WOODLANDS

OF

KENT

Geoffrey Roberts

WOODLANDS OF KENT

Geoffrey Roberts

With Illustrations by Philip Rutt

Timber trees, coppice and country park. Their absorbing chronicle, from wildwood axe to community planting.

Published by Geerings of Ashford Ltd.

Published by Geerings of Ashford Ltd., Cobbs Wood House, Chart Road, Ashford, Kent TN23 1EP. Tel (01223) 633366.

1st Edition 1999

Design and printing by Geerings of Ashford Ltd.

Illustrations by Philip Rutt

ISBN 1 873953 31 3

The publishers and author are grateful for support in this work from Kent County Council.

Illustration acknowledgments:

Canterbury Archaeological Trust: 21 top right; Canterbury City Council: 144; Norma Chapman: 68 bottom right; Peter Connolly: 31; Countryside Commission: 13 top; Stephen Davis: frontispiece, 35, 56, 137; English Nature: 28, 52; Forestry Commission: 155; Roy Keeler: 95 main, 111; Kent County Council (Ashford): 134; Kent Messenger Group: 87 main, 159 top right and below; Kentish Stour Countryside Project: 24, 68; Rob Liversidge: cover; Patrick McKernan: 45 bottom; Massey-Ferguson: 178; National Trust/Eric Crichton: 177; Julian Plumtre: 184 top; Royal Horticultural Society: 121; Surrey County Council/N. R. Bannister: 68 top; Topham Picturepoint: 146; White Cliffs Countryside Project/Eurotunnel: 13 bottom; The Woodland Trust: 40, 181, 206; W. T./Brian Aldrich; 173.

Looking out from The Devil's Kneading Trough on the
North Downs over the wooded landscape of Kent.

INTRODUCTION

In their journey through time following the last Ice Age, our forebears were dominated for several thousand years by limitless woodland. Then they subdued it. Human fear of the forest slowly changed to confidence as the skill came to hand of felling trees with wooden-handled stone tools.

The cut woody produce gave shelter, weapons, forage, fuel for warmth and better food and, eventually, the intense heat needed for smelting iron. Confidence nurtured mastery through many generations as these pioneers found that they could re-grow trees to meet their needs and choose woods for different purposes. The practicality of hardness or springiness was to be followed by shaping offerings of beauty to the gods. Woodlands were now taken into ownership by tribal heads and later by priests.

Always, while the long centuries brought society onward from primitive axework to cathedral carving, wood and woodland were a major presence in a people's life. And then, suddenly, they were not. After countless generations, in just a few years, the men and women of lowland England became free of dependence upon wood.

Yet now it is seen that woodland is still vital in the human environment. Because people no longer must themselves put it to daily use, our modern community has at first neglected and then become aware of the need, nevertheless, to sustain woodland. To do that, we ask about the natural beginnings of the land and the past progress of our forebears with their trees and underwood. In Kent, it is an absorbing chronicle.

CONTENTS

PREFACE

English woodland had always yielded a year-long harvest of rich variety. So matter-of-fact was it that history-tellers and commentators largely overlooked its presence, as they might earth and water. In a relatively few years people have left behind an inborn, unquestioning awareness of wood and woods that came from such dependence upon them. In my oak plantation or alder coppice, working without meeting another soul all day, that thought comes often. The past half-century has seen a leap ahead from axe and slow crosscut and woodland gangs of many men to the chainsaw and ecological debate.

Determined that the story of what went before should be told, I came quickly to the realisation that nowhere more than in lowland, maritime Kent is there so much rich material.

By concentrating on a single county, the narrative need not resort to generalities; it would picture at close range the meaning of woodland in the community. Researching for the book in this specific way has brought the benefit of many helpful and enjoyable friends and acquaintances who have relished its theme.

During the two years, there have been wise readers along the way: Patrick Hills and John and Joan Wood, foresters; Nicola Bannister, landscape archaeologist; Denise Rayner grammarian-historian. My daughter, Belinda, brought the long manuscript to disk with a skill and patience that lightened my work. Craftsmen-interpreters in all reaches of the county and Sussex have given their time: in particular, Damian Goodburn (Museum of London) on ancient carpentry; David Maylam (English Nature) on fuelwood and woodlore; and Chris Mulqueeney, gamekeeper to Lord Brabourne. Landowners, librarians, archivists, merchants, Forestry Commission officers and many other woodsmen have shown cheerful kindness - with which I hope they will encompass my not naming each person but recording here my warm thanks to everyone. Their wide goodwill must reflect the enduring appeal of our shared subject.

Geoffrey Roberts
Saltwood 1999

THE RETURN OF
THE TREES

At the Beginning of Kent

The construction of the Channel Tunnel yards near Folkestone presented an exciting opportunity for archaeologists. A kilometre square of rural land, until then penetrated only to the level of the plough, was uncovered to the subsoil for their skilled inspection. And this was not just a large sample plot which might be repeated in countless valleys across lowland England: it was at the shortest crossing point for early civilisations pressing outward from central Europe and finding here, on a new shore, a place to settle.

The modern explorers were intent on discovering more evidence of the daily life and work of Kent's early settlers. These first farmers had turned the virgin soil of south-east Kent about 4,500-5,000 years ago. They used an ard, the ancestor of the plough. Modern workers from Canterbury Archaeological Trust, as they photographed and touched the very marks left by the ard in the compacted earth, must have had a sense of wonder yet also an affinity with their pioneering forebears.

The first-footers from the central landmass had powers of reasoning vastly advanced over all other animals and a span of knowledge embracing what they could see, touch or be told about by their living elders. Their choice of which wildwood to clear of trees and bushes for good crops of grain came in this way. They had crossed to the chalky peninsula of a recently separated island. This new ground for their ard and herbage for their beasts was going to prove more diverse than most in soils and fertility; a feature that would order the agrarian pattern down the ages. The untreated soils, reflecting the rocks and drifted deposits beneath them, pointed a man to where he might plough, where graze cattle, where - eventually - to look for iron to smelt and where to leave the woodland as a provider of fuel, fruit, game and shelter.

The land surface, then and now, showed the very last-minute condition after awesome geological formations and climate change and distances in time. It is now calculated that from an accretion of dust and gas in space 4,600 million years ago Britain's oldest rocks were formed some three thousand million years ago. In the southern lowlands there are tiny outcrops of much younger rock, such as the Wrekin in the West Midlands and the Malvern Hills. These are of the late Pre-Cambrian Period, about one thousand million years ago. The surface of Kent's 60 x 50 miles (97 x 80 km) is the result of upheavals in the Earth's crust only one hundred million years ago and then hardening deposits of mud and chalk. To form the depth of just the top 15 metres of the final chalk cap took about a million years.

The shape of Kent, as we know it to-day, is established by the horizon of the high North Downs and the outline of the county's very long coastline. Of course, to-day's seashore is only temporary in the great geological scheme of things. The rock formations which underlie The Downs extend beneath the English Channel to beyond Boulogne, showing there the same top layer of chalk from the long Cretaceous Period (Latin - creta: chalk). The soft chalk was an unbroken canopy from Guildford to near St Omer and from Folkestone to Eastbourne. The cause of the domed shape of the once-flat chalk was a long, gentle upward movement beneath it of maritime Europe's rock crust. This firmed up to the existing shape of the region with its basins of Hampshire and London divided by rock layers pressed upwards to form the Weald heights. Before and after that time of immense surface reformation, for much more than 100 million years, south-east Britain was covered by either freshwater or the sea. The sediment laid down during that era, partly from the remains of marine life and partly from river and swamp deposits, solidified over the Jurassic level as distinct layers of rock, either beneath the surface chalk or exposed.

The ancient name Weald, from Wald - a great forest, was adopted by 19th century geologists for the form and series of rock types exposed in the area, a series now known world-wide as Wealden; technically a very large anticline, an arch-like fold in the rocks. The upfolding has the oldest stratum nearest the centre and the distinct layers match each other outwards to opposite sides of the arch. The layers became re-exposed or near to the surface as their chalk cover was, ever so slowly, eroded by the elements. Exposed, too, are bony remnants and petrified footprints of dinosaurs. The classic picture of the large creatures in the foreground of a vista of swamp and tree-fern and early conifer befits the Wealden area as it was about 120 million years ago. Those fossils are discovered in quarry or cliff-face, places where the older strata of the Wealden arch are at relatively little depth below to-day's surface. The distinct strata are so intimately close that, at Hythe for example, five geological categories may be crossed within two miles. It is a proximity unique in Britain and possibly in the world.

The oldest rock layer exposed in Kent is called the Hastings Beds which includes the sandy outcrops found around the highest part of the Weald, as at High Rock near Tunbridge Wells. The term Hastings Beds denotes where the layer can be seen debouching on the coastal cliffs. Within that layer, on the inland surface, are sub-types with names like Tunbridge Wells Sand and Wadhurst Clay, each one of importance for the modern soil and landscape it bears. Soil consultants use other vocabularies for primeval drifts of hillwash or windblown deposits which, usually in mix with the subsoil, have agriculturally important differences in texture. Farmers and foresters use less precise descriptions - loamy, alluvial, light sand, upland heath - for their broader descriptive needs.

Next oldest to the Hastings Beds is the Wealden Clay which forms the long vale of the Low Weald. Laid down in a period of fresh or brackish water, it stretches from Bewl Water reservoir nearly to Romney Marsh and is generally a poorly draining clay. Within the vale, however, is the rich agricultural land either side of the River Medway, some way south of the river's gap through the Downs, where it joins the Beult at Yalding. Abnormal evidence of prehistoric settlement in an otherwise forbidding clay land shows how early settlers followed river courses and exploited the good soils near the contemporary banks. The pioneers would have developed a deep lore to discern what soil value lay beneath the different tree species they found, and even more so the ground flora.

When the sea overcame the land waters of the region, about 120 million years ago, the new sedimental layer was what is now called the Lower Greensand. It does include some of what we think of as 'sand', in a narrow band of sandpits and rabbit warrens from the M20 at Wrotham eastward to Sandling by Maidstone and Sandling station near Hythe (ling = heather). This band is known as the Folkestone Beds which, with the Beds named for Sandgate and Hythe alongside, pursues a course parallel to the Weald Clay vale as far as the harbour town. The Hythe Beds are noted for the famous building stone, Kent Ragstone, but to answer the context of this chronicle their interest lies more in the high wooded slopes of Westerham and Sevenoaks. Just over into Surrey, Leith Hill is the highest point in the Weald, reaching 1,000 ft with the help of its ragstone tower.

At the foot of the North (and South) Downs is the outcrop of Gault Clay, a thin vale of singularly sticky and impermeable material which repels farmer and modern builder, for it is unstable too, but which grows fine oak and ash, especially where there is a drift of chalk over it from the nearby slopes. Of course, the exposed geological layers alongside each other on the surface do overlap beneath the surface and are affected by other factors such as underground water levels. At Frogholt, behind Folkestone, Professor Godwin's report in 1955 recorded the pattern found 200ft (61m) above sea level on the foot of the Downs. At a depth of 18ft (5.5m) the gross stratigraphy, the layers downwards, of the excavation - showed:-

metres 0.0 - 2.15   sandy earth

2.15 - 3.25   blue clay

3.25 - 4.6   peat

4.6 - 5.2   running sand.

To his researchers the interest lay in the peat, which had been preserved by the clay and sand above it and by the high water-table.

The North Downs, the chalkland of Kent, is the most open, and to many the most endearing, feature in an otherwise highly developed landscape. In prehistoric times, when the undrained water-table was higher and the woodland cover not too thickly daunting, these uplands made readily-won ploughland for the first farmers and acceptable pasture thereafter. On the north side of the chalk summit, the unsteep dipslope side, Kent's population has been most dense since man began to settle the county area. Here was the Thames estuary for canoe transport and the coastal land of varied but generally younger deposits of rivers and erosion. Fertile land could be found from Thanet to the Darent and Cray rivers. Only the marshland and, inland, the earlier London Clay in such areas as Blean Woods held back the farmer. Here in the north of the county is also the greater acreage of loess, the windblown topsoils such as Brickearth which are so rewarding for growers with the eye to find them. Across on the south coast lies Kent's supremely fertile area, known broadly as Romney Marsh. In its natural alluvial structure it had a partial tree cover which farmers would later denude, using the timber and saplings to protect the Marsh from the sea and enlarge it. (But this narration has leapt too far ahead!)

Long after the last, or latest, of the global plate tectonic movements to affect the Earth's crust and the landform of the European region, there came the relatively short periods of glaciation. The Ice Age of one-to-two million years duration, in probably four stages with warm intervals between, caused sea levels to rise on the coasts as the vast glaciers melted but also caused the land itself to rise or be depressed in response to the weight of ice at the northern centre of glaciation. These awesome effects on the lands of Northern Europe were combined with rocks being split by cold temperatures and with erosion, both incisive and rounding, as ice and water pushed huge boulders or a mudwall of stones across the still-frozen surface. Now wind, too, caused shifting deposits of fine soil. The great ice sheets never reached quite so far south as Kent, stopping just beyond the Thames, but the peripheral cold from the glacier gave tundra conditions. On Kent's half-frozen surface, water erosion could occur rapidly and loess, the windblown deposit, could reach us from Essex.

The last glacial period of the Ice Age (until the next? - we may be in just another interval) began to lose its grip on the climate here only 13,000 years ago. It is from then that may be plotted the rapid recolonisation by woody species, as we know them today, across North-West Europe. Unlike the giant horsetails, early conifers and other plants of so many millions of years before, these newer species recognisable by us had flourished in the interglacial periods. Although the periglacial climate of Kent had been impossibly cold for trees and discouraging to Homo erectus, the land surface nearer the Equator had remained warm: there were pluvials (rains) concurrently with our glaciations. Between glacial periods an evolutionary stage of hominids roamed Kent, able to use stone as tools but earlier than the Neanderthal people. The astonishing find at Swanscombe, near Dartford in 1935 of part of a young woman's skull from 250,000 years ago gives us a famous local link with prehistory. But after her time more than another two thousand centuries were still to pass before the first communities of families settled to agriculture here - about 6,000 years ago.

To give a dimension to the always amazing span of time and force which shaped our land, we recall that nine-tenths of that time had passed before primitive life on Earth was created. And eventually Man. To quote the geologist D.V. Ager (1975):

'If the whole time since life appeared on the earth were expressed as one year, then the first vertebrates did not evolve until about October 20th, mammals appeared on December 7th and Man himself only stepped into the limelight at twelve minutes to midnight on December 31st'.

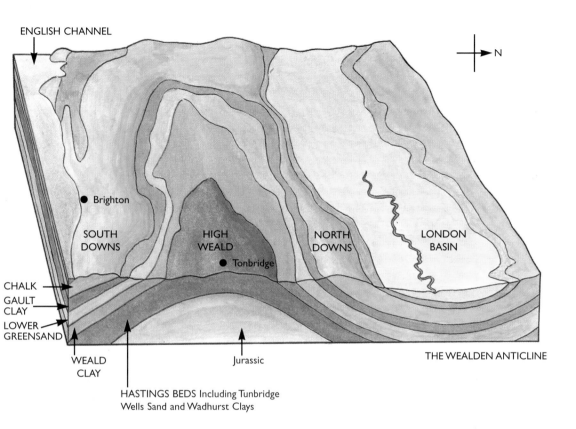

ENGLISH CHANNEL

N

● Brighton

SOUTH
DOWNS

HIGH
WEALD

● Tonbridge

NORTH
DOWNS

LONDON
BASIN

CHALK

GAULT
CLAY

LOWER
GREENSAND

WEALD
CLAY

Jurassic

THE WEALDEN ANTICLINE

HASTINGS BEDS Including Tunbridge
Wells Sand and Wadhurst Clays

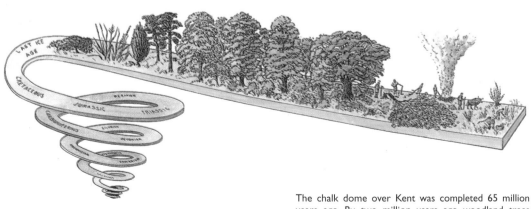

The chalk dome over Kent was completed 65 million
years ago. By two million years ago woodland trees
recognisable to-day had developed but because of
climate changes they died out here and then reappeared, at least three times. Their latest return from
warmer regions was during the last two millennia before
Britain's surface became separated by sea from the
mainland 8,600 years ago.

The Return of the Trees

Having reviewed at fast-forward speed up to the Ice Age, now is the stage to slow the pace. Interglacial warmth has returned to Kent and trees grow again. There have been 5,000 years or more of a warmer climate which spelled the end of the cold and wide open tundra, that good mammoth-hunting ground, and a return to the forest which densely protects smaller animals and impedes humans. The hunter has become the farmer. His are the skills which have left traces in Kent from about 6,000 years ago for us to see and wonder at.

How, even with thousands of good growing years, had the covering of the land changed so totally? Where did the trees come from ? All researchers, judging by their lack of mention of it, appear to be certain that there was no possibility of seed lying dormant in the frozen ground for thousands of years in order to rise up to renewed warmth. Surface plants on the tundra of southern England reached no higher than ground-hugging, wind-crazed shrubs of a kind not capable of developing the single woody stem. No, to bring back the landscape of the previous warm interglacial periods the trees must return from as far away as the Mediterranean and Transcaucasian regions.

Northwards they came, unhindered yet by an English Channel. The first to return that we would call trees were birch and pine, accompanied by shrubby hazel and willows. Birch swung round on the European landmass to reach its perimeter, Britain, from the east before being followed by Scots pine, which took the more expected direction from the south to north. Birch began to return earlier than 10,000 years ago; its ability for leaping into and across a low ground vegetation still often seen today.

From then until our first farmers of some four or five thousand years later the broadleaved forest trees which followed to cover England were, in date order, Wych elm, oak, alder, lime and ash. Their appearance on the landscape came not in monocultural waves, as diagrams are bound to imply, but in competition; circumstances allowing first pockets or mixtures then, sometimes, domination by one species. A few species, which we know from pollen analysis had been present here in the previous Interglacial, did not re-invade across the land.

In the post-Ice Age years there was, for the first several millennia, a wide and dry entrance from what is now Denmark round to Normandy. Indeed, the forming of the Dover Straits, so vital a barrier later, was not the final separation of our island. About 8,600 years ago, a few hundred years after water flooded through between Dover and Calais, the final submerging of the landbridge between Britain and the mainland came in the Dogger Bank area east of Lincolnshire. As Alan Mitchell wrote in *The Trees of Britain and Northern Europe* (1982), 'Then melting ice raised sea levels, Britain was an island, and no more trees could come'.

The dramatic sentence prefaces his listing of species termed British native trees because they arrived before the island separation, as distinct from introduced or naturalised trees.

He listed -

Conifers: only Scots Pine, Common Juniper and Yew

Broadleaved trees: Silver and Downy Birches, Bay Willow, Aspen, Wych Elm, Sallow, Alder, Bird Cherry (all early invaders). Rowan, Hazel, Holly, Ash, Sessile Oak, Small-Leaved Lime, Common Oak, Crack and White Willow, Wild Cherry, Black Poplar, Whitebeam, Hawthorn and Midland Thorn. (As latecomers) Wild Service Tree, Crab Apple, Beech, Field Maple, Hornbeam, Broad-leafed Lime, Box. (To distinguish them from shrubs, trees are generally accepted to be those woody plants able to grow more than 6 metres tall on a single stem).

In our time of wide awareness of the need to preserve ecosystems, the importance of native trees and their attendant organisms has been highlighted. Oliver Rackham defines a British native tree as a species which appeared here in post-glacial prehistoric times without human agency. Effectively that means before the landbridge was submerged. These, and not the later arrivals helped in by human hand, will have the best ecological pedigrees. He writes as our dating of a tree's establishment in Britain becomes profoundly more accurate through techniques developed mainly during the past forty years.

Pollen analysis, dendrochronology (tree-ring dating) and radiocarbon dating go on apace, leaving us ever more informed about organic prehistory but also less didactic. Pollen grains are examined from cores bored deep into peat or lake sediment. The method, begun in the 1920s, yields knowledge uniquely because the hard coat of the identifiable pollen grain has been preserved since a time for which other evidence of species is so difficult to obtain. The findings for trees are usually declared only when there is a significant pollen presence of the species at a given depth. The dates for their first post-glacial arrival in Britain may thus be unremarked. But there are species which leave specialists uncertain even beyond a margin of a few hundred years. Beech, as the most discussed example, is not recorded here until some 3,000 years ago in the major pollen work of H J B Birks, although from earlier work by Godwin we read of beech in use in Neolithic trackways 4,500 years ago and of beech pollen in that Somerset area as early as 7,000 BC. Beech is classified as native by Rackham (e.g. Tree News 1997) and by other authors but the timing of its arrival is still much debated.

Radiocarbon dating, which has done so much since the 1950s to increase the accuracy of our study of organic material from the past, has itself been given much greater dependability by the analysis of annual tree rings in ancient timber. Work which began in the USA with immensely long-lived Bristlecone pine was adapted for Europe by studying the patterns of slow or rapid annual growth in many shorter-lived trees of overlapping antiquity. In this way, work at Queen's University, Belfast, on semi-fossil bog-oak has led to records of climatic change reaching back over 7,000 years. The calibration with radiocarbon dating has been applied intensively to prehistoric wooden trackways in the Somerset Levels. Here the oak component of the Sweet Track is now radiocarbon dated very precisely as 3807 BC, or some 6,000 years ago. This would be well within Professor Birks' mapping of the spread of oak across southern England around 9,000 years ago.

The dating of pollen grains throughout Europe leads to an estimated rate of annual spread of tree species across the prehistoric land. For Britain, Birks drew isochrone, or date contour, maps of the geographic spread of trees, based on 135 sites. The Kent site was at Wingham where Godwin carried out one of the earliest tests (1960). The grains had been deposited in the conducive climate of the Boreal and Atlantic periods of 5,000 to 9,000 years ago and seedlings had none of the later hindrances of agriculture or urban barriers. But, even so, the calculated rate of spread seems too rapid to to-day's forester. Ash was thought to have varied from as little as 50 metres to 250 metres annual advance but alder, with water-transported seed, is given a more consistent 500 - 600 metres and lime a rate of 450 - 500 metres. There may be still a sense of caution in the author's notes: as in oak, for which a footnote adds that the rapid rate of up to 500 metres per year may have been influenced 'by birds - jays, rooks, woodpigeons'.

Among the species classed as native but of minor significance in most of Britain are hornbeam and the wild service tree which are considered native only in southern England. Wild Service, with its fruit of chequer berries, is at its best in east Kent but, for climatic or competitive or early human reasons, it did not spread strongly inland after its long journey of perhaps 3,500 kilometres from southern Europe.

The modern laboratory techniques for dating organic material run in parallel with the impressive range (one cannot yet say exhaustive) of other detective methods supporting our knowledge of trees in British prehistory. They are seen to their full effect in the monograph, *Elm*, by R H Richens (1983). Here is brought together the evidence from associated organisms, viruses and fungi, bugs, aphids, moths, butterflies, beetles. Vernacular names for elm across Europe are included in Richens' posse of methods used to pursue the identity of varieties as well as the more usual inquiries into leaf, seed and shoot. Then comes the exciting alliance of the source and distribution of the seed with the transportation along track and waterway of regionally identifiable Neolithic tools. The author's vividly reached conclusion, startling in 1983 in view of other vaguer findings, is that among all the elm varieties in Britain, Wych elm is 'native' in the meaning of the act, and no other - not even English elm. The typical Narrow-Leaved elm of east Kent, he suggests, came from the nearest point in France not by natural spread but by import from the tribe there who, in turn, had brought that seed from its region in the south. But, just when we thought here was a definitive answer, Dr Richens findings are profoundly doubted by Dr Rackham (1986 - *History of The Countryside*).

In 1976 Rackham cited three well known species as widely 'naturalised' - sweet chestnut, sycamore and Rhododendron ponticum. 'Originally introduced from overseas, they now behave like native trees in that they maintain themselves indefinitely without human intervention and have widely invaded native vegetation'. These naturalised species are considered ecologically less well-endowed than the natives. That can certainly be supported from observing the above three recent arrivals as habitats but we may need to reconsider the naturalised species from the Neolithic Age, those importations of seed to meet the farmer's needs.

The establishment of settled agriculture around 5000 years ago is a suitable period in this chronicle to take stock. By then the awesome fundamentals, the geological upheavals and deposits, the alternating fierce extremes of climate, the major surface changes to our region -not least the English Channel - had all happened. The weather and our flora and fauna were comparable with to-day's. The inventiveness of human beings and thus the talent for survival had become evident. The technical terms which follow offer the reader a cross-reference with scientific publications. From the literature, '5000 years ago' was, anthropologically, in the Neolithic Age of Homo sapiens sapiens. Geologically, the date falls in the Caenozoic Era (of some 65 million years) within which it belongs to the Quarternary period or Pleistocene (about 2 millions years). The more modern portion of that time of fossiliferous rock deposition is called the Upper Pleistocene or Holocene System. Biogeographically and phytographically, 5,000 years ago Britain was in the middle of pollen time zone VII in the sub-Boreal climatic phase of the Flandrian - in which period we still are. Flandrian is the name given to the period since the last retreat of the glaciers from northern Britain. It is more cautiously known as the Present Interglacial because the evidence points to another return of ice in the distant future. But only if Future Humankind refrains from skewing climatic events onto some unexpected course.

The Axe Cuts Into The Wildwood

When the site for Stonehenge was chosen, nearly five thousand years ago, the sun-(or moon-?) worshipping architects laid out their design of two miles in diameter upon chalk upland as grassy bare as it is today. A thousand years before their meeting that ground, like the whole of England, was certainly under the patchy canopy of the post-glacial wildwood. Some woodland clearings had been added to natural gaps by the hunters of the early Neolithic Age but the breaking of soil for farming began with the developing Neolithic culture. This was the herald of tremendous change to the landscape, the first to be wrought by human influence. By flint or stone axe, bark stripping and animal grazing the Neolithic farmers opened up about one-sixth of England. (With some rise and fall in the clearance rate and despite partial repossession by the wildwood, the agricultural advance continued. Helped on by first bronze tools then iron, it is reckoned that half of England's land area had been cleared by early in the Iron Age.)

In southern England the Neolithic woodsman/farmer began this great transformation acre by acre on the tillable uplands. The layer of topsoil, deeper in that age, was free of swamps yet had water nearer the surface than today for living needs. Semi-domesticated animals could graze the even terrain. On lower ground, around the river mouth by which he had arrived, it was the immigrant farmer's eye that chose good brown earth for arable and primitive orchard crops. In Kent, between the North Downs and the Thames Estuary, was the favoured area for these crops which would reward the labour of clearing denser wildwood to gain tillage on the fine loamy and silty soil. Not so on the southern slope of the Downs. From the hills the explorer descended to find the unbroken line of Gault Clay, to him a glutinous barrier. He had seen from higher up an apparently endless tree canopy that lay beyond and he imagined the Gault stretching to the horizon beneath it. Thus the forest between North Downs and South Downs was still intact when the Romans named it Silva Anderida after their Channel port (now Pevensey, Sussex). They knew the tree cover to be rarely broken for thirty miles northward from there to near the Thames.

During the four millennia up to the arrival of the Romans the clearing of the Kent wildwood made great advances outside the Wealden forest. The methods matched the needs, which were partly those of ground-baring for cultivation or grazing and partly the demand for wood for a multitude of uses. Modern investigators, notably since the 1970s, have created a flood of new information and surmise about the different methods employed by the early settlers and about nature's own course. The debate, kept fresh by continuing new developments, is very much alive today. It encourages a woodsman or amateur prehistorian, to make from the many hypotheses a choice influenced by personal experience and study.

In the history of trees of Britain the event given importance second only to the watery separation of our islands from the European mainland is that of the Elm Decline, sometime after 5,500 years ago. Perhaps its current prominence in debate is because the conclusions from a wealth of laboratory analysis of prehistoric pollen have featured in widely read publications of the late-1970s, just when the scourge of Dutch Elm Disease was altering our 20th century landscape. The timing of the prehistoric Elm Decline had a much more important juxtaposition; it coincided in England with the first animal husbandry and wildwood clearance by Neolithic farmers.

The dramatic reduction of elm pollen after that time has been ascribed to climatic change, to the farmers' preference for elm to be pruned or felled for cattle fodder, and to a pan-European plague of the deadly elm-bark beetle. Writers now give less support to the importance of Neolithic herdsmen feeding their animals palatable elm-shoots. After all, three-quarters of the land was yet uninhabited wildwood. Some natural cause must have been the decisive one, either a climate change or the disease. Rackham, with more certainty than in his earlier writing, said in 1989 (*The Last Forest*)

> In my opinion the only explanation which covers all the facts is that Neolithic men inadvertently let loose Elm Disease. (Men) by making farmland with free-standing trees, woodland edges and maybe pollards, created an environment in which the disease and the bark-beetle could get out of hand. The next time there was an epidemic it was a big one.

Scientists now believe that the killer-fungus resulting from the elm-bark beetle invasion has, itself, a pathogen which affects the virulence of the disease (Forestry Commission 1996). 'Little fleas have lesser fleas...etc.' but again, this is a matter of the balance of nature which need take no regard of the tiny presence of Neolithic people.

Elm, in its several varieties, was not at that time the dominant species in lowland England. Then, to our modern surprise, the chief constituent of the forest canopy was Small-leafed lime. For lime, too, there has been much discussion of its rise to dominance

following a late arrival in Britain, after oak, and then a deep decline like elm but less rapid. It is a quick-growing tree when young but scarcely more so than oak. It is said that it was cleared early from the most fertile soils, where it grew well. But in south-east England it seems from pollen counts that it grew almost everywhere. It was attractive for fodder but, like elm, it also declined throughout the unfarmed land. Because lime is a warmth-loving species there may be a stronger argument for a climate change being the cause of its initial downturn relative to other species.

In the Weald forest, where only hunters went until the search began for iron ore, researchers have deduced from analysis of charcoal at the foundries that lime was absent from the area by Roman times. However, studies in Denmark and Finland have confirmed that lime was a tree of manifold uses. In addition to providing good fodder it was easy to carve and shape and, most importantly, its inner bark or bast (an ancient word which the OED attaches first to the lime tree) was prized for twisting into cordage, harness, fishing nets and lines. It is, then, more likely that lime was present at the Wealden ironworks, although diminishing, but when it was cut it was separated from the piles of fuelwood. One also wonders, because the bast was so uniquely useful, why lime groves were not protected and regenerated or coppiced. Perhaps they were but, in Kent at least, never enough: there are only rare remnants of lime in the county's woodlands today.

The niceties of silviculture did not come first in the minds of men who crashed forward into the wildwood, urged on by mouths to feed and, eventually, the prospect of trading grain or cattle. How they did it has been questioned in great depth and breadth. How could such a small number erase a sixth, a third and then a half of England's forest and scrub with tools which lacked even metal heads until the last few hundred years of the main clearance?

Nearly 6,000 years after the Elm Decline of Neolithic times, the elm was almost universally destroyed in Britain by the Dutch Elm disease epidemic of 1975-1985. A few rooted trees survive among the dead, perhaps to provide immune seed. Picture: Hampton 1998.

In the Neolithic-to-Iron Age climate long periods drier than ours at present may have encouraged burning as a way of clearance but it would not have been effective in the predominantly broadleaved forest of the lowland except perhaps after years of high summer temperatures and low rainfall. We may dismiss the idea of fire, even natural fire holocausts, making a clean sweep of trees over great stretches of ancient countryside because enough would have survived to re-seed a burnt-over area too large or too difficult for the few farmers.

To-day, the striking visual change of land newly cleared for, say, a motorway is that it has become suddenly treeless and shrubless. Looking along a bare, ancient horizon of the North Downs we see that it, too, is treeless - but the big trees were probably not instantly clear-felled and removed. Neolithic pioneers knew from their use of bark for shelter that a debarked tree would die. Then there would no longer be a leaf canopy to keep sunshine from the growing crop. The primitive ploughmen, intent on breaking open the virgin surface, would avoid shallow rootplates and, all in good time, the part-desiccated, part-rotten tree would fall and its roots moulder away. For bigger trees the bark stripping away may have been done well ahead of the ground clearing. If not, even before its last leaf-fall the tree's understorey of scrub would have been hacked away to be used to best purpose or as a temporary fence against browsing.

We do not know, of course, how many trees there were to the acre. There is no reason to suppose that the larger ones were close set on the land first to be cleared; the chalk uplands and lighter well-drained soils. Our modern mind's-eye of woodland is conditioned by the ubiquitous planted acreage and occasional self-regenerated managed woodland in Britain or by television pictures ranging from rain-forest to savannah if we want to guess at the past. Indeed, 'we don't know' but, for lack of other evidence, we may surmise that to plough avoiding the bigger trees was the norm for Neolithic farmers and that the denser forest on heavy land still awaited the plough of iron tip and its attendant metal equipment. These points are, if anything, strengthened by current research into the Neolithic diet, which concludes that humans were less dependent on cereals than was previously thought.

It is thought probable that the Neolithic arable cycle, in its early stages, was to clear vegetation, break the surface, grow crops without manuring, and then move on when the soil became tired. It may be argued that the virgin soil did not tire quickly in lowland England but a more static practice would hardly have achieved clearance of the vast acreage per head of population now estimated, even over many centuries. If temporarily abandoned, the scoured land reverted to scrub which may have been poor in species of potentially high forest trees. That would have been due, not least, to wild animal browsing. Researchers often mention that a farmer's cattle kept regrowth in check in woodland clearings but there must, too, have been a larger number of red deer and roe deer, wild pig and other browsing species ready to relish the low-standing new shoots. In our own time the deer population has increased again for lack of hunters and we see how selectively deer browse the plump shoots of broadleaf stumps in preference to other nearby plants.

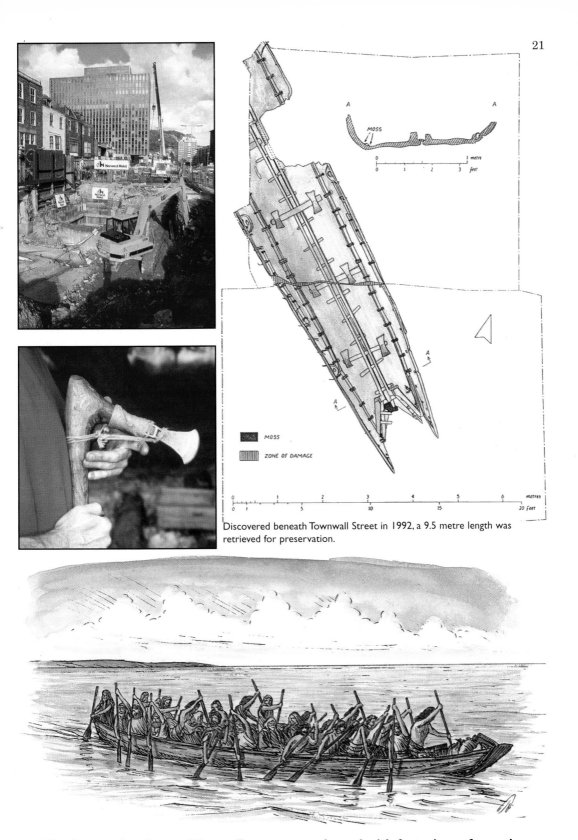

MOSS

A A

ZONE OF DAMAGE

Discovered beneath Townwall Street in 1992, a 9.5 metre length was retrieved for preservation.

The Bronze Age Boat of Dover. From great oaks and with fastenings of yew, the cross-Channel craft of 3,300 years ago.

For some three thousand years of opening up the wildwood, from the earliest Mesolithic hunter's animal killing grounds to the late Neolithic Age and even Bronze Age, the principal tool for the work was the axe of flint or other stone. There has been a large volume of modern inquiry into axes and axe-work because of the frequency of these indestructible finds with a wide variety of shape and weight. Here is the principal evidence of the method of clearance, supported by few enough other artefacts. The haft is normally missing, being made of wood, except when a bone or antler handle is found alongside a lightweight head. The method of felling is deduced from the remains of cut tree poles preserved in mud or peat which all have a 'sharpened pencil' end shape. This shows that the blade was struck at a steep downward angle to force splinters from the stem. Less is written about cutting the felled stem to a length. For the thinnest pole there would be a simple notching chop. Larger diameters would have been first cleaved with wedges for most end-uses. The thickest trunks to be cut for length, perhaps for a house beam, might have been burnt through but that seems unlikely as the timber would have been cut across while green and wet for ease of haulage. Certainly there were no toothed saws suitable for work of this size, although it has been said that small flint saws and teeth of flint set with resin in a wooden spine might have been used for sawing softer smallwood.

Axes were developed to remarkable efficiency, as shown in reconstructions. In Jutland in the 1940s, using an actual Neolithic polished flint axehead and facsimile wooden handle, it was demonstrated that a 15-inch (38cm) diameter alder tree could be felled within 15 minutes. (Iversen trials reported in H.Godwin *The Archives of the Peat Bogs*, 1981, and elsewhere.) The advance to be gained later from metal heads, especially iron, was the greater lateral strength from a narrow edge.

As men began to adopt a more settled farming pattern the need for woodware grew in volume and diversity. Coppicing, with the woodsmen now living near enough at hand to cut their crop a few years later, was a skill initially practised at least three thousand years before iron tools were known in England. From these straight-grown rods and by selection from mixed primary growth, the settler knew to choose wood of the right hardness or flexibility to suit hand-tools, arrows, bows, hurdles, posts, ploughshafts, stockades, house beams and grades of fuel. The craft of woodworking in prehistoric times is as much to be wondered at as stone or metal-work but so few artefacts have survived that we have an unbalanced image of the ancient world of the artisan. With the manifold demands for wood the craft of carpentry must have been the first to separate from the settlers' general farming regimen. The skilled exploitation of the medium of wood 3,300 years ago was marvellously revealed in the 1990s when the Bronze Age Boat was found at Dover. Thought to have been paddled by a crew of 24, it was made from oak beams 60 ft (18 m) long which were held together with yew withies twisted to give wire-like strength. The ability to shape the logs with axe and adze (see illustration) was deeply impressive to the modern craftsmen of AD 1996 who fashioned its replica.

The Advent of Metals and Communities

Beside the North Downs Way to the east of Wye there is a precipitous view down into a vee-shaped coombe. It is called the Devil's Kneadingtrough and has yielded an insight into the prehistory of Kent chalkland. The coombe's severe shape was cut by erosion of half-frozen ground during the Late Glacial period. At the flat-top, on the 170 metre contour, are faint signs of those square shaped plots which are usually called Celtic fields and probably these are from the Bronze Age of some 3,500 years ago. At the bottom of the near-vertical plunge the coombe is filled with chalk debris covered by hillwash which fanned out onto the level clay land. Below the dividing line of Chalk from Gault, in one-time marsh deposits, a team of scientists in 1962 found a richly rewarding presence of mollusc shells which have provided histograms of the changing ground and climatic conditions. Pollen counts and remnants of woody matter were also studied. The pioneer trees birch and pine were recorded from borings back to the earliest pollen after the Ice Age.

From these analyses, and others along the near escarpment the evaluation is that the wildwood on the height above was first opened up around 4,000 years ago but then the trees and scrub re-invaded and had to be cleared again in the Iron Age, some 1500 years later. Such a long interval between clearings - the same as our distance in time from the end of the Roman Empire - reminds us how generalisations might deceive when considering prehistoric Kent. After the shaping of the coombe all but the steepest, abraded surfaces will have provided ground for seedlings of trees returning from the sub-tropics until there was a full complement of species. Probably just before the first clearance by humans, the dominant percentage of lime would have given over again to oak which was mixed, if later local tree cover is any guide, with ash and hornbeam and some beech growing into the natural gaps. As lesser trees there would be holly and, interestingly, the study team found yew which may be evidence of regeneration after clearance. In the area would also have been the wild service tree in its Kentish foothold, whitebeam and wild cherry. High on the scarp, juniper still thrived and below the spring line in wet places would be alder. By these dates elm would be scarce, and the future sycamore or sweet chestnut still unknown.

Beneath the canopy, hazel was ubiquitous and essential. From the first stationary cattle herding and protecting of crops until almost modern times, agriculture in Britain demanded a huge annual making of hurdles, for which hazel was the quick-coppicing, flexible wand of choice. On the edge of clearances, mixed shrubs or minor trees prospered according to the ground conditions: viburnum, spindle, the buckthorns, elder and the sallows. In the woodland or at streamside would have been seen animals now extinct here such as the wolf, true wild boar, bear and possibly beaver. Most of to-day's species would have been familiar then but not the later introduced fallow deer, rabbit or grey squirrel. At ground level the prehistoric flora would have included those plants we now quote locally as evidence of continuity; such as woodspurge, wood anemone and herb paris. In abundance upon trees, shrubs,

Wild Service Tree. A 'southern' tree, best suited to parts of East Kent, it is found among other woodland trees. From the shape of the leaf it is often mistaken for a field maple.

stone and in the soil were the ageless lichens, mosses and fungi which revealed so much to the early Britons and now inform the natural scientists.

The second clearance of the land above the coombe was simultaneous with the earliest prospecting for iron ore in Kent and its primitive smelting. Evidence of smelted iron, washed down to the bottom of the coombe, was found by Kerney *et al*. The crude metal may have come from an exploratory working of iron ore in pits a mile away but, more probably, it could have been dropped on either of the two trackways across the head and the foot of the coombe. Early iron production pieces, like flintwork and bronze before it, were widely traded on these prehistoric tracks which, on the Downs, later acquired the name Pilgrims' Way. Where iron ore was found in Kent, the areas of woodland and scrub cut over for charcoal-making became afterwards indistinguishable from the general re-clearance for farming. Long before that, we may imagine pre-Iron Age folk journeying westward on their own restless search, even to the Wessex land of the wooden henge circles. Travelling woodworkers must have marvelled at the positioning of the erected posts and the huge quantity of timbers brought to one place for a burial longbarrow.

By the late Bronze Age, however, the eminence of the Wessex Chalk, and its rivers below, as the main southern England settlement area had faded; no more henges - wooden or stone - were built. The hub of trading had moved eastward to the Thames estuary and beyond again while an increasing number of settlers diverted into the Medway gap and other fertile watercourses in the North Downs. The pressure of an enlarged population, and its growing wealth and sophistication, is known to us in the modern unearthing of imported bronze artefacts in hoards or single finds, especially along the Thanet, Swale and Thames coastal areas. Although we know today about the ancient mode of travel along the shore, it is very likely that the early Bronze Age farmer in his fields knew little about the new metal from copper and tin, found far away, and he himself possessed none of it. Eventually, though, this first alloy to be suitable for weapons and farming tools became widespread on the estuarine coast and over the chalk, onto the Greensand land, and even into the Wealden forest. 'Indeed the spread of man's activity seems to reach its widest extent (in Kent) in this period with a very great range of soils being exploited' (T C Champion in CBA Research Report No. 48 - Kent). Later in Kent, nowhere more so, iron tools would spread quickly into common use because they could be made from local mineral deposits. Then, first in prehistoric and in Roman times, but dramatically so in the distant future, would the character of the Wealden forest be shaped by the iron industry's demands upon it.

Woodcraft and Tribal Forces

About a thousand years before the Roman army entered Britain through Kent, the complexity of this agrarian district became intensified. The population of Britain burgeoned: in several modern assessments it is calculated that the people of Britain numbered as many at the end of the Bronze Age as there were at the time of the Domesday survey some 1700 years later. This would have meant 50,000 Bronze Age people in the Kent county area of which perhaps 15,000 were able-bodied males; involved in many farming duties but with woodland clearance and re-clearance as a major task. The supreme question, to which the answer remains stubbornly fogged , is 'Just when did methodical wildwood clearance for agriculture in lowland England begin?' Without the answer the calculation of man-hour rates of prehistoric achievement is difficult and not, in itself, very rewarding.

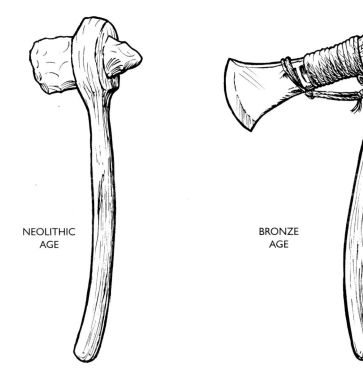

NEOLITHIC
AGE

BRONZE
AGE

The flint or stone axe wrought the first large clearances of the wildwood for Neolithic people. The shaping of wood for boats and beams became efficient with the first metal (bronze) heads.

It is the end result, the metamorphosis by clearance, which makes of this period the most arresting feature in our history of man and woodland. Oliver Rackham's dedicated research has led him (1986) to 'hazard the guess that half of England had ceased to be wildwood by the early Iron Age (500BC)'. He considered the Weald, however, even still in Norman times to be the largest wooded area in England. From this and Champion's observation on the effects of distribution of metal tools we must estimate that outside the Weald area much more than half of the remainder of the county had been opened up for arable use or pasture by the Iron Age. More than three-quarters ? To-day, Kent has an overall county percentage of 11-12% of the land under tree cover; including the Weald, now so much less heavily wooded. We can estimate that many locations in Kent now - however different in all other ways - are not dissimilar from the Iron Age in the size of their tracts with woodland cover. Visual comparisons would be less clear because of the disguising effect of modern hedgerows on unwooded landscapes.

Kent's wealth and population in the millennium in which iron replaced bronze for implements meant advantage being taken of the new metal to break ground with ploughs in heavier soils and also to reclaim some of the less fertile land on the uplands for renewed farming. More mouths to feed and, even so, more farm produce to trade, but the climate was becoming wetter and the conditions brought increased competitiveness. There was unease. It resulted, as always, in leaders persuading the people into defensive organisations. The cultural change of this age manifested itself throughout Britain in communal hillforts.

In the area which the Romans were soon to name in writing as Cantium, the people had long been used to, indeed were partly made up of, infiltering arrivals from the near mainland. Since the early Bronze Age the flow of traders, explorers and settlers-to-be had increased at this shortest sea-crossing. New practices and inventions were not the sole prerogative of more southerly Europeans but there the developments had been spurred on by the demands from military leaders of organised armies and ships; demands such as Britain did not yet know even in this age of iron. More recognisable to the inhabitants of south-east England was the looser, though warlike, tribal order of north-west Europe. For long now, immigrants from both regions had rippled onto the chalk shoreline, partly self-motivated and partly pressed outward by the splash of violent events at the centre. From the evidence of artefacts and from a few foreign travellers' contemporary written reports it would seem that the Cantii and their forebears, like the tribes to east and west of them, had previously assimilated the peoples of small invasions but now friction increased as self-sufficiency became harder to maintain and the newcomers increasingly warlike. Oldbury hill (Ightham) had long been inhabited but now it must meet the incursions of the so-called Belgae, a mixed Celtic and Germanic people, and other local threats. The hill was transformed into a fort measuring nearly one kilometre by half-a-kilometre. It was capable of supporting a permanent community, or of serving as a long-distance trading post or, at the worst, performing as a well-provisioned redoubt.

In Kent the puzzle for prehistorians has been that hillforts, so common across southern England that they are sometimes in view from opposing hilltops, have seemed quite absent to the east of the Medway except for the legendary but small Bigbury Camp above Canterbury. However, with recent excavations such as at Highstead (Chislet) and the work on the huge Iron Age cemetery site at Mill Hill, Deal, we are at a time of revision. Probably there was an Iron Age hillfort beneath the later Dover Castle. A feature of the forts was the strengthening of earth ramparts with timber and the use of heavy timber balks for defence gates. We read of Hambledon Hill in Dorset having ramparts, which stemmed from Neolithic times, requiring between 20,000 and 30,000 massive wooden posts (National Trust Guide).

Until the Iron Age hillfort era, and even afterwards, the chieftains of south-east England were not strong or well-organised enough to adopt a Roman military style but domestic, and now civic, developments were accelerating. In the south at least, coins were in circulation, signifying a growing sophistication of trade. At Pimperne in Dorset the pre-Roman farmhouse has been replicated to demonstrate the advanced construction using joined round-timber beams. For all these visible steps forward we still know almost nothing about the regulation of property and tenure, of ownership of fields, beasts and coppice in this wholly agrarian but developing society.

In Britain's south-eastern region facing Gaul, with Kent the nearest point, the two hundred years before the successful Roman invasion were a-buzz with change. The new patterns came not in the fundamental practices of working and domestic life so much as in political control and commerce. In Kent the greater importance of the tribe as a unit, and its demanding chieftains, came from the incursions and settling of the Belgae, those aliens from the Rhine and elsewhere. In times of calm, trade flourished mutually across the channel between troubled mainland and more receptive island. Iron Age Britons or Belgic immigrants in our south-east saw themselves, no doubt, as Modern; someone stressed by keeping up with what's new but fostered by a progressive land.

In our own time, at evening, stealthy on the hill of Bigbury Camp, we sense the awful wait for Caesar's legionaries. The imminent shattering of the scene, yet one so little changed to-day. Birch, a holly grove and once-coppiced oak. A wrong feature in time, the sweet chestnut plantation, but the true parallel of everything else. A moon in a cool, pale blue sky, jays quarrelling and a dog bark, woodsmoke and a chill mist in the young branches.

At a Point in Time

At this point in the nation's long history, perhaps more than any other country, our hindsight long suffered from a lacuna. Behind the dazzle of the arrival of Roman ways, the native society appeared dimly and to disadvantage, if at all. Two elements in the view were missing entirely. One always will be: the written word, the record to endorse tales from ancestors. Then there is the sparse physical presence of the building material of the era - wood. Moreover, the Roman dazzle has gained its light partly from the everlasting energy of our leading religion. In schoolroom minds the dates of the birth of Our Lord, Anno Domini, and the Roman invasions have been so close, and of such historical importance, that BC might equally well mean Before Caesar. By contrast with that mysterious world of 'BC', there is a rationality about 'AD'. It is the start of our measurable time and was deep-rooted by the rational Romans, who took up the first 400 years of it.

Since about 1960 the greater accuracy of dating and the sensitive practical skills applied to prehistory, with the parallel flood of published interpretations, have begun to fill the gap in the popular mindsight of life just before the Romans. The new abilities in detection allow, for the first time, the effect of climate on short-lived episodes to be assessed and this will help us to understand better many matters of woodland history and the usage of wood. In recent years we have come to know enough about the Kent of 2,100 years ago to be amazed that such an advanced people could thrive without a written language. From now on in our chronicle we will have the benefit of written records, richly to supplement what we can discern on or under the land.

Tudeley Woods coppice today.

ROMAN COLONY

Roman Kent and Classis Britannica

The year we now call AD1 occurred during the reign of Octavius Augustus, he who was the first to be named Emperor of The Romans. In Britain there were no Romans then other than a few traders, travellers and, no doubt, message-bearers. That year in Kent the eternal cycle of the four seasons must have been given a name and number by the local tribe, possibly a year of Eppilus who was a member of the same family as Cunobelinus (Cymbeline), the ruler of south-east England. By that year, whatever the Cantium people called it without being able to write about it, the seaborne raids of Julius Caesar were only childhood memories for the oldest folk. Perhaps they frightened their grandchildren by playing an early version of that scary Kentish game in post-Napoleonic times, 'Boney's coming!'

Certainly the Cantii knew all about the Romans. After his brief invasion Caesar himself had written graphically, 'The island is triangular in shape, with one side opposite Gaul. One corner of this side, situated in Cantium, is where nearly all the ships from Gaul land'. But, for all the cross-Channel Gallic migration and reciprocal trade, no Roman dominance was yet felt here in daily life.

It was the nearer inhabitants of North Gaul and the Low Countries who had brought new tribal loyalties and new trading methods with coins into Kent. Many of the developments of the time had come from the Europe-wide Celtic tribes, most potently the making and shaping of metals. There was among them in an early period a people called the Pretani from whom Britain had got its name, according to the scribes of the Romans and Greeks. The continental Celts, even in their most advanced cultural expression, did not write; nor did their northern Germanic neighbours. But out of the population stresses and movements came that Celtic people long-named (but lately debated) as the Belgae. Their loyalties spanned the Channel and they effectively ruled south of the Thames for more than a century before they were subdued by the Romans. Soon afterwards they saw their inland cousins retreat to highland Britain.

It is widely accepted by historians that iron ore in southern Britain was one principal reason for the Roman invasion. 'By the time the Romans arrived in Britain in AD 43 there was a vigorous and technologically well advanced iron-making industry in existence on the fringes of a region that was rich in iron ore and woodland' (Cleere 1985). In miles, Cantium was the nearest point to their province of Gaul but the Channel, known to the Romans as Ocean, repelled the non-mariner leaders and their troops equally. As the time for invasion approached, their fears of the strong tides and storm-tossed waters were only increased by the re-telling of the damage done to Caesar's ships. Eventually they embarked, a reluctant force of 40,000 men, in ships of a design now influenced by the traditional Channel craft of the Veneti from the mouth of the

Loire. Thereafter command of the waterway traffic fell to the Romans. In later years these ships were an arterial way of coastal as well as cross-Channel transport and, as classis Britannica, against marauders of the North Sea. The first ships were, Roman style, clad with planks abutting but later they had the overlapping or clinker design of northern vessels. The Romans, although skilled in sawing, still preferred cleft wood for ships' planks. 'Made in Cantium of local timber and iron' might well have been the ships' title of provenance.

The Celts, so widespread in Europe and in their way so skilled, had held sway in southern Britain through the Belgae, so what superior talents and force brought the Romans their success? The essence of the answer is that they could write and, moreover, calculate in writing. From the civilisations of the Near East and Greece they had arithmetic and Euclid's geometry. For the logistics of warfare here was a weapon which the Celts could not match; neither by runics nor by fervour. After the Roman military campaigns northwards through Europe, marked by rigorous discipline, the resulting civil government was made formidable by edicts that were calculated and recorded and displayed. Physical dominance of a settled land came from defence walls of stone quickly built and, as the epitome of military supremacy, straight roads engineered across the land. When the Romans arrived in 43, to stay, they brought with them the new skill of stonemasonry but, much more importantly, they had in their ranks of artisans the agrimensor, the numerate and literate land surveyor, and military engineers.

Forest Roads and Wooden Watchtowers

The first tasks of the surveyor would have been wholly military ones. The long miles of Roman roads were punctuated by wooden watchtowers and it is reasonable to suppose that as trees were felled to clear a route-line the first use of the timber would be in making the tower from which guerrillas or robbers could be spotted and the lie of the land plotted in a forward survey. The surroundings in the first days were virginally unmapped and unfriendly - even in Cantium where lived 'the most civilised of the Britons' as Caesar had written of them. Existing trackways evidently could carry war chariots but had been created by continuous wear, not by design.

The Romans brought metalled roads (To metal: a Latin word from the Greek 'metallon' = mine; in this case to mine or dig stone from the ground). With the cambered, stony surface draining off to side ditches, such roads lasted for centuries until they were buried, either by neglect or, more usually, by a later road on the same route. The first metalled road to be built by Roman orders must have been that from their landing port at Richborough (Rutupiae) to Canterbury (Durovernum Cantiacorum) and on via Rochester (Durobrivae) where the Romans built the vital Medway bridge, to London (Londinium). At this time, but also after the new road network had been established, all but the strategic roads were ways of beaten earth or short wooden causeways over spongy ground. In the 1970s at Wickhambreux, near enough to Richborough and its metalled highway, archaeologists uncovering a 1st Century wooden

water-mill found just such a causeway of coppice-wood leading from the mill.

The strategical Roman roads in Britain have their modern equivalent in main railway lines rather than motorways because they were routed to the very centre of cities and to harbour quayside. In Kent these heavy transport lines had to serve the supply harbours of Dover (Dubris) and Lympne (Portus Lemanis). Also vital, not least because of the weight of the merchandise, were the roads which could collect iron output from the Wealden forest; often for outward transhipment from those two ports.

The Romans brought writing, numeracy and new skills in carpentry for transport and construction.

The majority of the Wealden iron workings lay beyond to-day's county boundary in Sussex but from Tunbridge Wells to Tenterden were some of the sixty or more Roman sites. The interdependence of roads and iron output is shown by the routes in Kent. They were not all radial from London or from port to port, some being dedicated to iron such as the cross-country straight way from Canterbury over Godmersham Downs and Ashford vale, with a fork at Kingsnorth to the port of Lympne, then onward to Benenden. Another was angled from Rochester and Watling Street southward to Hastings via the rich iron fields near there. In part, these routes might follow the ancient Greensand ridgeways but the tree-felling and clearance through the virgin Weald forest must have been a prodigious task.

Tree-cutting to clear a route was, though, a minor item in comparison with the demand, during some 300 years or more, for charcoal to raise heat for the iron smelting. Henry Cleere, with the help of contemporary evidence from classis Britannica, the state owners who were an arm of the Roman fleet, has estimated that just six ironworks at Battle produced iron at the rate of 550 tons annually from the years 120 to 240. He calculates that each ton made required heat from the charcoal provided by 84 tons of wood. Oliver Rackham (1980) carries this through to being the annual output from 23,000 acres (9,300 ha.) of managed woodland. And all this for only six of the sixty Wealden ironworks....

Wood supplying was thus a major auxiliary industry: the hauling distance alone would have compelled the suppliers to manage woodland by coppice and pollard rather than to clear-fell and move on. Nearby, the arable farmer now had ploughing equipment able to take on more difficult land and he was being pressed by the Roman overlord for greater grain production as well as more meat from pastures. There is no doubt that this was the first, but not the last, instance of the woodlands of Kent and East Sussex being preserved because the woodsman's produce met a need greater than yet more farming output.

Woodland, its timber, coppice and fuel were of immense importance to the Romano-British but, rather like fresh water, this staple of life was so abundantly present here that there is little comment on it in the Roman writing that has survived. Caesar, in his brief forays, noted that 'there is timber (materia) of every kind as in Gaul, except beech and fir'. His remark about beech, still debated now, may have been a too-hasty observation: both beech and fir were far from leading species in his south-east corner of Britain. We now know from pollen-analysis (Godwin: 1960) that at Wingham, uphill from the Roman line of march, beech was present and even increasing in the Iron Age before Caesar's arrival. By inference from later years we know that, as now indeed, the woodland was unusually rich in its variety of trees and shrubs. However, the shape and size of individual woodlands is unknown to us. We know only that there was in total a vast acreage of timber trees, coppice and scrub in Kent but all cleared well back from the farmsteads and villas.

The different qualities of the range of species will have been well known to carpenters as they began meeting the orders of a more settled and, in parts, wealthy population. Roman craftsmen introduced the metal saw, previously unused in this country. The marks of saw-teeth on the beam or plank face, instead of cleavage along the grain by axe or beetle (wooden hammer) and wedge, are a significant double-check when dating ancient woodwork, the more so because when the Romans left Britain the use of saws ended. Perhaps it was, despite the reduction of the wildwood, that craftsmen of the north still had a wealth of trees to give straight knot-free timber for cleaving. Their counterparts of the drier, hotter Mediterranean countries would not have known these extensive areas of tall forest. That surmise is perhaps strengthened by the return of the rip-saw only after the coming of the Normans and their southern connections some 700 years later.

For all but a tiny percentage of homesteads the building materials in Cantium continued to be of timber, wattle and daub (rod and twig panels filled with mud or clay) and reed or heather covered roofs. In those buildings the main, or only, sign of change was the rectangular shape instead of the Iron Age round-house which was less demanding of joint work. In the later shapes of the

Romano-British era two-dimensional frame making became usual. This involved prefabrication on the ground; the frame of one side of the wall and gable was jointed together with a horizontal beam or plate (plat-form) for the base. The frame was hauled upright and set in place with trench and stones instead of postholes. For this framing the Romans used a cross-cut saw to make tenon joints as well as morticing by chisel. They also forged a range of axes for house-building purposes. An adze, however, was rarely used except on ships' planking.

To please the exacting few there were stone-built town mansions and the remarkable homes on the cantons or country vills of the Romans. Here, in addition to advanced woodcarving, were stone-dressing, tile-hanging and mosaic-tapping. The setting was one of wealthy indulgence and, with under-floor heating and bathing, of greater comfort than was to be achieved again in Kent for more than a thousand years. The great estate boundaries are not known to us and, indeed, in east Kent the remains of villas discovered to date are relatively few. That may have been due to the fact that the Saxon marauders along the Channel coast were fearsome to the degree that forts were built under the command of the Count of the Saxon Shore. Rural villas were, to the contrary, remarkably numerous in the valleys of the Darent and Cray and the middle reaches of the Medway.

Whether in east or west, we may picture areas of land under close supervision having advanced woodland management with controlled cutting for coppice products on the outlying lands. Teasingly for us, the surveyor Hyginus Gromaticus (not specifically of Kent), wrote 'If a settler has in addition to his holding of centuriated land a plot of woodland or mountain pasture, this may be recorded by hammering an extra piece of bronze on the edge of the map'. In the pastures, probably there would be protected regeneration of oak and other preferred species. Elm might be wanted for its toughness, ash for its shock-absorbing tool handles and wheel-spokes, wild cherry for its fruit and aromatic firewood. The sweet chestnut plant, to-day's Kentish woodland feature, was first imported by the Romans. The great spread of its coppice over the county was still far into the future but almost certainly it was being grown in the Sittingbourne area, where records of Milton Regis in the 13th Century imply that chestnut formed even then woodland of notable antiquity.

Away from the villas or mansions there were public woods for a community and these were marked on maps. The public might not be allowed access to all parts: for example, the local authority might grow trees and cut them for fuel to heat public wash-houses or some other civic purpose.

The Romans may have brought sweet chestnut to England for its fruit and versatile wood.

We think of stone as the dominant material of the time because it has survived but timber must have been the most usual heavy cargo. With the logistical skills that were their forte the Romans used the marine fleet to transport heavy deadweight along the coast as a superior method to land haulage even on their good highways. That it was a great traffic can be judged from the remains of Roman timber wharves found in recent years below the mud on London's Thames-side.

Tree-ring Counting

In our own time at the threshold of the 21st Century, London's waterfront has suddenly revealed new and accurately dated evidence of the Roman city nearly two thousand years ago. Excavations for new buildings and tunnelling have been examined using the latest state-of-the-art dendrochronology. This description of tree-ring counting was made for the Museum of London's Tower Hill Pageant:-

A reference graph is built up by overlapping the graphs from older and older timbers working back from newly-felled oak trees. In 1981 a continuous reference graph was produced from modern times back to 252 BC. The outer 25 or 30 rings of an oak, just below the bark, are living wood. If these are all preserved an exact felling date can be given. Otherwise we have to estimate how many rings have been removed.

Tree ring counting of ancient timbers is the most accurate dating tool for the years since the Iron Age in lowland England. This archaeological research method has added greatly to the interest and importance of wooden building materials of earlier times, especially where a water-logged oxygen-free environment has prevented biological decay. The mud-preserved sawn and cleft logs from an old London wharf site or beams used in riverside construction are now a source of much information; both intrinsically and in relating time to artefacts of other substances found beside them. In 1981, about 100 metres downstream from the present London Bridge, a massive box-frame was recovered which may have been a support for a bridge or a pier where Watling Street comes to the south bank to the bustling city of Londinium. Tree-ring evidence proves that this support was assembled after AD 78 but before 95.

The state owned all materials won from below ground-level, which partly explains why the initials CL, Classis Britannica, are to be found stamped on iron bars and tiles. The officers of the fleet acted as both works manager and freight handler. In Kent there is evidence that Wealden iron was brought down the rivers Rother and Brede to Lympne (Hythe) for shipment across the Channel or coastwise to the frontier areas of York and farther north. One modern specialist considers that timbers from the Weald forest may also have been shipped to York by this route. That seems less justifiable because the needed timber, unlike iron, would be to hand near York and the military craftsmen ready to convert it would have been in great strength. Almost the reverse perhaps: if the ships used ballast when not in cargo, a return load of timber or York stone might well have found its way southward to London.

Abandoned Alder Coppice

Northern Successors in Cantium

In the early 5th Century the Roman legions and their masters, military and political, began to abandon Britain. Claudius in 402 wrote about the legions returning to Rome from northern Europe, 'As when a herd of cattle has been scattered through some vast forest by a storm's violence and the beasts eagerly make for the sound of the oxherd's song or whistle'.

From this island they were the only incomers, either invaders or immigrants, to leave as a cohesive, though multi-tribal, people. When they withdrew to their embattled southern lands they left some Romano-British descendants, the remnants of a superimposed culture and their roads, always the roads. The effect was quite unlike the absorption of tribes, bands or families, that long line of other incomers, before and since, who have all blended into a mixture called the British.

In the lowlands, the vacuum left after the Romans showed in the absence of civic control, methodical taxation and naval defence. It was to be another six hundred years and more before such a unified control would be seen again in England. The tools of a distant government - its delegated authority, written records, lines of communication - all were to leave with the departing military force. In the next age a partial replacement would be felt from the ministrations of the Church of Rome. It would, though, be allied to a very different, northern, leadership.

We find it a strange thought, at first, that the English Channel was less of a deterrent to a people on the move in late prehistoric times than in our own. During the BC/AD period around 2,000 years ago, the crossing from continent to island was much the same for the North European tribes as making passage along the coast from one headland to the next. The culture and the Celtic language of southern Britain were similar to those of north-west Gaul. Even the Roman soldier, familiar only with Mediterranean waters, would overcome his fear of Ocean to find on the British shore a continuum (his word!) of the surroundings he had seen on recent marches through northern Gaul with its people of similar culture.

The nearest cultures to be different from the southern Britons were on the mainland but more to the north and east. Nearest to Britain in miles were the Frankish or Germanic people, who had a dash of their genes in the Belgic clans which spanned the Channel. There was, no doubt, a mix of the Rhineland Franks in the Saxons from further north and the same between Saxons and Angles reaching towards the Norseland. Although mixed in blood lines and often violently separated by war, these peoples (not yet nations) spoke a different language from the Celts to the south and their un-Romanised culture had gained little from the sciences of the Eastern Mediterranean.

Kent's best known legend after the landing of Julius Caesar is that of Vortigern and Hengist and Horsa. How Vortigern, either the man's name or the title of a high chieftain in Britain, invited two martial leaders from the Low Countries to take the Island of Thanet as their home in return for repelling the Saxon marauders. How the incomers reneged on the British and brought in their own people to dwell in Cantium and subjugated the native population. The story is not too improbable in view of the post-Roman collapse of rule and order in Britain but the wonder is that this new people, difficult to identify from contemporary evidence, should have brought and imposed a new law and lineage durable enough to stand for four hundred years and more. Indeed, the last remnants of inimitably Kentish laws of inheritance and tenure were not to be replaced by English practice until the 20th Century.

38

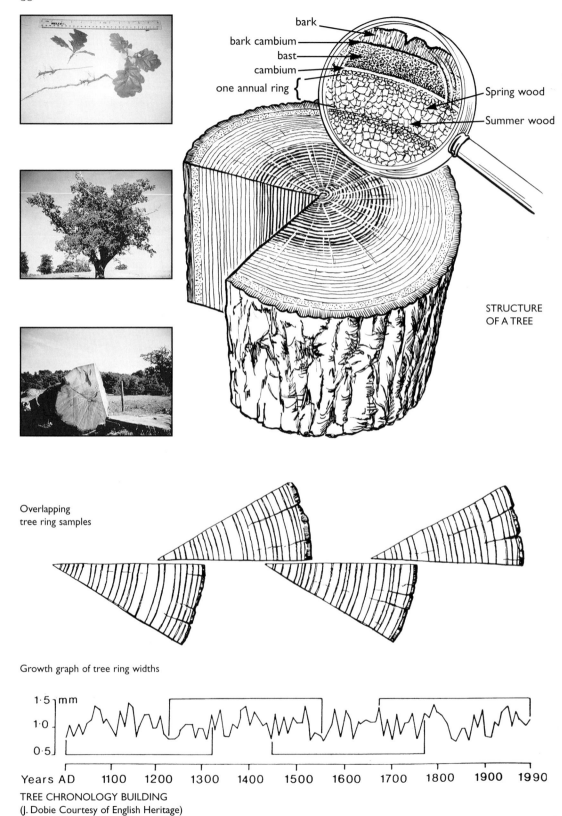

bark
bark cambium
bast
cambium
one annual ring {

Spring wood

Summer wood

STRUCTURE
OF A TREE

Overlapping
tree ring samples

Growth graph of tree ring widths

1·5 mm
1·0
0·5

Years AD   1100   1200   1300   1400   1500   1600   1700   1800   1900   1990

TREE CHRONOLOGY BUILDING
(J. Dobie Courtesy of English Heritage)

THE KINGDOM OF KENT

The Lathes Reach into the Weald

'A desart and waste wildernesse'....'stored and stuffed with heards of Deere, and droves of Hogs only'
(William Lambarde in 1570 on the early Weald.)

'With such generally nutrient poor soils, mainly sandy and podzolic, much of the rest heavy and unyielding and all prone to waterlogging, the High Weald has retained much of its woodland cover.'
(Report of the Agriculture and Forestry Working Group, High Weald AONB Forum - 1991.)

In Kent the High Weald Area of Outstanding Natural Beauty is the land within a boundary clockwise from Hever Castle south of Sevenoaks to Tenterden, then to Appledore on the Royal Military Canal and north again via Bodiam Castle and Bedgebury Forest along the Sussex border. East of the High Weald lies the Low Weald and clay. Here were the earliest dens, wood-pastures of the freemen in the vast common land of the 6th Century. Later the dens were subtracted from the commons as outland for new manors, a tide of possession penetrating up to the High Weald itself.

In prehistory and up to the departure of the Romans four centuries later we have seen that there was intensive development of the fertile soils between the North Downs and the Thames Estuary but that a much wider clearance of primeval woodland, the wildwood, had been hacked out across the Downs and inland at least as far as the vales of the Medway, Beult and Great Stour rivers. In the Wealden forest little agriculture had been attempted. The land did not merit it. Only iron deposits had drawn the early tribes and then the Romans into Anderida's vast folds. This the Jutish immigrants were to change; breaching the forest wall along a wide front yet with evidently close control, and doing it through the curious medium of distant swine-droving.

Horsmon-**den**, Bidden-**den**, Bethers-**den**, Tenter-**den** and all the other dens. The -**den** element means wood-pasture but, if that is all it means, why has it been perpetuated in hundreds of place-names in Kent, and relatively few elsewhere? The answer is that these were names given to new farms or settlements built at locations which did not lie close-in to parent farm or manor, although managed by them, but were notably far from home. Tenterden, the den of Thanet, some 35 miles (56km) away is an extreme example. The bringing of herds of swine such distances to their seasonal fodder of acorn or beechmast and maintaining droveways for that purpose is a Kentish phenomenon. The practice of wood-pasturing was commonplace in Anglo-Saxon England, and probably earlier, but elsewhere the herds were held closer to the parent farm.

The new rulers of Kent quickly appropriated the estates developed by their Roman predecessors on the well-cultivated slopes beside Watling Street, north of the Downs, and also the earlier-settled sites beside rivers breaking through that line of hills. The Jutes had recognised the value for arable cultivation of the

Acorns: symbol of wood-pasture.

topsoils above geologically recent deposits and the windblown brickearth but saw, to the south of their new homes, an expanse of woodland, mainly oak, on unattractive soils. The tree cover hung thick on the Downland's valley sides nearby, then next, but more openly spaced, on the level chalk and out over the east-west vale where Gault is followed by Greensand, (some beech there) and finally to the dense forest of the Weald with its soils either heavy or 'nutrient-poor'. The motivations for the immigrants were to preserve the good land for arable crops, to respond to increasing population numbers and the food trades but also, surely, from deep instinct to pioneer into new land. During many generations, wood-pastures were opened ever further south and west with drove-den staging points for the swine along the way. All this annual migration was despite the still large forests of Blean, Buckholt and Haradun between the Swale waters and the cliffs of Dover.

These so-called Jutes, soon to name themselves the Cantware, brought with them a way of life that appeared much more akin to the British than the highly advanced Roman predecessors. Roman towns were, in the main, shunned by Jutes who were used to an ungregarious rural life. Their homes looked little different from the Briton's of earlier years with walls of close upright poles and mud in-fill or wattle and daub panels, both styles with roofs of unkempt thatch, although the house shape was rectangular rather than a round-walled construction. They had reverted from the Romans' mass-produced pottery to vessels of wood and leather. The fundamental difference between the two peoples was that the lowland British had submitted to most of four hundred years of the Roman model of taxation, and degrees of liberty and progress whereas the north European Jutes (whoever precisely they were) brought their own self-generated tradition of rights and new artistic skills which showed their remarkable creativity.

Nevertheless, the immigrant artisans did not number scribes among them until some 150 years after the Romans had left. Then the scribes of Bishop Augustine, invited by the pagan king and his Christian (and literate) wife, Bertha, restored to Kent this Roman ability and applied it, not least, to writing deeds of property. The first charters were written only a few years after the mission from

Rome reached Canterbury in 597. Some five hundred of the Jutish-Kentish land and settlement charters drawn up thereafter still exist for our study - and our wonderment. The richness of the collection is surprising but so, too, are the early dates; the first being written in 605, nearly a century before any in powerful Wessex.

In our chronicle of woodland it is helpful that many charters were concerned with wooded common land; the act of drawing up was to define areas which would thereafter be owned by a manor for pasture and timber. Charter evidence is just one source for the meticulous research into records and fieldwork by which surveyors and historians have given us a marvellous depth and breadth of information about Kent's once-called Dark Ages. To-day, critiques are published which may refine or reject earlier theories about a royal lineage or the status of a lathe but they only emphasise the long-proven existence of a robust kingdom of Kent with rules which worked well, in grand design and in detail. There is a great indebtedness to the masterly studies published in the 1970s and 1980s by Professor Alan Everitt and by Kenneth Witney who, themselves, drew from the earlier dedication to Kentish history of J K Wallenberg on place-names (1931 and 1934), Edward Hasted with his astonishing single-handed county survey (1797-1801) and many other authors and editors of ancient manuscripts.

The 6th - 8th centuries in an expanded Jutish Kent saw the demands of the royal and, later, the manorial landowners peacefully rationalised into the divisions of land to be known as lathes. The connection with lathe as a turnery machine is a strong one; these being divisions framed or shaped by kingly decree rather than lands accrued into an estate. The nine (as per Witney: 1976) lathes amounted to a kingdom similar to the bounds of the early-20th Century County of Kent. The western boundary is now unclear, and perhaps was never rigidly defined. To-day, evidence of disputed ground may be seen in Joydens Wood (Woodland Trust) in Bexley parish. The ancient Faesten Dic is a mile-long defensive earthwork of zigzagging ditches and banks spaded up at the time of the westward march of the Jutes. It is a rare physical indicator of a probable land frontier line stretching from modern Crayford west to Croydon then south-east to Edenbridge and beyond.

For most of the lathes the shared feature, and a very distinctive one in land apportionment, was the long, narrow reach from the lathe's administrative centre on the cultivated land near the lower Thames estuary to the outlying and increasingly wooded tracts of the Wealden south. The boundaries made by royal decree were practical. They are also, for historians, the best partitioning, when combined with modern place-names, to describe the evolution of a kingdom from what the newly arrived immigrant families found in an already ancient land.

The old royal solution may have been a reasonable, even equitable, one but it should not mask the pioneering ambitions, the energy and fealty which powered this new kingdom. By now the Frankish influence, through marriage and trading contacts, added also to the material progress of this Christian enclave.

(See Appendices 3/1 to 3/3. The diagrams for Chapter 3 and the manorial list for Chapter 4 are based on Kenneth Witney's work, *The Jutish Forest* 1976, with his kind permission.)

To-day's woodsman sees as the outstanding feature of the lathe map the dependence of each division on having a share of the heavily wooded land, even to the extent of including swamp land in order to cross to the distant woods. A more predictable division might be one of squarer, more compact shapes, as in, say, the Sussex of those times and not unlike Kent's modern District boundaries. The reasoning behind the generally narrow Kentish lathes was the same wish for land use by different headmen; not just arable-versus-pasture but emphasis also on silvicultural detail. It seems that the royal vill, or the major settlement, preferred to dispose of its land needs, outward from the vill, like this:-

Arable	Near trading/farming road (Watling Street). Best soils. Cereals, early orchards.
Coppiced Woodland	(Not suitable for swine feeding). Essential for hurdle-making and every form of woodcraft for farm and household nearby
Timber Woodland	Part-cleared as wood-pasture but also for high timber trees, to avoid long haulage.
Pasture/Vaccaries	For cattle; separated from risk of illness from acorns, yew, etc. Also for sheep. Seasonally for swine.
Outlying Woodland	Swine wood-pasture (seasonal) and land for expansion.
Outlying Marshland	For sheep and cattle (seasonal).

With the major settlements strung along the generally more tillable soils north of the Downs, and with marshland or estuary north again of that line (and in the Limen river or Romney area), the north Kent landholder must look south if he wanted to keep the peace. First, to the south, he would seek spring-water and reasonable soil where the ground sloped up to the Downs. Upon the Downs he must allow for the areas of clay-with-flints which, as best, would provide him with thin grass pasture or open woodland. Descending south beyond the high land, and after the band of Gault Clay, he would have the attraction initially of the Greensand belt suitable for arable cultivation but then broken woodland on heavy clays or the risk of swampy ground along the vale of the low Weald. At last he would reach the copious woodland of the Weald Forest itself. At such a distance royal rights would be invoked and the first woodland edges appropriated. The freeman or tenant needs must penetrate still deeper into the forest to gain his wood-pasture. Now, such a land-use description is too neat, too schematic, but it offers an outline for filling out to paint a landscape of the times: its key feature the kingdom's vital woodlands, unusually abundant still but only partly accessible.

Chart Hills, south of Lenham. Crossed and re-crossed by Jutish drovers. Also called the Greensand ridge, this was a favoured settling place for later communities.

We can discern the course of the ancient droves more readily now than at any time since swine trotted along them, thanks to the importance given in modern map-making to minor roads, bridleways and footpaths. Earlier maps may depict woodland now vanished but they usually ignore the faint lines of prehistoric tracks, Roman roads and their contemporary paths not fit for wheeled traffic. The invaluable aid of K P Witney and other local historians gives us the Start, at the royal vill of the lathe, and the Finish, the location of the distant wood-pasture. We have the armchair pleasure of tracing the drove on a local map almost more clearly than by following it on foot. Here are a few examples from no less than 700 dens which, in their later life, were ascribed to 130 manors in Kent and whose records survive.

In the Lathe of Wallington

Now a satellite of Croydon, Wallington once headed the westernmost lathe of Kent. In 862 its manor of Bromley held five dens around Edenbridge. The herd no doubt followed the Roman road on the west side of Biggin Hill which is now at the edge of New Addington. A short stretch of the Roman road is the same as the modern metalled road but that then drops away below the scarp leaving only the line of the Roman road and droveway which crests the North Downs at Tatsfield (240 metres) and descends to the M25 by Clacket Lane Services station before rising sharply again to the High Weald. The demanding route for swine continued along a Roman road through the High Chart woodlands, in parallel with the modern Vanguard Way footpath at the wood-edge, before dropping down beside Crockham Hill to Edenbridge parish.

In the Lathe of Aylesford

In that still-distant future of the Domesday survey, although the king still held the manor of Aylesford itself, all but two of the other

thirty-six manors in this great lathe had been granted to the church
or to the powerful Bishop Odo of Bayeux, half-brother of William the
Norman and Earl of Kent; his position allowing him to acquire more
than two hundred manors. All this was a far cry from the Jutish
foundation. In simpler times, one early example among the manors
was Frindsbury which faces across the Medway river to Rochester.
Long before Odo's day and his building of Rochester's great castle
keep, this manor was granted to the church. As early as 764 two
charters refer to dens apportioned to it, including Ringden to the
south of Paddock Wood. It was more than 15 miles (24 km) away but
the journey was helped at the start by the Roman highway from
Rochester (and Watling Street) southward to Maidstone and
outwards to the iron field above distant Hastings; its line striking
deeply through the Silva Anderida. Probably the Frindsbury herd
left the highway at the south end of Blue Bell hill to go on through
the head town of Aylesford and by East Malling along an older iron
track which led to Brenchley and beyond. Ringden being still owned
by the manor in the Domesday Book survey, it is reasonable to
believe that great oaks were felled at this southern wood-pasture
and carted (floated?) to build the majestic Frindsbury barn. It was
erected in the early 14th Century and, at 200 ft (61 metres), it is the
longest covered barn in England.

In the Lathe of Lyminge

Ethelburga, daughter of the first Christian king, was widowed in
633 when King Edwin of Northumbria fell in battle. She returned to
Kent and became abbess of a monastery at Lyminge which was built
and endowed for her. Her wealthy manor at the centre of this lathe
possessed twelve dens, still to be recorded 600 years later in a
survey of the archbishop's drof-dens, those swine herd staging
points to distant wood-pastures. The drof-dens marked a line south-
westward through Woodchurch to as far away as Sandhurst (near
Hawkhurst). This shows how incomplete is our understanding of
the reasons for ownership of Wealden dens. At Lyminge, a lathe
dependent not on the Thames but the Limen, there were nearby
wooded commons, which became the Minnis, and many square
miles of woodland in the old Haradun (Hardres) forest. Indeed, even
in the late-18th Century Edward Hasted could report that Mr
Sawbridge of Olantigh had 'Westwood, near two miles in length' and
'altogether 700 acres of woodland in this parish (Lyminge), the
whole of his estate here having been formally appertenant to the
Manor of Lyminge'. That wealth of woodland notwithstanding, we
may place a ruler on a map to-day and see how a straight enough
line of quite direct minor roads joined up by straighter footpaths
leads from Lyminge via Sellindge past Woodchurch and on, on,
southward some 22 miles to the wood-pasture at Sandhurst. Who
knows but that this route may have been pioneered before Roman
roads existed; there was a prehistoric iron way going west-east to a
haven on the Limen or Rother.

In the Central Lathes

In the area covered by the lathes of Hollingbourne, Milton and
Faversham we see most clearly the unlikely effect of modern narrow

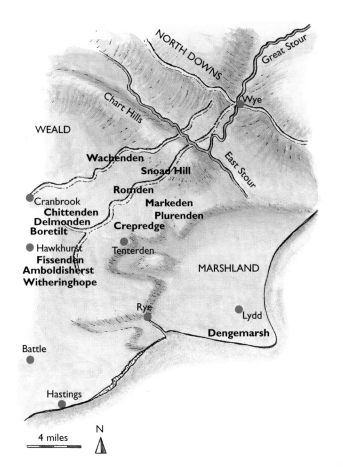

Dens belonging to Wye.

Jutish pig herdsmen kept seasonal wood-pastures in the common lands of the Weald and later settled there.
(Courtesy N. R. Bannister)

roads based on droveways which had been created only to go to wood-pastures and which are aligned north-south, across the natural lie of the land. Inside the area bounded by Chatham/ Faversham/Challock/Maidstone there is, apart from the 20th Century M2 motorway, no purposeful road from west to east whereas at least twelve vehicular ways cross the hills from north to south. Without question these are the dozen selected from the abundance of north-south droveways for tarred macadam surfacing around 1920. There are now some link lanes zig-zagging approximately west-east for the needs of local traffic.

Zooming in on a point at the edge of this area, one may focus just south of Charing which is mid-way between M20 junctions 8 and 9. At map reference TQ939503 to 953495 there are three minor roads within the space of a mile which, due to the generous road-surfacing programme of the early 20th Century, strike parallel lines to the south-west. Droveways. Being motor roads they are clearly seen on a 1:50,000 map but motorists who pause there will also see that the majority of footpaths are oriented in this direction. Two of these routes are associated with earlier iron ways. The western of the three roads and its attendant paths may be traced readily from Faversham (Ospringe) and Painter's Forstal over the Downs to Stalisfield Green, then Charing and the Chart Hills before a quick drop beyond the Great Stour to the Low Weald and the flat vale of Sherway and Beult rivers. Faversham held a den here between Egerton Forstal and Swift's Green. The three routes from near Charing all cross the Beult in the Smarden area among the royal and early dens in the commons acquired by Faversham, Canterbury or Wye. Climbing slowly again, still in rough parallel, the droveways pass into the High Weald between Biddenden and Three Chimneys.

Motorists will sense a leap of the imagination on an autumn day after leaf-fall, when the bones of the old land are most apparent. But the best feel for the trek of the swineherd and timber-wagon comes from walking the route; in the return direction with the sun over your shoulder to avoid the glare and lengthen the view. That the droveways crossed the grain of the land to reach the wood-pastures is emphasised for the walker. He crosses not only the railways and motorway, with their modern London orientation, but also the two westward long-distance prehistoric trackways on the dry ground, now picked out as public footpaths; the Greensand Way and North Downs (Pilgrims') Way.

The location of the early dens is far enough west and south in Kent to imply that there must have been very little remaining wildwood or secondary woodland between the Watling Street headquarters and its outland wood-pastures. We know that the Romans had demanded a huge surplus grain production in Cantium. Very possibly, as Everitt allows, to the south of the Tonbridge-Ashford line the heavy flat ground had been broken into by the ploughs of the Iron Age or Romano-British but later abandoned to revert to trees and scrub, perhaps not initially rich in acorn crops. Looking north next, at the higher Downland, can we equate the idea of clearing sparse but usable tree cover in the 5th Century with the snail-and-pollen investigation at Brook (Chapter 2) and its suggestion of earlier high hill clearances in 2000 BC and again in 500 BC? Three times cleared? That possibility moves up the scale to probable, given the thousand years or more of regeneration between each felling. Who is to predict what portion of our land will be tree-covered one thousand years from now?

In the 6th Century, so unfettered was the freeman or ceorl, who then gave his loyalty directly to the king, that he could make his own pasture clearing in the commons of the Weald or other large woodland areas such as the Blean on the clay caps of the north lands or the Haradun forest south-west of Canterbury. Presumably, in these outbacks away from the royal centres the immigrant freeman fraternised and interbred with the 'Britons', those immigrants of previous tribal movements now seen as the natives, who had not moved away to western Britain. For both cultures the method of ground clearance can only have been with implements hardly advanced beyond those of the Iron Age Belgic forerunners in Kent.

The Jutes took very little advantage of Roman skills in urban administration and technical knowledge. They must have imported iron implements from afar, yet they did not cut timber by saw. Astonishing as it may seem to us, the incomers used Roman tracks to the Weald but ignored the ironworks at the end of the trail. They did, though, take over iron sites, not for metal but to adopt the already cleared or coppiced woodland around the site for wood-pastures. K P Witney has elucidated this from Kentish locations in the Edenbridge-to-Penshurst area with place-names ending in 'field'. There is, in Kent, only a minor occurrence of this Germanic component in descriptive place-names when compared with the 'dens', already noted, and with 'hurst' which means 'wood' in the sense of a **separated** wood. Otherwise the word wood must have been so unremarkable as to have no value in identifying a place. All etymologists give warning that we should not try to squeeze out of a name information which was never there. One fallibility can be seen in 'tree' names. A location named after a tree species may very well indicate that the species was **not** plentiful in the district but rare enough to be noteworthy. Similarly, the absence of certain tree names does not indicate the lack of that species in the area; oak being the best example in Kent.

'Hurst', though, is a major place-name component today. Its area of use, mainly in the Weald, and the implication of a detached wood indicate a later place-naming than 'den'. J K Wallenberg believes that the prefix of objects or animals, e.g. Staplehurst from stapol - post, pillar, staple, or Hawkhurst from OE_heafoc = hawk are probably the earlier pre-conquest namings while a personal name, e.g. Shadoxhurst, would have been chosen later. What is not clear, either from the landscape or the names themselves, is why a ring of towns and large villages should have 'hurst' as a locally grouped name in south-west Kent and across the kingdom's border among the Saxons: Goudhurst, Hawkhurst, Lamberhurst, Ticehurst, Wadhurst etc. Possibly in the early-exploited forest of the southern Weald the 'detached wood' settlement names were so many that the apparent grouping became mathematically likely. These become fewer westward into Sussex where the iron 'field' endings soon replace 'hurst' as the dominant element.

The English but alien-sounding word 'transhumance' (Latin trans/across + humus/ground,) is the precise term for moving livestock to another ground. 'Droving', though, is a Germanic word to its earliest roots among northern tribes and the fact that it has come to mean, especially, moving livestock over long distances is appropriate to the swine herding across Kent. We have already offered a topographical explanation for such distances from parent pasture to outlying woodland but probably, and increasingly so as manorial dens became formed out of the commons, the distance to these outlands needed to be justified, if possible, by farming advantages.

We know that acorn crops vary widely in their annual weight and time of fall; one good crop in about four years is expected after the tree is some thirty years old. For the swineherds the weather as crop time approached could affect the conditions of the home pasture as well as the state of the long, maybe mud-bound, track. We in Kent have been influenced by the Domesday Book use of 'pannage', an area assessed by the number of hogs it could feed, to exaggerate the importance of acorns or beechmast. These fruits would be a welcome part of the animal's intake when it rootled also for fungi and bulbs. The more so because there were then no bountiful root-crops for fodder, as we know them today, in the home fields. Cattle were left at home because acorns reduce their milk yield, and forage from cutting tree branch and bud would be palatable only in the Spring (except for iron rations in severe winters). It seems that other compulsions or attractions had to be sought to make worthwhile the difficult annual migration.

Certainly the resting of the home swine-fields would be an advantage, just as would moving the sheep from marsh to high ground. The two herdings may have been carried out consecutively. At least one charter tells us that the swine-feeding season, the pannage, at the distant wood-pasture lasted seven weeks. In that period the herdsmen, perhaps with their families, would undertake more than overseeing the hogs. At the risk of mild fines, a little tilling could be done - and more next year - the living shelter could be improved and enlarged and, above all, permitted sizes and amounts of wood must be cut. Apart from cutting wood for shelter and fuel for the den, the charters tell us of duties to bring home loads of hurdle wood, of fuelwood for hearth or for salt-panning and sizeable timber for the manor.

Settling of New Rural Communities

In time the herdsman, like the freeman before him, and more particularly his kin would feel settled enough by several seasons to look for assured rights to live permanently at the den. Meanwhile there is the hazy picture we conjure up with great curiosity of the long droving with its overnight outspans. So many questions still unanswered. The use or not of herd dogs, the belling of pig herd leaders, the number of pigs herded? The arrival after days and nights in unpeopled country at a half-clearing with hurdles needed for new fencing and what sort of shelters, and were there wolves as predators? The return journey, with animals on the hoof or already in a wagon, slaughtered and salted?

The part of the Weald that is in Kent covers some 260,000 acres (105,000 ha), about a quarter of the whole county. A particularly close look at it has been taken in this Jutish chapter because of a unique transhumance, acknowledged in the narrow shapes of Kent's lathes. To-day its heavily wooded High Weald country of tumbled contours is a contrast to the broader North Downs passing a few miles away. The North Downs area, at first glance from the foot of the sixty-miles-long scarp, is seen as relatively treeless but its originally complete tree cover has been replaced by a substantial secondary woodland on the flinty plateau. Like the Weald, the North Down's Jutish settlement, or perhaps human re-settlement, began in the 7th Century; much later than the burgeoning communities of the Watling Street line and the rivermouths. The pressure on those fertile lands may have reduced in the late 6th Century when large numbers of martial sons who preferred conquest and booty to the pastoral life emigrated to the Mainland or along to Southampton Water.

Thereafter, in some parts of the northern Kentish uplands, new settlements from the already ancient rivermouth and upstream sites began to lead off, 'layering' in the forestry term, upward and inland on the course of small tributaries and dry valleys to the high ground. One factor in this settlement pattern was to secure wood-pasture and timber en route, as it might be said, to the eventual clearing of land on the upper contours for grass pastures and homestead, and arable tillage wherever the land was suitable. It was land acquisition in the style of previous ages but in settings where it had not before been thought necessary to settle

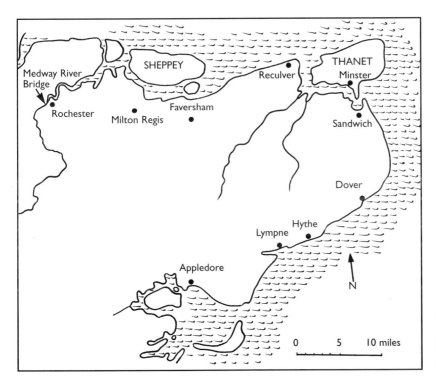

Kent coast in the 9th Century: the coast was the highway. But now Danish raiders threatened channels and inlets.

permanently, even as single farmsteads. In the north-west, above the Cray and the Darent, these upland extensions were few initially because of the Saxon frontier but the pattern was found here, too, in later centuries. Along the central stretch of the Downs, as at Hollingbourne, there were incursions into the hillside to the north but a competing attraction was the line of lower Chart Hills immediately to the south. It seems therefore that the first valley-to-upland settlement lines were in East Kent, notably in the Bourne area between the Stour river and Deal and influenced by the early total forest clearance of the Thanet and Deal arable lands.

All over the North Downs plateau and intervening valleys the later community developments and the devising of Christian parishes were to echo the earlier dependence on woodland. As Everitt has shown in his fascinating study, many of the parish boundaries above the Elham valley of the Nailbourne or along Stone Street from Hythe to Canterbury were devised around the homesteading in order to allow all users a measure of woodland, just as did the original lathes of the kingdom.

A Landowning Hierarchy

During the 7th Century the rapidly strengthening influence of the Roman missionary church became a power to equal the kings of the Esking line. In 604, while Ethelbert was still king, the Canterbury priory was quickly followed by bishoprics at Rochester and in London; the choice of old Roman cities reinforced the Imperial link. The secular world became graded by classes of preferment by the king. These institutions could only restrict the freedom of the pioneering years and the written word was here in the land once more to help enforce decisions of property ownership. Witney says of those times:

> From the early seventh century onward a succession of royal grants of land were made, first to the church and later to the great men of the king's household, grants which included numbers of free tenancies and the rents and services owing from them. In this way ecclesiastical and lay lordships came to be formed interposing between the freemen and the king; and out of them, in due time, the manors developed through grant by the lords of land to their own retainers or (more often in the case of the church) by farming out different parts of the lord's estate or the appointment of stewards to administer them.

The eventual ownership of hundreds of dens by more than 130 Kentish manors will remind us of the importance of distant wood-pastures to the surging ambitions of the church estate managers and the senior Jutish, or Cantware, families. Witney's map showing various formations of the manorial dens (see Appendix 3/3) will tempt the reader into further exploration of this critical and enthralling stage in Kent's woodland history.

Great Landowners of Church and State and Their Wide Trading.

The urge to make gifts of grandeur to the holy church was first manifested in King Ethelbert's grant to Bishop Augustine in 605 of the whole lathe based on the royal demesne at Sturry (that kingly site once chosen as a centre to avoid the Roman-built Canterbury). For the previous one hundred years the king's lathes had been as much agrarian holdings as administrative districts. His power was applied directly in the farming of the land as well as in laws and taxation. Ethelbert's demonstration of Christian generosity, therefore, was the greater because of the worth of the rich soil he gave up in the northern grain-growing area rather than the heavy clay or hungry sand in the west of his kingdom. This open-handed nature of the donations to the church continued until at least 725, when the first Wealden dens were granted specifically by King Wihtred to Minster Abbey. In later times the church in Kent accrued a vast acreage of timber land, not necessarily wood-pasture, presumably because there was no need for quick money returns from its land when there was so much assured wealth to hand. In a similar way, but into the distant future, the lord of the manor would be obliged to let poorer relatives or tenants have sufficient annual-crop land and thus he kept much timber land in his own demesne.

By the 7th Century these Jutes, Cantware or Kentlings had already made a substantial body of law which was to be known as the custom of the land, hence the Custumal of Kent. Within that was the developed tradition with its better known name, gavelkind. A woodland chronicle is not the place to embark on what William Somner (1660) delightfully entitled *A Treatise of Gavelkind, Both Name and Thing* but its mention here is to signal the growing importance of Kent's own laws in matters of land and property and, in a more amenable way, of service. Kent laws, notably of tenure, were to be allowed to continue after the Norman imposition of new legislation, unlike those of the rest of lowland England. For the Kentish landowner the 'custom' that regularly touched on his daily life concerned requirements of services. Although quite soon to be replaceable by money rent, these are often quoted to-day because they throw light on his pastoral world. In Kent the woodland and wood-pasture rights and duties were to continue with less alteration after the Norman conquest than in those many districts which would come under royal laws of afforestation; the variably wooded Royal Forests and their armies of office-holders.

The names we find quaintly recognisable like firebote and cartbote and the group word for such rights, estovers, are all of Anglo-Norman etymology but the laws they describe are similar to those already practised in Kent. Firebote referred to wood for fuel; here meaning the domestic use of firewood by the lord's tenant or other rightholder on his land. It is said that our modern phrase 'by hook or by crook' had to do with scavenging only that wood which might be hooked, that is bill-hooked, or pulled by crook out of a tree without cutting, presumably by axe. The bill-hook interpretation seems too generous for simple firewood. Hedgebote was the term for fencing material; usually cut by 'hook'.

Timber trees were retained for the lord of the manor.

These rights, often mentioned, should not mask the huge volume of small woodland produce cut for industrial use, however mundane. The dependence on hurdles, and wattle, throughout the economy has already been mentioned. Firewood had to be cut and carted for hearth and kiln and, in coastal Kent, for salt-panning. A grant in 732 by Ethelbert to Lyminge Abbey made an annual allowance of 120 laden wagons of wood to fuel a salt-pan at West Hythe. One pan only, or more? At Chislet, with its royal vill on the edge of the Wantsum channel marshes there were said in the Domesday Book to be 47 pans. Firewood was carted to the salt-makers who did not have a peat supply nearby. Charcoal would have been lighter to transport but it would crumble to dust in transit (a punishable offence in later times). To make salt the seawater had first to be evaporated to a brine, by heat of sun or fire. The brine was then put in vessels or kilns to be fire-heated until only the crystalline salt remained. The product was not needed to add to the normal diet but was a condiment and, above all, a preservative for meat stored through the winter months. The local Kent industry lasted until imported salt was plentiful and cheap enough from across the Channel or the West Midlands brine pits. Leland, speaking in the early 16th Century of the forests around Droitwich, estimated that about six thousand loads of wood were burned at the furnaces there each year.

The terms cartbote and housebote came into the larger wood category we would now call timber. As a perquisite it would probably have come from a hedgerow grown or windblown tree. Prepared timber of large size and in quantity would be felled more usually to an order from the lord of the manor to his woodsman. The best recorded example in the 7th Century was for the rebuilding and then maintenance of the great bridge over the Medway at Rochester (*Traffic and Politics*: Yates and Gibson 1994). The demands for bridgework material were largely imposed upon the territory of the lathe of Aylesford. It must have been practicable at that time to find sufficient 'trees of oak, elm or chestnut to yield beams 50 ft (15m) long with' a square section of 1½ft'. Those timber lengths, moreover, would need to be fairly free of branches and their knots because the lengths would have to be cleft with wedges and then square-sided with side-axes. From evidence retrieved in recent time from river mud, Damian Goodburn of the Museum of London confirms that the rip-saw known in Britain in Roman times was not used in the Anglo-Saxon period for lengthwise cutting, nor even a saw for cross-cutting; in which it is notably more efficient than an axe.

The deficiency in sawing did not mean an inability to handle timber. (Consider the later Viking ships of strength and beauty of line - using no sawn wood.) In this and in many artistic or worldly aspects the Cantware had reached by the 7th Century a stage at least as advanced as any other northern kingdom. Their working of silver and gold at Faversham demonstrated that standard which also carried into iron for tool-making. The Jutes gained politically from their Frankish connections and from the keen interest of the Roman church in this island.. The two pillars of support, at first, added a disproportionate power for the small kingdom over others in Britain. Along the Thames estuary, Kent was becoming a great entrepot between the European mainland and the increasingly populous Saxon hinterland. Canterbury was an Amsterdam or Antwerp of early times with its ports at Sarre and Fordwich. In addition to agriculture and fishing, international trading had become a main wealth provider for Kent.

Trading evidently was more important than exploiting the iron resource of the Weald, for both Jutes and South Saxons. Nor was iron brought from the Forest of Dean or the troubled north. Heavy goods were best transported by water, making a reciprocal cross-Channel trade with the Rhine area more businesslike than shipping iron bars around the coast of Britain from the Severn. English oak would have been shipped from the Weald down to the Limen haven at West Hythe and across to harbour towns which had no immediate land source of timber. The navigable Wantsum channel with its two entrances around Thanet provided an all-weather haven at Sarre, as did that only other Jutish realm, the Isle of Wight and the Hamble river. Between the two havens lay only Chichester of any account but with the unexploited Weald at its back. The theory that the Jutes made clever use of the two-way vantage points of maritime trade bears scrutiny. Certainly the Kent sea-promontory location was to be the great prize for the almost landlocked Mercians in their savage invasion through Kent in 798.

Could it be that the original Jutish incomers of the 5th Century knew better than most the maritime attraction of Kent and thus chose it over, say, Anglia? They had sojourned for long enough on the Frisian low-lying shore and river estuary until the inexorable rise of the salt sea level had forced them out. From that experience they could see the value of Cantium's location and a promontory facing their Frankish mainland. They would well know how best to farm alluvial soil and marshland. And they would be inured to long haulage and droving to woodland. That the people, ousted by partly natural means from Frisia, should have had so straightforward a design, and a leadership to formulate it, may be too demanding in concept. The reality, nevertheless, was the chosen settlement of Kent by a people which preferred wealth to conquest.

Six Centuries of Rule Await the Norman Hammer-Blow

The 5th Century to the 11th, loosely known as the Anglo-Saxon period, for Kent was really three very different episodes. The first two spanned the time of the kingdom of Kent, some 350 years of independent existence to 820. Of those centuries, however, the marked difference was the relative ability and growth during more than 200 years of the descendant kings of the Esking line and the turmoil across Kent thereafter. The Roman church, with its enormous importance in the minds and lives of men, came to Canterbury and prospered during the Esking succession. Royal grants of land and property to the church were fulsomely generous and the church lands grew to be greater than the royal lands, the more so because royal grants were being made at the same time to secular lords.

From about 785 the erstwhile mainly peaceful kingdom of Kent, other than a brief alliance with Wessex, was battered by the more powerful Mercians and their dominant overlord, Offa. There was destruction and rebellion and there was a rift with the church. Soon there came the new and equally fearsome threat from the raiding Danes or Norsemen. During all this turmoil the cleric managers of St Augustine's Abbey and the community of Christ Church at Canterbury were able to protect their landholdings and increase them in times of low buying prices for the ravaged countryside. Archbishop Wulfred (805-832) could easily afford a Mercian fine for which he forfeited a large manorial acreage in, probably, the Ickham-Wingham area. At his death the complexity of landholdings in Kent did not hide the fact that the church was well on course towards the position found by the Domesday surveyors, 'with something like a third of all the lands in Kent belonging either to the archbishop or the community of Christ Church' (Witney, 1982, *The Kingdom of Kent*).

Through the 10th Century and into the 11th, with the backing of Wessex, the Kentlings could pursue their civil interests. The Danish raids were brutal but launched for plunder, not for settlement. In Kent they left no place-names from their language. In the third episode of the Anglo-Saxon Period the small kingdom was politically reduced. It was to become an earldom under Norman rule but until that last invasion from across the Channel the nature of the region was to change little. The people of Kent laboured for their livelihood or, at the higher secular and church levels, to amass more possessions in the land they knew so well. The region did not change its economic character, with agricultural richness on the northern littoral and there, too, its strong international trading routes. Almost everywhere else it was a quiet land and hard to work with the people depending vitally on the staple products of the great forests.

NORMAN OVERLORDS, THE CHURCH AND THE LONGBOW

Feudal Pressure on the Land

In southern England the second millennium of Christianity opened, like the first, with a century of invasion and alien domination. The year 1043, one thousand years after the Roman invasion, was the first year of Edward the Confessor. Acceding to the throne after the collapse of King Canute's empire, Edward brought with him the manner of his upbringing in Normandy, and his friends, too. The Norman impact on England as a whole was to have many points of parallel with the Roman transformation, most notably the vigour of the civil administration hammered home after Duke William's invasion in 1066.

The picture of Kent in the twenty years before William 'the conqueror' is seen only faintly through the dazzle of his onslaught, in the same way as those last years in Cantium before the Roman invasion. Lowland England in AD43 was more settled, more prosperous and of a higher culture than brief histories can portray. We know that this was true of 1043, this time from the written records of clergy and court.

The large land estates were in place. As landowners, the kingly predecessors of William had gained from their hunting rights over vast areas but the designation of the Royal Forests and their fierce laws were first imposed by the Conqueror. The intellectual improvements begun by Alfred more than one hundred years before were now part of the fabric of the lay courts and bishoprics. Decades before the Domesday survey of all landholdings and dues, there was an attempted analysis of custom throughout England known as *Rectitudines Singularum Personarum*, the Ranks and Rights of the People. Edward 1, eventually canonized, was dedicated to churchly matters; the great physical evidence is his building of the abbey at Westminster. The military governance of the nation was in the hands of Harold, Earl of Wessex, soon to succeed for that fateful ten months as King of England.

The difference between William's England and the country of his forerunners (Harold having had no time to prove otherwise) is shown by the comparison of the looser survey of the Ranks and Rights of the People with the totally materialistic and effective Domesday Book. The manorial land apportionment of Kent which had been developed in Saxon times was adopted swiftly by the Conqueror to reward the Norman knights who had fought with him at Hastings or were otherwise well-favoured. His lavish gifts were often strategic placements but included acts of conscience, notably the founding of an abbey on the site of the invasion battlefield for the souls of the fallen. To endow Battle Abbey he gave the great manor of Wye, the Saxon royal possession which in Jutish times stretched from the vill of Wye to the extent of its lathe south-westward to Bedgebury.

Overall in Kent the church had become by far the largest landlord; the king's main estate was the half-lathe of Milton Regis, a large area but a tiny holding compared with his lands in other counties. In this county the dominance of the church as property tenants-in-chief, and perhaps the complication of Kentish laws of possession, may have slowed the granting of new lay tenancies but this did not deter William's half-brother Odo. (See Appendix 4/1). As Earl of Kent and also Bishop of Bayeux, he acquired huge tracts of land in Kent and beyond. A minor property skirmish is preserved for us by a charter, written in Latin and Anglo-Saxon, when Odo exchanged land with the monastery of Christ Church, Canterbury.

'Odo, bishop of Bayeux, to Lanfranc the archbishop and Haimo the sheriff and to all the liegemen of the king in Canterbury greeting. Be it known to all of you that I, Odo, bishop of Bayeux and earl of Kent, hand over to our mother-church of Canterbury, which was built in honour of the Holy Trinity, that four denns of land, to wit, Losenham, 'Adalardendena', 'Blacecota' and Acton, to be possessed by archbishop Lanfranc and all his successors for their perpetual use. I do this for the redemption of my lord William, king of the English and for my own salvation and for the salvation of those whose redemption is especially incumbent on me to procure. I do it also in exchange for 25 acres of land which are contained within my part of Wickham'. (Wickhambreux.)

The increasingly rapacious take-over of estates by his half-brother must have caused constant nervousness to the king but mostly it offended the church. Eventually, William's own-appointed archbishop, Lanfranc from Normandy, brought Odo to court at

Wild garlic - at the southern foot of the North Downs.

Penenden Heath, the traditional Kent meeting-place at Maidstone, and after this famous confrontation Odo was forced to give back to St Augustine's, Canterbury twenty-five of the manors which he had taken. Six years later Odo was banished from England forever for inciting rebellion. King William's tenants-in-chief, not excluding the church, were the senior of his vassals, all of whom owed him knight's service on a military and a hereditary basis. The control was of the strictest, down to the least sub-tenant manor. In the strategically vital position around Tonbridge, William had placed fitzGilbert and his Lowy lands. With that exception, and his unwise tolerance of brother Odo, he seems to have contrived that no man, other than the church, had too large an expanse of land and command of people in any one place. And his sons had none. Other land-swaps were made, no doubt, to give the holder a better mix of arable, pasture, woodland and water. From all these manoeuvres, large and small, it is not surprising that in 1086, twenty years after the invasion, the king caused to be carried out the astonishingly detailed survey of assets and obligations. Whether done to improve the collection of tax or from cupidity or for fear of opposition, the Domesday Survey, with its depth of detail and speed of completion, put the Norman mark of ruthless administration on the land and on the people like a great seal to a parchment.

The detailed vagueness of Domesday Book woodland

And yet, for all its zeal of inspection, the Domesday Book frustrates our wish to learn about the woodland of that time. There are reasons for this, introduced with the words of Dr Harvey in The Agrarian History of England: 'The primary purpose of Domesday Book was to record the assets and income of the tenants-in-chief from their lands'. King William's inspectors were auditors not surveyors; they recorded the acreage of the estate but not its boundary, and for the woodland not even the acreage. For Kent and for much of England the asset of woodland was listed only by a notional 'pannage'; the capacity to feed swine, and the dues for renting it as a wood-pasture. In Kent, especially, the mystery of woodland was yet more complicated by the numbers of dens recorded, by pannage, under the manor placename but located far away. For example, Battle Abbey's manor of Wye had many wood-pastures, of which twelve lay 20 miles (32km) distant around Hawkhurst.

The stocktakers of the 11th Century could record woodland only as an asset most difficult to quantify. Its value as swine pasture applied fully only in a short season of two months in a good year. Its smallwood products were valuable, and annually so, but the long tradition of common rights meant that the realisable value might be very little for the tenant-in-chief. The natural asset of game in the woodland was far from negligible but uncountable. (Soon that consideration would lead to fenced deer parks.) The high value of selected timber trees had long been recognised, with swingeing fines for their misuse: in Saxon times a fine of sixty shillings might be levied for wrongly felling a tree under which thirty swine could stand. But how to value a naturally growing timber asset some 80 or 100 years before its sale puzzled the surveyor then, and still it does now.

The woodland, as with water and rough pasture, remained in immense sufficiency at the location of most Kentish settlements. These were not assets to be carefully detailed, although rapid losses might be noted. Apparently, in East Anglia the Domesday Book comparison of the years 1066 and 1086 deduced that pannage for more than 10,000 swine was lost over the twenty years. No reason is given. Perhaps, too, the Norman surveyors were conscious of woodland being only one remove from pasture. Large tracts of Kent woodland observed in 1086, even in the Weald or Blean or Buckholt, had been part-cleared one thousand years before but the tree-cover regenerated after a decrease in population and the lost Roman demand for grain had meant less land needed for agriculture.

For Sussex, Hampshire and Kent a large area of each county is almost blank of placenames in the Domesday Survey because of the light and shifting population in the Weald. As England's largest woodland area it was to continue to put the three counties out of balance with the lowland norm of land utilisation. That spurs us to try to overcome the failure of the Domesday Survey to estimate the acreage of woodland in Anglo-Norman Kent. Oliver Rackham (1986), with a double question mark as warning, put at 70% the woodland coverage of the Weald, including wood-pasture, in 1086. His 13% for the rest of Kent was also tentative but that figure falls midway in his estimate of lowland counties coverage. We know that the Weald in Kent represents 260,000 acres (105,000ha), which is about one-quarter of the county's surface area.

Using those figures, expressed in acres, the woodlands of Kent in the 11th Century accounted for 28% of the total land; a tree-cover of 280,000 acres among Kent's ancient one million acres total (now 913,000). The comparable figure over the whole of Domesday England, according to Oliver Rackham, was 15%. The Saxons and Normans attacked the Weald harder and for longer than most other English woodland but despite that, and the depredations of the 20th Century, Kent's woodland cover is to-day, as at Domesday, twice the average for England. Its 100,000-plus acres are 11-12% of the county's total land area. The county's population is more than thirty times greater than at the Norman invasion and the modern per capita demand for land to be rendered vegetatively sterile due to housing, transport and industry is, of course, enormously increased. Yet the county has 74,000 acres of ancient woodland sites (pre-AD 1600) still wooded. The survey for English Nature in the 1990s showed that Kent had retained more acres of ancient woodland than any other county.

To return to the chronicle. When King William's inspectors and their local informants strode across a typical parish, what they saw would be recognisable to us now but simpler in most respects. The manorial woodlands were still largely managed under the priorities for their use listed in Chapter 3. Their boundaries would have been less hard-set than to-day. In outlying oak woods, the majority species by far in Kent, the wood-edge was still one of shifting wood-pasturage and of trees being grubbed up for assarts of additional ploughland. Continuing from more ancient times, the line of a stream or natural bank might form a boundary to which would be added hazel hurdles according to temporary need. Hedge-growing was practised nearer to the manor and here, too, a ditch-and-bank as an obstacle to slowly moving cattle but not yet the high-banked and palisaded barriers for the Norman's imported fallow deer. In the wood, large dead tree-trunks might lie unremoved but the forest floor would be cleared of brash as the peasants made kindling for the master and then took firebote rights for their own use.

The scene at the wood-edge will have been simple, indeed, in colour. As spring turned to summer the flower-colour, below and above, was white: the plain white of wild garlic, cow parsley, may or whitethorn, then the sorbus range of rowan, whitebeam and wild service tree and the fading fluff of sallow or willow. Not yet the white candles of the 16th Century horse chestnut and none of the now-common colour spectrum at the wood margin of exotic trees such as laburnum or early summer cherries. The new leaf canopy bestowed its beautiful early summer tinting from the coppery-brown of the aspen to the yellow and vivid lime of English oak. An occasional dark green signalled the holly and yew in the understorey and the rare two-needled pine, but evergreens were few, no Kentish holm oak. The dull green broadleafed sycamore, too, was still a future tree.

This scene was familiar to manors across much of Kent and unchanged by the Norman upheaval in ownership. How the manors related geographically to the pre-conquest world of lathes can be seen to an extent by their grouping as given here in an Appendix 4/1 from the work of K P Witney.

In the Darenth valley, that most idyllic of Kentish settlements, the green-and-white backdrop of early summer would have been enlivened by the hay-meadow flowers. Along the river the meadows were unusually large; their size was noted separately in the Norman survey. On the Darent's straight course, but broader then, up from the Thames to Sevenoaks lies the particularly favoured stretch of five miles from Sutton-at-Hone (the Jutish royal vill) southward to Otford and lands given to Archbishop Wulfred 250 years before the Domesday survey. Today, with faint whispers of old settlements one upon the other from Neolithic times and then a great fanfare at the Lullingstone Roman villa, we should stand on a field slope below the diminished woodland, here to ponder on the complicated Norman tenancies that have led onwards to Kentish landholdings even of the present. Our raised viewpoint might show us the tower of Otford church which was added to the little nave and chancel first built in stone only a few years before the Survey. Parishes there were already; and Hundreds, too, had been interposed on the lathes of Kent in the previous century. The basis of land measurement for its wealth, nevertheless, was the military service obligation to the king from his dependent knights.

At the Domesday survey, Sutton-at-Hone was listed with Dartford and the joined manor was owned by the king. Next southward, Farningham was held of the archbishop by knight's service. At Eynsford, too, the manor was held of the archbishop by knight's service. Here, though, like Farningham and other manors in the Tonbridge area, there were links with the Lowy, the castle-dominated region run by the Clare family (or fitzGilberts), who were to become Earls of Hereford and Gloucester. Lullingstone manor was held by the infamous Odo, Earl of Kent. Filston-in-Shoreham was at the time still part of the archbishop's Otford manor but later was assigned to the Clares of Tonbridge. Finally, Otford manor was the holding of the archbishop as tenant-in-chief of the king. Otford's immense ecclesiastical estate was composed from the settlements of Otford, Dunton, Shoreham, Sevenoaks, Sevenoaks Weald, Halstead, Chevening, Woodlands and Penshurst; it had then a total population of at least 600. (From *Otford in Kent*, Clark and Stoyel 1975.)

To the description of the status of the manors in that heavily settled five-mile stretch must immediately be added their detached woodland areas in the Weald. The brief items of pannage in the manorial listings along the Darenth valley referred also to dens much farther south, away over the Sevenoaks hills, beyond the river Eden, as far off as Ashurst bordering south Saxon country. The Conqueror had positioned Gilbert Clare at the strategic point of Tonbridge, and the king and archbishop were to assign more land to that powerful family, including dens along the old iron-carrying road from Hastings to London.

It was the matchless combination of alluvial soil, gradient, water and communication lines which had attracted settlers down the ages to the little Darenth valley in the west of Kent. Otherwise, larger attractions lay in north-east Kent with the expanse of good soil and sheep marshes, salt and fish, and the Roman road to the continent, then latterly the growth of the Channel ports.In the coastal hinterland, based on England's mightiest church at Canterbury, the land was dominated by the church holdings and, more particularly, those estates granted to Christ Church, the Canterbury cathedral community of monks. The ecclesiastical lands in east Kent included much of the great woodlands of the Blean, mainly plateau clay with gravel, and elsewhere along the North Downs and reaching towards the Channel sea. This did not deter the church from having a large stake in the Kentish Weald woodlands and, indeed, Wealden Surrey. Even Lyminge, a holding of the archbishop heavy with timber trees near to the manor, included those dens on the way to and within the Sandhurst-Hawkhurst area. It was probably this ecclesiastical ubiquity in Kent, as much as the strange property laws, which dissuaded the king from carving out Royal Forests in the county. In south-east Kent, Hugh de Montfort was the lay tenant-in-chief posted there for security by King William. From his base at Saltwood his staff must have overseen much of the wooden defence works of the coastal area. At Canterbury, on the main thoroughfare between London and France, houses were demolished soon after the invasion to make space for city defences and a new, but still timber, castle bailey. (It was to be superseded little more than a generation later by a castle of stone.)

In the Darenth valley that green-and-white of early summer 1086 changed, as every year, to autumn colours. On the western slope the leaves of the beech were 'the first to turn and last to fall'. The villeins, cottars, bordars and slaves had been tabulated as never before but it made little difference to their seasonal round. The swineherd setting out with his charges passed by the resting plough being made ready for the fallow field and the listed beehives to be emptied of their own summer asset. As his cart and recorded oxen team creaked and lurched up the old chalk holloway, the peasant reckoned nothing to that surveyor talking foreign to the masters. His own concern was with the den to be reached to-morrow, the hard-lying and the cold clay but also with the hope for more freedom and gain and even work on a grant of woodland with better soil to be cleared, perhaps even to live upon it.

For in this reign of William I the great swine movements were slackening, after five hundred years, as new settlements and cash fees began to allow the permanent development of the outer Wealden forest. Now, towards the end of the 11th Century, the new Anglo-Norman feudalism upheld the strongest monarchy in Europe. The sometimes brutal order had disciplined the landlords in England but ensured a base of developing confidence for those knights and monks who managed the countryside.

Grim Keeps and Magnificent Churches

From 1100, and the first year of Henry the First, there began a long progress of national events, often turbulent and with life held cheaply, which added up to an immensely positive period. It would take the Norman and Angevin rulers of England into the 1200s and

Rochester Castle. Built by the Normans to secure their communication line with the Continent.

that 'magnificent 13th Century'. At first the outlook was dour. In Kent the two great building achievements, suiting the temper of the times, were the grim keep of Rochester castle in 1139, the tallest in Europe, and the most massive keep of Dover castle fifty years on.

Troubled times and baronial rivalry of earlier years had seen the erection, throughout England, of hundreds of lesser wooden fortresses. The timbers for a high keep raised above an earth mound (motte) and the fencing for the yard (bailey) beside it came from trees and underwood hewn and shaped and raised by local men in addition to their burden of manorial labour. Before these unapproved defences could gather history Henry II ordered most of them to be removed, leaving us with only the lettering on an Ordnance Survey map at some barely discerned knoll topped with trees. A few were strengthened by building a keep of stone, followed by a gatehouse and an outer stone wall. The outstanding example in Kent of an un-royal yet important castle transformed by stages from timber to stone is Tonbridge, still powerful to behold. The fitzGilberts (Clares), with royal encouragement, were to adopt the mound and adapt the building through two hundred years after the family had exchanged it for their castle at Brionne in Normandy.

Church building, or in many cases the re-building in stone of wooden Saxon churches, also resumed in the 12th Century. Often, in little settlements still deeply rural today, a rebuilding of the church was funded by the recently enfeoffed knight or by his secular lord. One such is at Upper Hardres, near Canterbury. After the disgrace of Bishop Odo the manor was granted to the Clares and occupied by the family of Hardres for the next seven centuries. (A handsome estate church after its reconsecration in 1160, it was eventually gutted by fire in 1972, devouring some eight-hundred-years old timbers. Happily it was restored as best could be). Philip de Heac Hardres set out in 1189 with the excited band leaving for the Third Crusade under the new king, Richard I, and his mainland confreres.

The Canterbury of that year was a hubbub also of pilgrims; in increasing numbers they arrived to pray at Thomas Becket's tomb in the crypt below the place of his assassination. Above them there was a dust and din of wondrous new work by masons and carpenters to replace the choir which had burnt down in 1174, four years after Becket was slain. It is the same choir today. Philip de Hardres' family, like the Clares, was French-speaking; his forefathers had probably come to England with William of Normandy and found little need to speak the peasant tongue. The crusader knights felt no strangeness in leaving England.

Yet the Upper Hardres manor was well established and a local provider of Kentish produce for the house and for the priory. Timber from the demesne woods and worked by local men for the little church may well have been followed out by more, to be carted along the metalled Stone Street five miles to the cathedral. In this reach of the deep Buckholt woodlands the Norman family, with its own church of Kentish ragstone, flint and oak, was being assimilated into the very soil. Throughout the shire, in the agricultural lands along Watling Street, across Kent's central vale and among the Wealden dens as far as Westerham, supervision of the king's and the ecclesiastical farms and woodlands became delegated through a more numerous but still feudal hierarchy. The vast Canterbury church holdings were by now divided between the archbishop, Primate of All England, and the priors of Christ Church. It was to the monks that King Richard gave from the Blean a wood known then as Sorotte, later Shoort and now Church Wood, in gratitude for his stay when marshalling the Third Crusade.

In urban England, for us it is the towering beauty of the 'Early English' cathedrals which symbolises the magnificent 13th Century. We can sense faintly the consuming awe in which they must have been held then. New achievements abounded in stone and in brilliant glass pictures. The architecture showed a dramatic development away from the Norman style because the pointed, not rounded, arch, previously achievable in wood only, could now be created in stone. The architect aspiring, literally, to more lofty stonework called for large quantities of straight-grained timber. More advanced jointing was needed and carpenters sought finer mouldings. Surviving examples of wood-carving definitely from the 13th Century are rare but a well-proven fragment of the Canterbury cathedral screen which was the work of a Master Jordan may be seen, and touched, in Adisham's church where it is propped against a wall. A carpenter, although as important as the stonemason, was likely to be a local man with a wide range of work, whereas the masons were far-travelling men who tracked the few great buildings requiring dressed and sculpted stone.

In later years, at the end of the 14th Century would be seen the delightful fine-chisel carvings of wooden pew-end and misericord. For wooden framing, the joints in the timber are not now easily seen but the rare examples show that early medieval framing was developing in strength to give a more durable building construction. The tenon (the insert) and the mortise (the hole) were more carefully fitted even though that work was still done without the aid of a saw until the 14th Century. Stronger frame joints, made firmer still with wooden through pegs, and the, by now, usual base plate to square the frame and keep the upright posts from the rotting earth combined to prolong the life of wooden structures by hundreds of years.

The members of the timber frame were now as likely to be fashioned by rip-saw as by axe. The rip-saw was seen as a completely new invention in those Angevin times unless any worker could deduce from old buildings that the Romans had used the tool in Britain eight hundred years before. The method of sawing a log leant against a trestle, first cutting one-half the length then see-sawing it to cut the other, had not changed. The tool must have been brought back into use by French craftsmen in England as the surge in the building programme caused a shortage of 'sweet', straight-grained tree trunks for cleaving. The revealing saw-teeth marks, with a cutting angle changing at the middle of the piece, distinguished trestle sawing from the device in later centuries of sawing timber over a pit deep enough for the junior of the pair of sawyers to stand in it. Even in later years the trestle continued to be used most at the building site, to meet daily or changed orders, while for more predictable planking for stock or boxing (squaring) and dividing a knotty tree's length a sawpit would have been constructed near a copious stand of trees.

The Church Leads Woodland Management

By the late 13th Century, Wealden woodland laws or customs had moved from a priority of interest in pannage to the conflict of protection or destruction of standing timber and underwood. Here the seasonal wood-pastures were expanding with settlers and the new locals had a keen eye for much more than pig fattening or firewood duties. In east Kent, that larger portion of the county east of the rivers Medway and Teise, religious foundations pursued their ancient customs through a forceful staff of stewards, bailiffs and under-bailiffs. The peasants, by those times, were boldly aware of their right to plead against their lord in the king's courts. In the southern Weald, it was possible to gain good profit from timber by shipping it on the age-old waterway down the river Rother to Smallhythe harbour and by the Brede to Rye for coastwise deliveries or for sale through ports across the Channel. Distant manors, such as Northbourne, near Deal, brought home by sea the timber and smallwood from their own Wealden dens. The same advantage might have applied from time to time to the Blean and Buckhurst forests, sailing from Fordwich. However, wooden building works at Canterbury, needing to be repeated after each of the many fire outbreaks there between 1161 and 1298, must have meant a buoyant local market for timber, board and wattle.

In north-west Kent during these years and into the 14th Century the woodland situation was different. Wooded dens had become hard-won farmland, at Leigh for example, and near rivers many new manors had demesnes encompassing the good soil with outer tenements reaching into the vale of Kent and the High Weald. The population was increasing rapidly in the anciently settled parts, its ripples spreading southward from the Thames estuary. Inward from the Downs, timber and smallwood had not held their value relative to farming produce, partly because there were no navigable rivers for heavy loads to by-pass miles of miry tracks. A different but important factor was that a series of manors was passing from church hands to control by the Clares (by now the Earls of Gloucester) and lesser secular tenants of the king. These transfers of land, to less commercially adept managers, were initiated by the successive archbishops of Canterbury because the burden of providing knight's service to the monarch - or cash fees in lieu - had become very heavy.

From 1272 to 1377 the English monarchs were the unbroken, if far from untroubled, line of Edwards I and II and III. Their state affairs were dominated by Scotland and France, leaving southern England as a supplier to courts and armies with the liberty and profitable purpose to study closely the condition of its manorial economy. Woodland management in the 14th Century was carried on with an increasing awareness that timber and undergrowth were not unlimited. There were more frequent appeals to law. Mainly from ecclesiastical records, we know of disputes involving the archbishop and the priors as their tenants tried to prove a right to woodland produce or were accused of misusing it. During the first Edward's reign, for example, the tenant's pressure upon Battle Abbey resulted in their being granted full timber rights in the lord's woods of twelve dens around Hawkhurst. Other cases were resolved more usually with the large timber being retained by the owner. All this litigation, recorded in Kent in the Black Book of St Augustine and other sources, encouraged more careful forestry accounting, particularly of underwood.

In *A Survey of the Manor of Wye*, researched in 1933 by Dr Helen Muhlfeld (Columbia University), we are impressed by the surveyor's confident measuring, pricing and sense of awareness in The Extent of the Manor, drawn up in 1312. We can hear the clerics, John de la More and Walter, and another John, the serjeant of Wye, propounding with their local knowledge to Henry de la Rye, seneschal of Battle, for him to balance their opinion against his wider knowledge. With a different priority from the Domesday survey, more than two centuries ago, they list woodland clearly after the description of the church, home farm and water-mills and fishery. The following extracts show the depth of detail:-

> 'And there are in the wood called Melecompe 21 acres 3 roods of large timber (grossi bosci) and undergrowth (subbosci) and the undergrowth is valued at 40 pence per annum and not more. The latter should be divided into ten parts for cutting and thus every tenth year can be cut down'.

That the correct translation for *subbosci* is under<u>growth</u> not under<u>wood</u> seems justified —

> '...the wood of Helonde 18 acres of timber and undergrowth and the undergrowth of this is worth 2 shillings and not more because it is for the most part thorns and thistles (fere spire et tribuli). And there is also one acre of timber at Swainlonde and no profit can, as yet, be derived from it. At Ocholte... the undergrowth is entirely cut over...(and) will be worth 40 pence per annum as soon as it can be cut....(and) Schrewingehope 6 acres 3 roods which were assarted from Kingeswood according to the statute of Winchester ... (and) within Wylyet 3 acres of brush of which each acre is worth 4 pence a year'.

Thus the abbey writers concentrated on the value of the smallwood, partly no doubt because they were assessing its worth to the tenants, who apparently had rights on the lord's land to cut wood for repairs. Indeed, from a Customal of Battle as late as the 16th Century we learn that if a right for the tenant to take wood on one land could not be met the lord had to find the wood from elsewhere. Having been recorded, the large timber need not be priced until the time came to fell it. It remains a puzzle that, despite the close detailing, neither *bosci* nor *subbosci* are identified by species. Around Wye in these earlier days the naturally dominant trees, in number and size, would have been oak and ash; the underwood being a mix of their self-regenerating progeny with elder, hazel and willows. However, the woodland acres described in The Extent of 1312 may well have been cut over for so many generations that the underwood types wanted by the users had gained the ascendancy; a selected growth become quite uniform across the land. Or was the naturally found undergrowth so intimately mixed that in any one locality it had a sameness and only the grades of quality and growth - bottom grade being *fere spire et tribuli* - were to be noted?

As the demand for timber sizes grew and availability reduced, one stem per stump was left, as of yore, to stand and grow on after future cuttings of the regenerated coppice. Planting of seed or transplanting by cuttings was practised for hedges, for orchards and ornament but is not recorded for woodland timber trees. The 'standard' or 'store' tree allowed to grow on from the stump (stool) would have a clean bole, avoiding knots in the eventual main length of timber, because the surrounding coppice up to twenty feet (6m) high would prevent light from stimulating buds to make side-shoots on the bole. The species for building timber was nearly always oak. Oak's proneness to recurring side-shoots (epicormics) meant that special beams for church or hall, longer than twenty feet, straight and fairly knot-free became ever more difficult to find.

Although woodland management was much more than the growing of tall, well-favoured, trees, this was the subject of most contemporary letters. From the late-13th and early-14th Century many communications at workaday level can be found in the Christ Church Priory archives at Canterbury. Passing from Latin into anglicised French the talk is of *boys* for woods/woodland, *le meryn* for the timber and *cheverons* for beams. In 1334 an order to a wood-reeve translates (*Literae Cantuariensis II 55*):

> 'Greetings. We order that you deliver to J de Coggeshall, our good friend, (nostre bon amy) six beams of the length of thirty feet in our park at Bocking. And take care that no damage be done in our said park by reason of the said timber so cut down. And we desire that you cause the stumps (souches) of the said beams to be marked so that the Warden of Manors at his next coming may see which trees you have given.'

Eventually in east Kent the ecclesiastical hold on the woodlands and their produce was to become less strict while the lay lords were not as unyielding, or were less vigilant over the minor tenants' commoners. The increases in price which tempted timber tree sales by the owners were incitement to plunder in the farther dens and perhaps to smuggling abroad in Flemish boats at Rye. Sought-after, clean timber was probably as scarce then as it would be at any time for several hundred years to come. The prior of Christ Church might even decline to oblige the heir to the throne, albeit a young boy then but to become the Black Prince, of Crecy and Poitiers fame. (Literae Cantuariensis II 715, translated from French): October 1341

> 'To Lord Sir Edward from the Prior and Convent of the Church of Canterbury. Most honourable Lord, we have received your letters (which are for us, as far as we are able, equivalent to commands) asking us to give to Peter of Guldeburgh, your Treasurer, twenty-four oaks, sound and suitable for building timber in our Wood of Heselyng. But because our said Church is so insecure and dilapidated this small wood of Heselyng has for a long time been reserved from cutting in the hope of great help from it in the time of our need, which cannot be postponed more than a short time, and in that unfortunate case we should not be able to supply ourselves within twenty leagues around.'

'Heselyng' existed still on the 1st Edition Ordnance Survey map as republished in 1819; a wood about 1/2 mile-by-1/4 mile, then spelled Hastling and lying just west of Bramling. But the OS edition of 1933 gives only a strip remaining, a shaw on the flat top of land to protect the orchard planted there.

From the second half of the 13th Century there had come a breadth of convincing evidence that the English kingdom was, if only selectively, more prosperous. There was building work on great cathedrals such as Canterbury and Rochester and a host of simple naves-with-towers on all quarters. Exports of wool to Flanders were huge at this time. In law there was a confirmed establishment of trial by court hearing, instead of by combat, for property disputes. In learning, the century saw the founding of the first colleges at Oxford and Cambridge. The rich indulged in deer parkland.

Deer, Woodbanks and Cattle Pasture

Deer parks had been known since earlier Norman times; the oldest by document was at Trenley Park Wood, just east of Canterbury. Put together by Bishop Odo of Bayeux, it was his determination to complete the park by gaining a 25-acre plot in exchange for no less than four dens which explains the charter, and the bargain, quoted earlier. Also among the earliest was the parkland of the Clares whose chase is still inferred by the surviving name of Cage Green in Tonbridge. Into the 14th Century, at nearby Otford the Great New Park was fenced to enclose 700 acres (283 ha) for the archbishop.

An example of the average size and grandeur was the deer park at Stowting, that forgotten rural hub which once enjoyed the right to a Tuesday market and annual fair. To-day, the land still not built upon, one sees clearly how the park was spread outward from the mound that marks the Norman motte and wooden bailey and the watermill. At the likely boundary around the bowl in the hills is the evidence of the name of Cage Farm. The park can be judged to have covered 200-300 acres (80-120ha). Stephen de Burgh was granted a gaming-right licence of 'free warren' early in the 13th Century and perhaps his descendants were further encouraged to empark by a gift of fallow deer. At nearby Elham Park, we know (Lit.Cant.I. 491) that in 1332 six deer were given on request by the Prior from his Westwell Park to Sir William Clinton, Warden of the Cinque Ports. Anglo-Normans, with increasing wealth and being envious of life in southern Europe, had looked for more fresh meat and variety in their diet. Winter fodder for beasts was not yet a developed staple and, so, for even the rich man the winter norm was a monotony of salted pork, and not enough of that. In a Kent not policed by Royal Forest laws, wild deer was a dwindling meat resource. Roe and red deer, the natives, were not amenable to fenced parkland but the imported fallow deer was. These enclosed deer were helped through the winter by cut fodder and in May, their most voraciously hungry month, by tender shoots from oak and other pollarded trees.

At first many live fallow deer were transported across the Channel but their dependable birth rate in captivity promised one fawn to each doe every year from her second year for some six years. The demand increased but was sustainable locally. Tied feudal labour to dig and maintain the perimeter was also dependable and increasingly plentiful. Only the Black Death in 1349 and its attendant troubles would halve the growth in the number of Kent parks which probably had reached towards one hundred at its peak. Thereafter, the practice of laying out parkland was modified but it continued as a setting for many manors. Although Elham Park remained as a name, the emparkment there, like Westwell, was abandoned before the writing of Lambarde's *Perambulation* in 1570. Stowting remained but, itself, was disparked, at some date before

I

The puzzle of banks and boundary markers

1. Bank profiles
2. At Thornden Wood, Blean
3. Old meandering lines
4. Boundary stubs; hornbeam and maple
5. Dead hedge
6. Fallow deer; young menil buck

parish/
hundred
bank

field
bank

wood
bank

2

3

4

5

6

the next survey of Kent, by Hasted two centuries later. The thirty or so which still contained deer by the end of the 16th Century were complemented by pleasant land of general grazing and widely-spaced, spreading trees. Some of the huge pollarded oaks to be found in the vicinity of deer parks may just be survivors from the enclosures of the 12th - 15th centuries. Most of the old giants, venerable nevertheless. are pointers to later, post-Civil War, landscape management, with or without deer. At Lullingstone Park, with Susan Pitman's 1983 study, the walker can follow with pleasure the history of a medieval deer park which, unusually, retained deer until recent times.

From their Norman beginnings deer parks had cages for close control of the high-leaping fallow when it was needed. On the perimeter surrounding the park there must also be a quite formidable barrier against their escape. The park area of pasture and trees was usually circular or oval, that shape being enclosable more efficiently than an angular one. A ditch was dug, to perhaps a metre, with its spoil banked on the outer side to present the greater height from within the park. Atop the bank, deadwood was piled or a dense hedge grown to complete the pale. This enclosing bank-ditch for the docile but agile new imports was the opposite in construction to other traditional boundaries which marked property in general, and coppiced wood in particular. Browsing animals had to be kept out of the latter until the new shoots (or 'spring') had grown to a safe height.

In the Blean, by Canterbury, property woodbanks at Thornden were set up before 1252. The boundary now appears as a bank two metres or more across. Here, it is also seen in the form of two parallel banks with an ancient way in between. The way is named a 'radfall' which is thought to derive from 'rod', the old linear measure, and 'fall' as in tree-felling. The implication of that, with apparent felling between the banks, is that the banks dictated the ancient way. The reverse, of course, is possible - an existing way divided two properties and boundary banks were formed by both owners.

Wealthy owners found bank-and-ditch barriers a worthwhile long-term investment towards their coppice industry by providing a protection with relatively little maintenance, other than for topping when necessary with deadwood or hurdles if there was no hedge . Ancient boundaries at the wood-edge took every advantage of natural bank, gully or stream. Their seemingly haphazard line, to-day, helps to distinguish an ancient woodland site from a modern one with straight boundaries made easy by powerful machinery. A few old properties even had such anti-browsing barriers dug to surround sub-compartments within a large woodland area for use in the repetitive coppice cycle. However, to-day's possible evidence of an internal boundary might equally well be the profile of a drainage ditch cut beside an old working-track. To-day's woodland archaeologists win new insights from the experienced study of linear features on the ground and the living plants entangled with them.

The manifestation of wealth in the reigns of Edward I and II and the early years of Edward III did not imply a concentration into few, large estates as was happening elsewhere in England under laws different from the gavelkind of Kent. Here the unique way of dividing inherited property and other factors were allowing steadily more freemen to obtain land as they came to afford it through their improving income from wool or grain. The source of nearly all wealth was still agriculture, with fishing, and by the end of the 13th Century Kent was relishing added profits from sales to London and exports through Sandwich. Across most of the county, woodland was now to feel the last great attack by axe and ploughteams for hundreds of years to come. Pasture, too, was ploughed up for arable crops in these boom years and some of the heavier land then eased with marl (quarried clay-lime) for better yields.

At three of the distant corners of the county the soil was good and the tree cover had been sparse or nil since prehistory. The treeless marshland beside the busy port of Rye lay there in contrast to the heavy seagoing traffic in timber from its hinterland. On the peninsular island of Thanet and the thickening Minster marshes the soil had long invited the farmer and only a rare placename hinted at past woodland. In the north-west was that land area to be deducted from Kent county in modern times. The ground there changes beyond Crayford and Croydon from chalk or alluvial richness to heath and the clay of the London Basin. By the 14th Century the deciding factors in land use in this area were the demands from nearby London, whether it be for food growing, for parkland such as the one thousand acres of the first two parks at Eltham Palace, or coppice wood to supply the city's ravenous ovens and hearths.

These county corners were indeed peripheral to the Kent woodlands which massed from the Blean to the High Weald. After about the year 1000 until 1300, undeflected by changes in kings and causes, the axeman had fought the trees for agricultural land. The reduction in woodland from some 300,000 acres (121,000ha) in Saxon times to 100,000 acres (40,000ha) to-day was largely achieved in those three centuries of arduous manual clearing.

Black Death spurs the Kentish rebels

To gain even second-rate crops for the rising population much of this new soil had to be improved, adding to the Herculean labours. But the dependence on climate, everywhere, was still total. Great storms, such as the one which changed the course of the river Rother overnight in 1284, were followed in the next century by severe drought, and then pestilence struck the farm animals. Clearing and marling of newly-won marginal fields declined as lack of money to develop the land made the small return no longer worthwhile.

Within that ill-fated generation recurrent plagues, some lethal to humans, increased in severity. What was to be named the Black Death came, therefore, in the autumn of 1348 not unexpectedly. But its whirlwind savagery had no precedent. Among every ten living people, three or four or even six were suddenly dead. So shattering was this plague that in other European countries the whole fabric of society was threatened by behavioural extremes of reaction, from flagellism to advanced hedonism. In England, firm rule held and perhaps, indirectly, brought a new sense of urgency to daily work.

Certainly the monarchy and the courts recovered their way quickly. In the second half of Edward III's long reign war was prosecuted in France and Scotland. Parliament produced many and varied Statutes, notably the far-reaching Statute of Labourers, as soon as 1349. This, with its re-enactments, was a speedy attempt to force the dramatically reduced number of labourers (but a greater portion of them now made landless) to work for wages fixed before the plague. The penalty for refusing was imprisonment and family destitution. The statute was a dismal point along the arduous course from a society of local custom, of personal and feudal service, to one of a nation-wide economy.

Feudal employment ties, and the perquisites that went with them, had slackened already. The term yeoman might now be applied to a freeman holding more than twenty acres and that of husbandman to a peasant with a smaller parcel of land to work. With the risky freedom of action and new responsibility for many came, too, the assertion of practical thought and the need for many minds to communicate their viewpoint. Old terms to define conduct were losing their force. The people of Kent, not for the last time, were in the vanguard of the opposition to the self-interest of their masters in London. In 1381, with the yeoman Wat Tyler at it's head, the throng from Kent and Essex came close to causing the crown to fall. The young Richard II saved the day by instinctive behaviour but only after the Chancellor of the Exchequer, also Archbishop of Canterbury, had been killed. His successor, Archbishop Courtenay, built Saltwood Castle's magnificently high gate-towers - no doubt, to impress the rebels of Kent rather than some invading enemy.

Archbishop Courtenay's gatehouse towers at Saltwood.

Top: St Mary's Church, Wingham

Above: 14th Century carpentry in oak

Right: Timberwork in sectional view to West
(Courtesy of Canterbury Archaeological Society)

The Yew - holy provider of the longbow

The intermittent war with the French was still in the first half of its Hundred Years. The victories at Crecy (1346) and Poitiers (1356) had come a couple of years on either side of the climax of the Black Death. The yew tree held a now revived religious significance; in East Kent it was called the palm, for which it substituted in holy ceremonies. From Crecy, through Agincourt (1415) and on for more than two hundred years, the name yew was to be equally famous, but practical, for the weapon of English battle-supremacy.

In woodland, from whence came the poles for the six-foot longbow, the yew was probably never a major species. Along the North Downs and the Chart hills, where yew groves are mostly found, the truly ancient specimens are not in the wood but in the churchyard. The older of the two yews at Ulcombe church dates from early in the Iron Age; it was already some 1,750 years old when Crecy was fought. There is, however, no written record of churchyard yews being cut to make bows, except a reference in anti-clerical Cromwellian times. The dark groves of relatively young yews within woods had been sought out for weapon-making since before the last Ice Age, when a spear found at Clacton was made. For the longbow, the yew provided the best combination of weight, strength and flexibility; ash was a flexible but lighter alternative.

Following his success at Crecy, Edward III issued an early proclamation via his sheriffs of London demanding that men strong in body should 'use in their recreations bows and arrows' and not waste their leisure on ball-games or other fancies which did not assist the defence of the realm. For it was the defence militia, the home guard in every settlement, which brought all men to some knowledge of weaponry. The English, and South Welsh, bowmen are said to have kept their supremacy for so many generations because of the body stance they learned; throwing their whole weight into the bending of the bow's wood. At Agincourt, archers still dominated the battle, in John Bowle's words, 'with their six-foot yew bows and their long arrows, accurate up to 250 yards in a sleet of silent death'. Even into the 16th Century, Hugh Latimer, later the martyred Bishop of Worcester, could describe how his yeoman father had taught him the English skill.

Proclamations and Acts to secure supplies of the longbow and skills to use it continued at least until the Elizabethan Act of Bowyers. This, and Acts in previous reigns, set the prices for longbows and it is noteworthy that imported bows were allowed to cost three times as much as a bow from English yew. The 1545 publication *Toxophilus* by Roger Ascham explains that the six-foot bows might be made from the branches by pollard cutting, or the trunk. Regrowth from the stool or by striking cuttings would be very slow. It is possible, maybe probable, that the majority of bow lengths came from imported yew grown in southern Europe which offered less knotty branches and, therefore, trees which would be more likely to survive the bowyer's cutting than English-grown. Imported yew bow-lengths were higher priced, perhaps for their better quality. Or was it simply that yew supplies from English woods, never plentiful, had been exhausted and the continental merchant could demand prices high enough to make worthwhile the exhaustion of his yew groves in turn? Supplies kept coming, as we know most recently from the raising of the flagship of Henry VIII, the Mary Rose, with her provision of 139 bows and 2,500 arrows. However by Elizabeth's time the Bowyers Statute bade the makers to stock a preponderance of elm, witch hazel or ash over yew. These inferior species, in archery terms, may have been an important factor in the bow being superseded by the gun.

In English archives there is a surprising lack of references to yew woods being exploited for bows or, apart from royal exhortations to do so, new plantations cultivated to meet the long-term need. Considering that the archery butts of a town were an established commonplace, it is strange that little evidence remains of yew plantations on the town's boundary. For most people the naturally regenerated yew grove, cavernous and gloomy, was a place of ancient, unchanging awe. But to the bow-maker, during the long success of English archery in the 14th - 16th Centuries, the yew grove beckoned invitingly amid a wintry woodland. In those days it was unique as an evergreen grove, having no colour competition from the Scots pine of the past or the rare new appearance of the imported Holm oak and none yet from plantations of Norway spruce; which species was just being re-introduced after its absence since the last interglacial age.

FROM LATE-MEDIEVAL KINGS TO IRONMASTERS

The Rise of the Woodward

The drastic loss of woodland acreage in medieval Kent came about because of the striving without end, as it was seen then, for more farmland. Resuming quickly after the Norman invasion, it continued as far as 1350 when the conditions culminating in the Black Death brought a sudden halt. Now were to come another three centuries throughout which men expected that another intensively productive regime must go on for ever, but this time within the woods. When that era, too, faded, around 1650, fossil coal was still known as seacoal or pitcoal to distinguish it from the familiar fuel of the lowland woodcollier. Steam power was even then one hundred years away. From after the Black Death, and the oppression that led to Wat Tyler and the Peasants' Revolt, until the days of Cromwell and his Commonwealth, the woodlands of Kent were to be worked as never before.

A suitable setting in which to consider this long period in local history is King's Wood, a mile south of Leeds Castle and near enough at the centre of the county. The wood is one of many to have been given that name when the early Jutish kings divided their land monopoly between themselves and the warrior class of the ceorls. That was many centuries before a castle of stone and a priory were built beside the Len stream at Leeds following the Norman arrival. King's Wood covered the land without a break from Langley Heath to Fairbourne Heath; some 1500 acres (600 ha). It had, then, a traditional woodland cover of oak with hazel and birch on a ground of stony, gravelly, loam. In the early 15th Century there was the prosperous cloth industry down the hill at Headcorn. Stout buildings in the locality, both Wealden hall-house and castle, were adding new demands to the woodland activity which already must supply all the material for more-humble dwellings, farm stores and field fencing and charcoal and firewood and the special needs of wheelwright, millwright and wagon maker and bowyer. Indeed, it is a wonder that the man in charge - be he named woodward, bailiff, woodreeve, serjeant, warden or forester - could cope with all the traffic in his domain.

The feet-on-the-ground management system of King's Wood in the 15th Century is unclear to us now. Its western reach belonged to a priory at Leeds, hence the name Abbey Wood to-day, but in general the forest area was under the king of the moment or his tenants, or wives indeed, at Leeds Castle. After a history of siege and hangings and royal witchcraft the castle had settled into relative calm by 1450. A century later Sir Henry Guilford was made constable and also had a grant for life from Henry VIII for the parkership of the Langley deerpark (not long before it was disparked). Direct management by the king existed in Kent but the record is hazy. For 1533 the annual accounts have been preserved of William Payne, deputy in Kent to 'Robert Henneage Esquier, Master of the Kinges highness Wooddes'. The sales recorded, stretching from Eltham to Tonbridge, were only small lots of coppice and tops. The implication is that nearly all wood sales were handled by manorial staff. The four manors of Langley, Sutton Valence, Bromfield and Ulcomb all had their interest in King's Wood, but it was to the lord of Ulcomb, Sir Anthony St Leger, Lord Deputy of Ireland and friend of Henry VIII, that Leeds Castle passed finally from the Crown (Edward VI) in 1551.

The manorial tenants of the monarch had, in Kent, long kept a very different administration from the Royal Forests. The rigid, and often suffocating, management of those royal lands is much written of to-day, partly because of the quaint laws and names of office-holders. The best-quoted source is John Manwood, lawyer: '*A Treatise and Discourse of the Laws of the Forrest. And what a Forrest is in his owne proper nature, and wherein the same does differ from a Chase, a Park or a Warren.*' It is an amazing book of 180 pages covering every detail of that privileged and artificial world, so called because it was outside (foris) common law and custom.

> '*The dignities of a King and his royall prerogative to have Forrests where he will appoint. Which are beast of Forrest and Venerie, or of Chase or are beasts and foules of Warren. What forfeiture and punishment will grow to him that commit waste within the Forrest or that doth commit an assart of the Forrest in his own woods or lands. How Hue and Cry shall be made after an offender of the Forrest*'. And so on.

This world, with its Verderers, Regarders and Boys, was not known in Kent. Readers will find the most realistic account of it in C E Hart's *Royal Forest - A History of Dean's Woods as Producers of Timber* (1966.)

That Kent was spared such an imposition, stemmed perhaps from the Conqueror's acceptance of Kentish laws in that old kingdom but also from his having bestowed nearly all the land he might have retained upon his half-brother and the Clares. At King's Wood from the 15th century woodland supervision was local and, for want of evidence to the contrary, we may presume that adjoining lordships did not often dispute between themselves. When peasant or yeoman freeholders and tenants of fractionating manorial estates became more numerous and confident they also must become the customers of other men's woodlands rather than recipients of anciently-bound largesse. The woodward was now accountable to his lord or yeoman master for profitable sales, which revenue was important to the family's economy. The greater care, even hoarding, by owners of their woodland was another element in slowing the loss to agriculture. The more assiduous development of timber and underwood gave a better protection of existing woodland than any royal Acts might bring.

Changes of this sort in the ordering of everyday life were absorbed equably enough but others were ill-received; a reaction which culminated in Jack Cade's Rebellion. Starting in Kent, it reached a national scale in 1450. With a new independence of thought, determined gentry and yeomen in large numbers from west Kent and the Weald showed their resentment against maladministration of government. An enlarged, organised force occupied London for three days and Lord Say of Knole was beheaded. Eventually a free pardon was offered and accepted but not by Cade, who struggled on until he was killed at Heathfield. Thereafter a high-level Commission was set up to examine the Complaint drawn up by these influential landholders.

But the rural seasons were unchanged. For medieval woodland stocked mainly with oak the quieter season came in late summer. The farm labourers were busy at field work except when using the hot months to haul tree-trunks and poles out over the hardened ground. Horses, if there were enough, would be preferred over oxen to weave between obstacles on surer, wider hooves. After harvesting the fields the men and women could come into the wood and along the hedgerows to collect and bind fallen or cut small branches and twigs into faggots or bavins. Bavins were tied with bands (wifts in Kent) of sallow and used for quick heat in bread-baking ovens or to start the fires in larger kilns. Birch slivers were good for kindling but the inclusion of twigs was otherwise essential; there was no resinous conifer wood in lowland England to produce 'firewood sticks'. These and some of the larger underwood products might be taken home as of ancient right of the common, though usually dispensed by the manor. Firewood gathering was, however, very different from the casual gleaning often pictured.

Faggot making: The method has been passed down to a few to-day. In East Kent, David Maylam can show it still. The gathered brushwood is augmented (as ancient decrees insisted) with branches of, say, 5cm diameter to give the faggot a steady burn. The collection is forced together by the crossing of two thick sticks, roped at their base and poked into the ground. The all-important tie may be made from a bramble which has been de-thorned by a 'dolly', or hazel fork, and kept flexible (in stream water and then by twisting the fibres) so to allow knotting of the faggot bundle.

Underwood trade in the year 1461/62			
Items selected from research by A Wheaten into the Accounts of Woods of Canterbury Cathedral Priory			
LONG BECHE Forester - Thomas Olyfe			
		Forester's Costs	Sale Price
Belet *(billets)*	17,000	10d per 1,000	3s 4d per 1,000
Talwode	4,000	3s per 1,000	13s 4d per 1,000
(bundles of wood pieces)			
SHORT WOOD Forester - John Smale			
Courtfagot (no.)	44,500	8d per 1,000	- -
Salefagot	950	2s per 100	6s 8d per 100
Halfagot	1,450	6d per 100	3s 4d per 100

To describe firewood collecting first among wood products emphasises that fuel was, although the least remarked now, the biggest demand upon woodlands for most of their history. It was particularly important in north-west Kent where the London market was insatiable and to which the light bundles could be hauled. The crowded population of the capital would soon equal the whole of Kent in number. From the 13th Century to the 16th the various forms of fuelwood merited written description. In his *Ancient Woodland,* Rackham gives the meticulous specification of underwood sizes from twigs to billets which is preserved in the account of Beaulieu Abbey, Hampshire, in 1269/70. None is known from Kent in this period but Christ Church monks in the 15th Century, even for in-house consumption, carefully graded the products of their nearby underwood with yet more descriptive names: curt fagots; stumbyll (?); kitchen fagots; carboun. The size of the output from woods such as Thornden and Short in the Blean was astonishing, as Alexander Wheaten, woodland historian, has shown by his extracts recently taken from the Account Rolls relating to the woods of Canterbury Cathedral Priory (pre-Dissolution.) The archives have figures of 30,000-40,000 curt fagots in a year; for example, 34,000 in 1513. The inexorable rise in use of fuelwood prompted, in Queen Elizabeth's time, the Acts of 1558, 1581 and 1585 aimed at reducing the effect on woodland (most of all in the Weald) of the iron industry's demand. But by then the domestic demand for timber had widened, too, well beyond the owner's traditional needs in manor buildings, farm and water-mill.

As woodland autumn advanced, the portions or coups (or cants in Kent) of coppice and timber to be cut were allocated by the woodward. His need to maintain a sound rotation of his forest growth was quite as important as getting a good price for some timbers selected according to a builder's fancy. The builders, either from the lord's estate staff or the local independent carpenter, were not divided into the trades that we know now. 'Carpentry' spanned a wide range of occupations. The highest carpenters in the land were masters of cathedral construction. Such men might go to a forest to ensure a supply of special sizes of oak beams but would not themselves work on them to shape the timber to their plan. Most carpenters went to the wood to 'fetch some timber', as did Chaucer's carpenter on behalf of the Abbot, but not to select from standing trees. A commercial builder meeting the order for a half-timbered hall-house in Kent was likely to do his own converting to his rough dimensions in the wood and then the jointing and fashioning in his yard or at the building site. He might also fell the trees or coppice poles himself but this was more usually done by the woodcutter employed by the manor. The climax of raising the assembled sides of the frame on their foundation was speedily completed with local help.

These gradations of the same occupation applied, to some extent, to the millwright and wheelwright while the hurdle-maker often made for his own masters and for sale. (Strong and mobile hurdles are here distinct from wattle work.) Brief as they are, these descriptions of the woodward's customers show how essential it was for him to maintain a growing plan. If, for example, he allocated an acre of oak coppice to an outsider, the woodward must first mark the half-grown standards to be left uncut. If he thought it time to fell a selection in a stand of tall trees for timber, he would do better to fell those most suitable to his plan and sell the felled trunks rather than let a customer walk through and choose standing trees without thought for the pattern of future growth. On the other hand, that plan may have included growing some of his finer oaks into their slower years between ages 90 and 130 with the hope that a bespoke buyer would reserve them for work needing rare dimensions of timber. In 1450 this was justified, not least, by timber values which were rising faster than other agrarian commodities.

Felling of most species could be winter work but for oak, whether timber tree or coppice pole or rod, the cutting down was timed for early spring, 'bud burst', the moment when the tanbark is at its softest and can be axed or peeled away easily. After the winter or spring felling and coppice cutting came the conversion of misshapen branches and any smallwood of more than about 2 inches (5cm) diameter into firewood billets or cordwood piles of mixed sizes of piece. Lastly at the newly-cut area, fencing might be erected to prevent deer or stray farm animals from feeding off the young re-growth.

The woodland, so unlike to-day, was never still. Between coppice growing cycles a clearing of any large expanse was a site for woodcolliers. Their huts of turf beside the smoking kiln were temporary dwellings, for these independent producers were often men of moderate property. In the autumn, tree nutting, berrying and mushrooming provided significant food for local families. Throughout the year deadwood was sought for fuel. Nothing in the woodland was wasted and access was not barred. Through all this activity the owner and his friends threaded their way or rode the fields at the wood-edge in their pursuit of game - and so, too, did the poacher in the quiet of night.

At King's Wood the soil to-day is much as it was in medieval times; the same mid-brown gritty look which soil scientists describe as a thin podzol under mor humus. But sweet chestnut coppice and conifer plantations were not thought of here in the 15th Century when the mainly oak coppice may have been well mixed with other native woody species. Ash and thorn, alder and willows where wet or birch where dry, and hazel are not unexpected but C E Hart and Oliver Rackham feature 'maple' in Forest of Dean coppice and Bradfield woods in Suffolk. The continuing frequency in Kentish hedgerows of the amiable field maple, the one native maple, makes it likely that anciently in southern England it appeared wherever light allowed it throughout the woods. In Kent the hornbeam, which is more amenable to shade, would also have been present within the wood more usually than elsewhere in England.

What the records do not tell us is when the practice began of encouraging only one or two species in coppice, which certainly became more important when coppice started to be grown primarily for sale. At some time before the wholesale replanting of one-species coppice, usually chestnut, there must have been an era of encouraging the natural occurrence. One way to augment chestnut, still used in Kent today, is to make or find a gap for growing and there to bend a strong rod from an existing stool and peg it twice to hold a short length beneath the soil surface so that it will root itself.

A larger scale method than this 'layering' is described in a later chapter.

Down the southern slope the East Sutton deerpark had not yet been created. In the 1400s the exciting feature was the construction of new houses with their appealing outline of all-over roof and jetties of oaken beams set wider than the ground floor walls. The thickest concentration of these 'Wealden' houses, it has been pointed out, is not on the Weald but on the Greensand. To this most characterful of end-products from Kentish woodland we come next.

Makers of the Wealden House

The period from the Late-14th to Early-16th Centuries, which we might better describe here as 1,350 to 1,550 years after the Iron Age, produced the wonderful flowering of English carpentry and wood carving. Its creation began in prehistory and its force came from countless tiny steps forward in the method of converting wood for human use. The fashioning of it was by blades of metal essentially unchanged since Caesar. During all those years the carpenters continued within the unaltering parameters of their work; always talking, touching the wood with finger-tip or palm and eyeing it - instructing and learning by patient example. The timber-framed house reached its zenith not from sudden inspiration or new invention but from an astonishing coalescence of a hundred small practices. It came from a very long roll of sentient craftsmen with a mastery of oak, their animate material for construction.

Just north of our particular King's Wood lies Leeds Castle which, in 1370, was being rebuilt by William of Wykeham. It was one of many large secular demands on carpenters and on timber resources at that time in Kent. From contemporary records we see that the thronging occupation of 'carpenter' stretched from the hewer of freshly-felled timber to structural carpenters, joiners and carvers of adornments. On the Isle of Sheppey there were 173 carpenters working on Edward III's favoured castle and being paid wages varying from sixpence to threepence. The dreaded Statute of Labourers had been amended in 1360 to ensure that carpenters worked by the day, not the week, for their graded wages of 4d or 3d or 2d and, more importantly at the time, that they should not form chapters or take oaths to strengthen their bargaining. But far above the level of even the 6d earner were those few master carpenters who, with master masons, designed the structure of great buildings.

The work of these craftsmen-engineers was amazingly bold. In 1400 the King's Carpenter, Master Hugh Herland (one of the few whose names we know), completed the hammer-beam roof of Westminster Hall which is described now as 'the greatest single work of art of the whole of the European Middle Ages'. Dr John Harvey goes on to say (1971) 'No such comparable achievement in the field of mechanics and aesthetics remains elsewhere'. It is one of the largest timber roofs unsupported by pillars in the world. Eighty years later, in Kent, the principle of the hammer-beam with collar arch was applied to the splendid palace of Edward IV at Eltham. That was England's third largest unsupported roof, and it too, remains to-day. The architectural style in England took an independent turn from the European continent during the years 1375 - 1485. The style and its period are given the name Perpendicular because of the slender perpendicular columns supporting much higher windows and their less-pointed stone arches above. It is allied with the slightly later glory of stone roof vaulting with Tudor fan tracery; a design which came from timber work. The whole effect is one we have been brought up to love for its Englishness. The fact that only a very few buildings were afforded stone tracery does not diminish the beauty because the contemporary wooden roofs were often of superb craftsmanship.

Master Herland's new roof design admirably met the royal wish to do away with the oppressive effect of the wall-to-wall tie beam strengthener above the floor areas of large assembly halls. Another medieval impetus came from the diminishing resource of oak beams of anything longer than thirty feet (9m). It demanded the greater use of those short and knotty pieces which could now be converted by the trestle saw set in a frame. The alternative of building-stone was not widely, or cheaply, available in England south-eastward of the limestone ridge stretching from Gloucester to Peterborough. In Kent, one type of ragstone and some flint were used for church, castle and palace, but for nearly all other buildings the raw materials were timber, underwood and clay.

Just south of King's Wood, in the years from 1400, rural and separated properties were built for the wealthier yeomen during three generations. In East Sutton's parish alone there remain and prosper no fewer than nine 'half-timbered' houses listed in the gazetteer of the Royal Commission for Historic Monuments. Here was a most desirable location. The first owners were either the limbs of the august St.Ledger family at Ulcombe or those who-would-like-to- be; the newly wealthy cloth and farming families. East Sutton is convenient for, but sloped above, flat Headcorn's market and the good alluvial soil along the river Beult. The southern slope was sheltered from Kent's cold north-easterly winds and, essentially, it also gave good drainage for the new houses. Just how this tract of land was owned or parcelled to allow so unusually many Wealden halls upon it at that time we do not know.

This chronicle of woodland will not presume to explain timber-framed building construction. For readers who are new to the subject, and not at ease with the many technical names, there is an agreeable way into it through *Discovering Timber-Framed Buildings*, an often-reprinted little book written by Richard Harris while Research Director at the Weald and Downland Open Air Museum. It has a short list of further reading. For a second local writer of national repute, one would recommend any work by Kenneth Gravett. Best of all is to spend a day on the airy downland at Singleton (north of Chichester) to study and touch the woodwork of medieval and later period buildings rescued from modern developments in south-east England.

At the museum, talking with to-day's craftsmen makes it clear that the basis of the architecture, as well as the actual woodworking, depended on the ageless accumulation of feel for the material; using to best advantage its natural, animate properties. The acme of the outward appeal of 'half-timbered' buildings became realised when enough money was available to build farmhouses and small manors from the best timbers still to be found locally. A moderation in overall size is slightly outweighed by the generous breadth of timbers. The strength and lasting appeal came from these factors and from the, often unseen, work methods which increased longevity.

Photographed at the Weald & Downland Museum
Top: Beam joint locking and tightening
Bottom: Wattle woven over diamond-shaped uprights

Tenon and mortice joints were made firm by the use of pegs through the joint in a hole cunningly offset so that when the peg was hammered home it increasingly drew the shoulders tighter together. Even in making panels of, usually concealed, wattle an extra element of design came from the long-accumulated awareness of the material. The horizontal woven work could be made of slim rods of hazel or other flexible species or occasionally cleft oak. For the vertical formers, however, a round rod of sufficient strength must deteriorate, unless it had been tediously trimmed, because of the sapwood surrounding it. To achieve the rigidity needed for these stakes a straight oak or chestnut coppice pole was cleaved down the grain. (Elm, otherwise suitable, does not cleave easily.) Then, with two more strokes the cleaver converted the length from a wedge-sided one into stakes of a flattened-diamond shape. This gave not only sufficient strength and freedom from sapwood but a much smoother 'flow' to the lateral woven rods which helped the wall panels' draught-proofing. The economic production of quantities of pieces cleft along the oak's medullary rays, the radial food passages, probably led to the shape of weatherboarding; that thin wedge shape being retained for its efficiency in overlapping boards long after powered sawing was introduced.

After the relatively easy cleaving, sawing or carving when the oak is freshly felled there comes a short spell when the material seems fibrous to the craftsman and, although not yet hard, quite difficult to work. There follows the further drying (seasoning) and then the years of weathering in position which leaves oak like iron in its hardness. For sawn wood which has a very large surface relative to thickness, such as for panelling, the carpenter relies again on cuts along the line of the medullary rays. This way the fibres are equal in tension and there will be no distortion in drying. Much of the medieval imported timber was cut in this way, 'on the quarter', for final working at a later date.

Quarter-cutting by saw is, however, time-consuming and wasteful of wood. For all structural carpentry the conversion of the tree was more simply done. Early load-bearing posts and beams were hewed into a squared shape around the heartwood - 'boxing the heart'. This, too, produced timbers relatively free from future distortion but it required a profligate felling of growing trees. From older trees several scantlings (timber beams of small cross-section: OED) could be won between heart and sapwood. If cleft, with the cleavage following the rays, there was little distortion. This method also offered a better strength-to-thickness ratio and was used for ship's side planking long after sawing had become the usual method of conversion. If sawn 'through and through', as dictated by all but the cleanest, knot-free tree trunks, the several scantlings were prone to twisting when dried owing to the uneven stresses between the heart side and the outer side surfaces. (Modern sawmills cut out and discard the heart of large logs to avoid distortion, but at the expense of wide planks.)

Squaring the sides of housebeams when boxing the heart was usually done, while the wood was still fresh, with a side-axe (flat on one side), not with an adze. The return of the saw to England after the 12th Century encouraged the conserving of oak trees until they reached larger dimensions now that they could be converted more readily to timbers of the required size. The boxed-heart beam from young trees was much less used. This and the increasing price of felled trees ('round timber') led eventually to smaller cross-sections for many of the structural beams. The exception remained the vital horizontal beam to support the joists above the ground floor of a building. Named the somer or bressomer, it kept its reassuring cross dimensions, usually upwards of 12 x 10 inches (30 x 25 cm). The impetus to form an upper storey was aided even at the start by ready-sawn floorboards imported from the Baltic; there is record of a specification of 'Baltic board' for the Brewers' Hall, London, in 1423.

The origin of the expression 'half-timbered' still provokes debate. It is probably not from the external appearance of a house - half woodwork, half plaster or brick - but from the act of halving round timber poles for use as joists or, more visibly, as wall studs (OE studha = pillar, post) to carry horizontal laths. In both cases the rounded face was not a disadvantage so long as the flat face could be used and the other, with crumbling sapwood and even the bark left on, would be not too evident.

The effect given by the simpler 15th Century houses, not boastful with contrived decoration, was of an entity arisen from the soil and its trees. The owner's later insertion of a bedroom floor and a fireplace and chimney stack of brick to complement the clay roof tiles only broadened this oneness with the land. Of a number of basic English house styles, one that is often pictured did not feature in Kent: the cruck frame, with gable ends of massive curved tree trunks meeting at a top point, is found mainly in Herefordshire. The walls of 'black-and-white' effect are also more common in the West Midlands and Wales. It comes from the old practice of coating exposed timbers with tar for protection. The treatment perhaps has more purpose in the wetter west but was never really justified for oak with its outstanding close-grained hardness. In Kent, the intentionally-chosen curved timber is usually seen as a secondary brace at a right angle of the main frame. It was cut from a lower branch and is usually quite thin in cross-section. On the other hand, close-studding is often a Kentish wall feature, as on the old parsonage at Headcorn.

Inside Headcorn church the 16th Century nave is credited with having the best open-timber roof in Kent. North-east of our King's Wood is Lenham church with its richly, delicately, carved pulpit of the same period. The money from parishioners which endowed these church buildings was bestowed, too, by the wealthy upon their new homes. What we are now unlikely to discover is whether the carpenters of all that fine oak work in central Kent came from, say, Westminster Hall to be taken on by prosperous locals or if perhaps this high level of skill was fostered in the area and then gained royal patrons. The style of yeoman's house which originated around 1400 on Kent's Weald and Greensand is known as Wealden. From whatever creative background, this standard type of timber-framed house, says Alec Clifton-Taylor (1972) is 'easily the finest'.

The Wealden hall (or house) style always has a rectangular hall ground plan with an overall, monospan, roof and the walls jettied out above head height over the ground-floor walls. The overhanging jetty was a feature before the common insertion of a floor to make an upper storey. The Wealden name is also applied to the style in other parts of the south-east and East Anglia but it was first the design built for medieval mid-Kent men, the successful farmer and cloth maker, the upward families. Households such as these, with their new freedom from constraint, were the backbone of Cade's rebellion of 1450, the mid-way point of our foray into the building carpenter's world. Sarah Pearson, in her superbly executed survey for the Royal Commission for Historic Monuments, points out that central Kent improved in its wealth assessment from among the lowest in England in 1334 to one of the highest yielding parts of the country by the time of the lay subsidy inspection in 1524. With little suitable stone for emulating palace building, the Wealden hall-house of timber became an impressive alternative.

Trees for Tudor Timber

From the early 15th Century the changing pattern of wealth which encouraged men to compete among themselves with their houses also made easier their buying of mature timber for the required substantial beams and planking. In depopulated England after the Black Death many fields of heavy soil were uncultivated and no pressure was felt to clear woodland for the plough. The value of timber, however, began to rise. Tenants, thereafter, sought to ensure that the woods on their land could be exploited by them, not reserved for the landlord as was traditional. Concerning Rolvenden, twelve miles south of King's Wood, we have this from Archbishop Warham's rental book of Michaelmas 1512:-

> '6 shillings received of John Mongham and his partners for the dene of Rolvynden,belonging to the manor of Aldington, that they and their heirs may in future times dispose of all the wood growing upon the same dene, and that which shall thereafter grow in it, at their pleasure, in addition to the ancient rent and services formerly due and accustomed therefrom.'

Robert Furley, from whose *History of the Weald of Kent* this extract is taken, adds that it conforms with the course followed by Battle Abbey, Christ Church Canterbury and other religious houses in allowing the tenants of the dens 'to acquire the important right of converting the timber to their own use and cultivating the land as they thought most to their advantage'. As the nation turned into the 16th Century there were steep and, at that time, unusual bouts of inflation. To Furley's thoughts in the 1870s we could add from our own inflation-fearing age that the tenants had extra reason to look for the control within their leasehold of long-growing timber trees. And perhaps the impulsion to invest in a dependable long-term Wealden house.

The manor of Aldington was held by the archbishops of Canterbury but in east Kent the dominant landowner of all was Christ Church priory, an exceptionally rich monastery. The religious Reformation across Europe was adapted by Henry VIII to transfer the rights of the pope to the crown and, as a consequence, in 1539-41 the king subdued the monasteries (not the archbishops' properties) and redistributed their wealth. His seizure 'by the cartload' of the treasure of Becket's shrine was not resisted and in general the Dissolution caused little turmoil among the citizens. Indeed, the change from priory to deanery, both in property and in office-holding, often was smoothly done: in mid-Kent in 1540 the dismissed Prior Walter of Boxley Abbey reappeared immediately as Walter Phillips, Dean of Rochester. Some priory woodlands in Kent have thus had undisturbed deedholders since Saxon times. That is not to portray a lack of change in the county. Demands on the monarch and economic pressure on the church caused widespread transfers of land to laymen.

Dispersed ownership meant that an increasing number of woodland managers could make available at least a small portion of their maturing trees. The carpenter had a wider choice of woodland source and he knew well where the oak grew fast to give him sweet-working wood with its plump summer increment. The price may have seemed forbidding but oak was the name. He was attuned to working with oak and would find that substitute material presented him with converting problems. Elm, for example, being difficult to cleave, was foreign to him. An age-old instinct for this wood, born from generations in pre-sawing days, would not be in his hand. For durability and size, however, this tree from hedgerow rather than woodland became the second of the species used for construction. At Singleton, about a tenth of the material in the ancient houses is elm. A case is known of a house made of elm except for its frontage of oak, which underlines oak's cachet. Sweet chestnut, long thought to have been used as an equivalent to oak for beams, is now known to have been a rarity. In Kent the best known instance is the splendid roof of the Great or Baron's Hall at Penshurst Place. Attributed to William Hurley, Edward III's master carpenter, the great timbers have their apex sixty feet above the floor and employ a system of king posts resting on collar beams which are in turn supported by enormous arched braces. A similar, more intimately observable, use of sweet chestnut is in the line of arcade piers for the nave of Wingham church.

Sweet chestnut in medieval Kent, before the great planting to supply hop farms, was probably found in a woodland sub-industry which is little remarked now but had an enormous output, numerically, in its prime: the making of laths. Usually riven from oak or beech, the lath was a strip about five feet long by an inch wide and half-an-inch thick. Its purpose was to carry roofing or the plaster of walls or ceilings. Made both of heartwood and sapwood, together the output was prodigious. In *Building in England down to 1540,* L. Salzman mentions that the stores of the works at London Bridge in 1350 contained 87,000 laths. At Langley (Bucks) in 1441 twelve oaks produced 7,000 laths. The craft must have been similar to, and perhaps shared by, the hurdle-makers.

Yeomen wealth at the level of Wealden houses was still new and rare. Even in the county of gavelkind inheritance most families paid someone rent for what was little more than basic shelter of wattle on a wooden frame with a small plot to grow food. They were dependent on others for building materials used in repairs while the remnants of the old housebote system lingered on. Where there was a shifting population, for instance between farming and cloth centres or, after 1500, in iron-making, the accommodation must have been flimsy and of impermanent timbers, such even as willow. The frame members of better wood were re-used until they broke and then again as shorter lengths. (The erroneous thought that 'ship's timbers' were commonly re-used in houses arose in recent times, most probably from the sight of curved crucks and braces. Also unlikely is the suggestion that the term was in the past a general one for high grade timber, as in the modern 'marine grade' plywood.)

Whether mobile or static for generations, the population had to be housed and this meant the supply of timber and underwood for

The archetypal Wealden hall/house with unbroken roof line and jetty at each end. Old Bell farmhouse, Harrietsham.

the thousands of premises in the county which have since disappeared without trace. It is surprising that by this date, despite the great traffic in wood, there is still no record in Kent of a timber merchant per se. In London in 1410, we read from Salzman, there were timbermongers by trade name and medieval timber importers did business at the Steelyard. But then, in London we know there were Roman warehouses for timber, presumably shipped in by classis Britannica and sold on by middlemen. In the Weald, timber which was sold from the estates of the Bathhursts and Osbournes as late as the 16th Century was converted into a wide variety of scantlings, rails and wood utensils not by a timber merchant but by a Kentish thatcher and his partner (Agrarian History vol.4).

Somehow the demand was met for a county population which had recovered by Tudor times to about 80 - 85,000, as is closely estimated by M.Zell (AC 1984), or rather more by others. The family unit was about five souls. Given an annual rate of re-building or new building of perhaps ten per cent of premises, the county needed timber and smallwood for, at most, two thousand houses and attendant buildings. Continuing with these extremely broad figures and combining them with the acreage figures in Chapter 4, these two thousand premises a-building annually had some two hundred thousand acres of predominantly oak woodland to sustain the work. At 100 acres (40ha) of woodland for each 'house' there was no problem of resource, given careful growing cycles. However, the reservoir of larger trees, upwards of 15 inches (38 cm) in diameter at breast height, became more limited after a period of relative plenty in the early 15th Century, and the price alone of oak rationed its use for humble dwellings.

Back along the Greensand slope, the southern aspect might well have been in the mind of the Reverend William Harrison when he wrote in 1577, 'The ancient manors and houses of our gentlemen are yet, and for the most part, of strong timber, in framing whereof our carpenters have been and are worthily preferred before those of like science among all other nations'. On the ancient drove roads the pannage herds were already a past legend but sheep and cattle and humans of the prospering 16th Century continued along the miry way. Timber wagoners cursed equally the drop downwards from King's Wood and the climb from the clay vale. To and fro the woods they encountered journeyers still bucolic, indeed, but becoming abruptly more aware of manufacturing. Tales from the next villages of the new fulling mills were capped by the ones about the pressure for more iron output.

The demands on the woodlands were not only for house building and traditional uses but for every developing industry. With the increasing population as well, thoughtful men began to wish for a rational silviculture even though it would be difficult to sustain. It encouraged the Kentish nobility, gentry and yeomen to conserve their woods as family assets. Within the next century their trees were to become a surprising and vulnerable target of envious enemies in civil war.

Iron and Cloth and Wealden Coal

The oral sound that is to us <u>coal</u>, yet also <u>kohl</u>, the Arabian eye cosmetic and <u>koel</u> the Indian cuckoo, is very early and widespread speech for <u>black.</u> The collier was the man who made wood black - he made coal. To heat until black and thus to achieve a superior fuel could refer only to wood before the days of fossil fuel from underground, and that new arrival had to be distinguished from the traditional coals of wood by an affix, <u>pit</u> or <u>sea</u>. After a time, the black fossil fuel became, simply, coal. In that wonderfully haphazard way of word-breeding, charred wood was relegated to its modern minor role and renamed, not as <u>charwood</u> but <u>charcoal.</u>

To create usable metal, higher temperatures are needed than can be got from the flames of burning wood or peat. We may easily imagine Neolithic people recognising and understanding how a lump of congealed ore lay with a certain type of clay among hot ashes, but from that stage to their achievement of shaping iron artefacts is a journey staggering to contemplate. At some point they taught themselves to make in an efficient way the charred wood which could be re-ignited to burn at the required superheat. H L Edlin (1949) gave a woodsman's description:-

> Charcoal is made by heating wood in the absence of enough air for complete combustion. The water contained in the wood is first driven out, followed by all the volatile compounds, including creosote and tar. This leaves behind a residue of black carbon, together with a little mineral ash. The process of wood decomposition becomes, at one stage, exothermic, producing more heat than it absorbs; this fact explains how a small fire, lit at the heart of a heap of wood, can cause the whole to become charred, although only a fraction is actually burnt up.

Charcoal-making in west Kent and Sussex is a story now closely linked with that of iron smelting and shaping. Before concentrating on the blast-furnaces and forges, we should note that charcoal was a staple made all over the county in woodlands which supplied mainly local artisans' small forges. The shipwright of Sandwich hammered iron for his strongest fittings and the jeweller at

Canterbury practised his metal artwork. The Jutes and Saxons of Kent wholly neglected the iron ore source but charcoal was still essential for forging their implements or weapons and for their metal finery, all of imported iron. A local collier could readily meet these demands. He would be little troubled by larger competitors from afar because charcoal, although relatively light to carry, was bumped to dust over long distances. For his woodstack burn this collier may have favoured either small diameter coppiced wood or larger billets from pollarding and felled or naturally fallen trees. These modest requirements did not dictate the local woodland regime.

In the Wealden iron-bearing lands of western Kent it was a different story. Iron ore was to be found by digging in the Wadhurst Clay and Tunbridge Wells Sand; the geological base gave a topography of forest and pasture upon clay vale or narrow-sloping ghylls and sandstone outcrops. Small rivers, too, which were to be so important to the later ironworkers. The first sustained processing of the ore, from about 500 BC until when the Romans left Britain one thousand years later, was at a level and a concentration, at least in Sussex, which even then made necessary some degree of coppice-cycle growing of wood (see Chapter 2.) These large areas of coppice then had a long respite of at least six centuries, if they were not over-grazed or cleared for ploughland and settlement, until the Normans and Angevins began to win iron from the Weald.

From early medieval sales lists are found items such as in the archives of the Archbishop of Canterbury, whose Weald of Kent forges in 1242 supplied the Crown with 8,000 horseshoes and 20,000 nails for delivery to Porchester (Portsmouth harbour). The earlier medieval English iron bloomeries were still a simple smelting process: metal was extracted from the crushed ore by melting between layers of burning charcoal in a clay-capped mound, a bloomery. Other records tell of the small Tudeley bloomery at Southfrith, Tonbridge, owned by the Clare family. There, it has been estimated, was an output of 4 tons of iron in a season, requiring for each ton about 2 acres of coppice annually. Eight acres per year and (for round figures) a 12-year coppice cycle meant a woodland area of some 100 acres to sustain indefinitely the fuel supply for that early bloomery.

From the European continent, in late-medieval days, came improved production methods from blast-furnace and forge which depended on water-power to work the furnace bellows and hammer. Thus the great expansion of Wealden iron-making could begin in the early 16th Century, and with it the demand for a huge acreage of woodland fuel. The demand lasted for more than two hundred years.

The expansion was stimulated when French sources became closed to the English. The Wealden Anticline, which also forms part of north-west France, had given rise to one thriving iron centre in the district between Dieppe and Beauvais but there, in time, agriculture won the battle for wooded land. The ironworkers were encouraged to emigrate and find work in Sussex and Kent. From their Pays de Bray they brought new skills to the English furnace and forge, which was set among scenery familiar to them.

One major end-product of the Wealden ironfield was the cannon. During the militant reign of Henry VIII, gun-founding was a busy activity at Calais, to which both iron and great quantities of timber and fuelwood were dispatched from the Cinque Ports in addition to their home coastal trade. Equally as important was the energetic building and re-building of fortifications along the Thames estuary and Channel coast, the frontier for an increasingly isolated England.

We have to consider if, unlike the woodlands of the Pays de Bray, those in the Kent 'iron area' were preserved by the demands of the military. To go with the guns came orders for prodigious quantities of materiel, almost literally the nuts and bolts of a belligerent kingdom aided in its funds by the Dissolution of the Monasteries. (At the new Sandgate castle alone, the site blacksmith in 1539/40 worked through 4-to-5 tons of iron.) In contrast, the powers in France, for about one hundred years from 1550, were beset with internal differences; the task of suppressing rather than fortifying. England, too, had its brief share of religious fratricide: an Ashford pamphlet listed the martyrs burnt in Kent's town centres during the years 1554 - 1558 as no fewer than 48 men and 23 women. However, in general the civil aspect of Kent and Sussex was encouraging. The population trend rose upward and London food markets were buoyant. Yet agriculture did not take over the wooded valleys and vales of the Weald.

A table from *The South-East from AD1000* (Brandon and Short 1990) shows, in simplified form, that Tudor ironworks were nearly five times more numerous in Sussex than in Kent:-

	Forges	Furnaces	Others	Total
Sussex	67	88	2	157
Kent	17	16	—	33
Surrey	12	6	—	18
Hampshire	—	1	—	1
Total SE	96	111	2	209

But the positioning of the works in relation to rivers and cross-border ownership (the Sidneys of Penshurst were mining at Robertsbridge, for example) meant that the pronouncements of the Crown and much of the economic and social debate treated the sites of Kent, Sussex and the corner of Surrey as one resource. The longest and noisiest part of the debate was about woodfuel supplies. The fierce, and sometimes entertaining, proclamations and jury testaments must be read in the context of a south-east England which, apart from imported sea-coal in London, had no other fuel. No gas, no oil, no electricity - only wood.

For the many complainants against the ironworks, whether their grouses were commercial or humanitarian or aesthetic, a trigger to their polemics was the almost impassable condition of the roads. Guns and timber deliveries for the Crown were delayed in transit, sometimes for months. For many of the works the rivers Medway, Teise and Rother offered only limited relief by waterway. A later,

Elizabethan, edict required that for every six loads of charcoal or one ton of iron carted between October and May a load of cinder should be spread on the road or equivalent money paid for its repair. Apparently to no great effect. The claggy, stumbling, strength-sapping mire, an everyday penance for the locals, was first to arouse the indignation of literate observers. Their writing survives for us to read the mounting reaction against the loss of tall trees and the pollution from flaring furnaces, sulphurous cinder piles and thumping forges.

In Kent these monsters lay scattered, nearly three dozen of them, over a twenty-miles-by-ten strip along the Sussex border; an area bounded by a line Bough Beech to Tonbridge to Biddenden and Bedgebury. The inhabitants became used to the degradation in their short daily radius, and many lived by its cause, so that what were hideous offences to the sensitive might have been pardonable but that iron-making was also blamed for a loss of wealth in other trades. The complaints arose most strongly from cloth and shipping interests in the middle of the 16th Century.

Nationally the iron industry's appetite for charcoal had created high alarm. Shortly before his death King Henry had enacted that, from Michaelmas 1544, when a wood was cut there must be left twelve tillers (or stores or standills) per acre to grow on for timber until they were '10 inches square three feet from the ground'. The felled area must be fenced for four years and not cut again for fourteen. However the Weald was exempted from this and similar statutes, either because it was so relatively heavily wooded or because it represented half England's iron production.

From all these pressures it was little wonder that the local opponents of iron in Sussex got agreement to a Commission of Inquiry in 1549. Among the questions were:-

1. How many iron mills and furnaces for the same be now in Sussex ?

2. How much great wood by estimation is yearly destroyed by the said mills and furnaces ?

3. How much the price of a load of wood is already enhanced in divers places in Sussex by occasion of the said mills and furnaces ?

4. Whether the said mills and furnaces be of great detriment as well to the inhabitants in the towns of Calais, Guines, Boulogne, etc as also to the inhabitants of many towns and parishes in Sussex concerning their fuel.

The full question-and-answer of the Commission is given in the most interesting chapter, Fuel, of Ernest Straker's *Wealden Iron* (1931 and 1969). The jurors, he records, estimated that each of the fifty iron mills then in Sussex 'spendeth at least yearly 1,500 loads of great wood made into coals'. The term 'great wood' is usually taken to mean from mature trees not coppice wood, but here there must have been an accepted, possibly intentional, vagueness.

At the time when Kent's new water-powered ironworks were seen to be savagely affecting the roads and woodlands and, above all, the price of fuel, the cloth industry was hit by Queen Elizabeth's Act of 1566. It required the clothiers centred on Cranbrook to sell only wrought (finished) cloth and that meant, effectively, that the cloth needed to be dyed if it was to sell. The dyeing process was the only stage in cloth-making to use large quantities of fuel; prices for wood and charcoal had thus not been a significant factor to the clothier before that date. Similarly in timing, a new peace with France in 1559 had meant a lapse into apathy at the Calais garrison and a reduction in timber and other freight to it from Hastings, Rye and Hythe. Such timber and underwood cargoes as were shipped along the home coast increased dramatically in cost to the shipping merchant because of the ironmaster's demands. Both Cranbrook and the Cinque Ports complainants did, with reason, recruit to their cause the harsh effect on domestic users of fuel price increases but the clamour of protest was often thought to be against an actual shortage of wood. Charcoal for industry increased in price far more steeply than other commodities; it quadrupled in the sixty years after the Commission of 1547.

Within ten years of the Commission, the weakened garrison at Calais was easily overcome by the Duc de Guise, resulting in a transfer to the Weald of the garrison's gun foundry work and reduced exports of wood. The Queen's law makers in 1574 devised new south-eastern legislation which prohibited the use of wood for charring within eighteen miles of London and eight miles of the Thames. The Privy Council required all suppliers of cannon to enter into bonds not to manufacture iron within fourteen miles of the Thames and no new ironworks were to be erected within twenty miles of London. The distances again excluded anywhere south and west of Tonbridge, thereby increasing the pressure of orders upon the Wealden works. At much the same time, 1573, the Cranbrook clothiers, themselves, calculated that wood needed for general use, including dyeing, in the area around their town was one-fifth more than that for iron-making.

Near the end of the century an Act specific to Cranbrook was passed to aid the Kentish cloth industry, and the iron industry was again seen as the ogre.

> The trade of making and dyeing cloth has, for a long time, employed the poor people within 20 miles of Cranbrooke, and the greatest number of the inhabitants thereabouts have lived thereupon. It is feared that unless speedy remedy be provided, the said trade will fall into decay by reason of the great spoil of wood lately made within the same circuit, chiefly by ironworks or mills lately erected.

But by 1637, John Browne, ironmaker to the Crown and exporter, was able justly to claim still that the clothiers could change to sea-coal for their heating whereas for iron-making he must perforce use charcoal.

Ironmaking: Woodland Destroyer or Conserver ?

An accurate assessment of fuel output from the woodlands in Tudor times is not easily made. As the iron industry progressed, the manufacturing of iron became more efficient, terms of measurement changed, or perhaps varied between districts, and coppice cycles varied in the number of years. Contemporary descriptions reckoned a 'load' of coal as either 30 sacks or 40 and the 'sack' might hold 3 bushels or 4. An acre of coppice was said by some to convert to 4.5 loads of coal but, by others, less than 4. Again, different dimensions of a cord of cut wood were found, although to-day's traditional measure of 8ft x 4ft x 4ft was then in common use. A cord of smallwood, weighing, when fresh, perhaps 1.5 tons (a figure to be argued over even to-day) was said to produce both 30 and 40 bushels. Of course, the yield of charcoal from wood, nominally one-fifth, varies according to species, size and the collier's skill.

In 1607, John Norden, cartographer of the south-east and writer, made a stab at quantifying the consumption of charcoal which was typically hesitant in wording

> I have heard there are, or lately were, in Sussex neere 140 hammers and furnaces for iron......which spend each of them in every twenty-four hours two, three or four loads of charcoale, which in a year amounteth to an infinite quantitie.

Authors of the 20th Century, notably Straker, Hammersley and Cleere, have investigated thoroughly the required acreage of coppice woodland to sustain the Roman, Medieval and Stuart ironworks of the south-east. Their assessments come together in

Even in the iron-forging process, the dependence upon large timbers was immense.

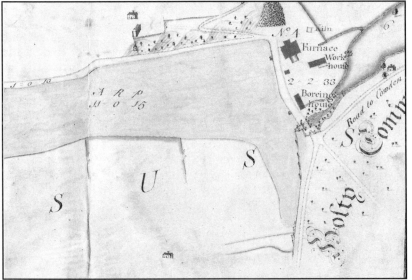

The Cowden iron-master's map was by John Bowen, 1748.

Cleere and Crossley (1985). In the *'Iron Industry of the Weald'*, the latter two authors estimate that an average 16th Century Wealden blast-furnace would need 2,500 acres of coppice to perpetuate its coal supplies, with a further 1,500 - 1,600 acres for its forge. This Tudor industry requirement would approximate to 200,000 acres of regularly coppiced woodland. They assess the land area embracing all the Wealden ironworks as 900,000 acres (364,000 ha). Because this countryside was, and is still, among the most heavily wooded in England, it is possible to accept that as much as nearly one-quarter of the land area was under coppice management dedicated to iron-making. But that amount certainly explains the pressure on fuel prices, the outcries from other wood-dependent industries and the actual shortage felt by householders in some districts.

The Civil Wars and the republican Commonwealth, from 1642 to 1660, saw damage to woodland on some of the estates of Kent by disaffected persons but the political turmoil did not greatly alter the iron industry's progress except to slow its decline. Here a distinction must be made between the Wealds of Kent and of Sussex. The Kentish Weald contained only one major chase, that of The Frith at Tonbridge; its ownership changed from the Duke of Northumberland during the Tudor iron-making period to the holders of Somerhill estate. Sussex, on the contrary, had more than 40,000 acres of Wealden forests or chases with a stronger tradition of seasonal common rights than remained in Kent. These wood resources of Sussex, particularly on the 20,000 acres of Ashdown Forest, appear to have been wantonly used for charcoal by the nearby ironmasters, thus giving force to the early protests against spoliation. After the Restoration of Charles II the Wealden iron industry was past its prime, and coppice-for-charcoal was by then a long-established regime. Several contemporary authors came, hesitantly, to the conclusion that the practice had actually protected Wealden woodland. This theory was then strangely abandoned until the silvicultural writings of the 20th Century.

Back in 1663, John Evelyn published *Sylva*, his seminal *Discourse of Forest-Trees to the Royal Society*. His challenge to conventional thinking began

> '.....twere better to purchase all our Iron out of America, than thus to exhaust our woods at home, although (I doubt not) they might be so ordered as to be rather a means of conserving them.'

He goes on to cite the case of Christopher Darrell of Surrey who had been specifically exempted from statutory restrictions on wood-cutting

> '....though a great Iron-Master; because he so ordered his Works, that they were a means of preserving even his Woods; notwithstanding those insatiable devourers: This may appear a Paradox, but it is to be made out; and I have heard my own Father (whose estate was none of the least wooded in England) affirm that a Forge, and some other mills, to which he furnish'd much Fuel were a means of maintaining, and improving his Woods; I suppose by increasing the Industry of planting and care...'

Evelyn's relatives were gunpowder manufacturers in Surrey but this possible influence on his thoughts probably did not apply to other writers such as Thomas Fuller and Andrew Yarranton. In 1677, the latter helped us to picture the contemporary debate as in

this extract from his *England's Improvement by Sea and Land* :-

> The second manufacture to be encouraged to set the poor people at work is that of Iron. But now I am sure I shall draw a whole Swarm of Wasps about my Ears. For say some (and many too who think themselves very wise) it were well if there were no Ironworks in England; and it was better when no Iron was made in England: and the Ironworks destroy all the Woods and foreign iron from Spain will do better and last longer.... The next thing is Ironworks destroy the Woods and Timber.

> I affirm the contrary; and that Ironworks are so far from the destroying of Woods and Timber that they are the occasion of the increase thereof. And as to making Charcoal with Timber, in these parts so much talked of, it was and is most notoriously false; for Timber in all these parts is worth thirty shillings a Tun, and a Tun and three-quarters of Timber will make but one Coard of Wood. So let all rational men consider whether an Iron Master will cut up Timber to the value of fifty shillings to make one Coard of Wood when he pays for his Wood in most of these places but seven shillings a Coard.

At Mereworth, with river transport to the nearby iron works and later demands such as for tan bark, this oak coppice has been cut regularly for 450 years.
Roy Keeler, Head Forester.

Perhaps to avoid weakening his point, Yarranton did not add that some areas of timber trees must have been clear-felled, including those not at best girth, because they would fetch a good price for the main trunk (the butt) and a ready sale for charcoal of the branches and lop-and-top, and then leave a woodland more opened up for coppice regrowth. After that operation the cut area would be kept free of grazing animals so that the stumps (stools) produced coppice rapidly and straight-growing for another cutting in seven-to-fifteen years' time. Early cutting had the advantage for the users that small diameter charcoal lumps are less likely to crumble in transit.

John Browne had been right at the time when he told the Cranbrook clothiers to use sea-coal and leave the charcoal for him. Not for another hundred years could ironmasters use the alternative. Then, after a generation of development from 1709 to 1735, Abraham Darby arrived at a method using coke from pit-coal which, with an improved blast-furnace, was suitable for smelting iron. This was the key to using fossil fuel for all metal-making, and it was the coup-de-grace for the Wealden iron industry. The often quoted effect of imports from Sweden and Spain could have been averted by Government embargo. The miry roads of the Weald and the unreliable waterflow of its streams were indeed local hazards, as was a shortage of good ore, but a shortage of wood, once coppice-regimes had been adopted, was not a factor. The dwindling sales of iron for urgent rearmament and civil use stopped at around the same time as those of the old competitor, the Wealden cloth industry. By the 1780s Cranbrook, too, had fallen victim to cheaper production elsewhere.

Woodlands - and the Colliers - Survive

Wood colliers survived beyond this Kentish 'iron age' but in reduced numbers. To the ironmaster the cost of charcoal had been half or more of his expenditure, implying very high employment in its making and carting. In the Robertsbridge area in 1546 at the Panningridge Furnace these fuel workmen had numbered five times the ironworkers. Alternative industrial customers for the colliers remained many after iron and cloth. For gunpowder-making, alder was the preferred wood source for combining with saltpetre and sulphur. Far distant from the ironfield, alder was plentiful at Faversham, which offered the added attraction of safer transit by water for the imported chemicals and the outgoing gunpowder. Wood ash had its uses, as at Crayford. Andrew Yarranton described the bleaching grounds there in 1677. 'Six score acres in extent' the bleaching meadows from Crayford House to Barnes Cray, seen from the hill above, resembled a great lake. The 'great coppice woods in the neighbourhood' provided the ashes used for whitening; ten acres of whitening ground consumed 80 bushels of ashes.

Nearer to London, however, the collier was out of his element when selling to households and artisans. The collier's man would bring his load to the suburbs where it was taken over for door-to-door selling by local spivs. Or so says an Elizabethan pamphlet quoted by Lyn Armstrong (1978). The street-wise pedlars would 'dirtie theyr hose and shoos on purpose to make themselves seem countrie colliers' and then give the urban cook or other customer very bad measure. For the rural collier the serving of a single industrial customer or employer had its attractions after all. Now, the increase in lime kilns and in brick making would help to sustain his market.

Tudor colliers of the Weald spent several months of the year living in their conical huts of poles, brushwood and turves because the woodstacks could not be left unattended during a burn of several days' duration. It is sometimes held that, like firewood, the collier had his favoured species for charcoaling but, comparing an

John Evelyn's drawing of the process for *Sylva*, 1663 and (below) modern charcoal making, and modern protection for the makers, at Mereworth.

analysis of species done for Straker with the natural availability in the Weald, it is likely that most kinds of underwood were acceptable.

Among those few that were not would be elder, because of its pithiness and, more positively, straight hazel rods because of their range of other uses in flexible small diameter. Whatever its contents, the meticulous preparation of the stack of cut wood, the burning and dousing of it, was a handed-down skill with the intricacies of any treatment which involves the controlled use of fire.

The ironmaster or clothier who leased or owned the woodland often was the collier's sole employer but elsewhere the collier was more usually not an estate worker but a specialist who bought the wood crop for cutting and charring. Woodcutter, burner and merchant might be one

person or three but the image of the collier was that of a man of blackened countenance rather mysteriously following his woodland craft. As the huge demand for the product in the Weald fell away in the 18th Century, younger men took up one or the other of the seasonal trades in which their collier fathers occasionally worked. Not only in the Weald but across the county, the myriad continuing uses for coppice-wood were a major provider of work. Now the Kent cutting cycle could be tuned to provide poles for what was already, nationally, more than 30,000 acres (12,000 ha) of hop gardens.

This chronicle has dwelt long on the period of the Wealden iron industry. It was not until Tudor times, outside the Royal Forests, that the increasing demands upon woodland output were generally recognised. Iron - in the Weald more than anywhere, but also in the Midlands and Scotland - formed the catalyst which fundamentally changed the approach of owners to their woodland management. Although iron was to become independent of wood fuel, it had pointed the way for woodsmen to control their resource with unnatural planting and a disciplined growth.

Nowadays, so frequently is it seen in print, the reader could be excused for concluding that only the ironworks (and perhaps the dyer's vats) saved Kent's woodland; a twist of conservation to the extent that the county now has the largest acreage of pre-1600 woodland sites in England. This over-simplification is as fanciful as Yarranton's contemporaries who concluded the opposite - that 'Ironworks destroy the Wood and Timber'. Remembering that the ironfield in Kent was only a western tenth of the county, even within that area different outcomes may be seen. The largely-wooded Southfrith, for example, some 5,000 acres (2,000 ha) south of Tonbridge, was allowed for tree-felling about the year 1550 and was afterwards converted mainly to farmland. Parts of the land were adaptable for arable cultivation and, soon, hop gardens prospered there. Yet in the same district, and well within the charcoal-carrying distance of iron works at Barden, Vauxhall, Southborough, Postern and Cage, were considerable woodlands still extant at the end of the 18th Century and even to-day. Ashour Wood, still looking over the Medway at Penshurst, is recorded as supplying not charcoal but hundreds of loads of myne, the iron ore itself, in 1577. At the far end of the Kent field, Bedgebury's Furnace is remembered by the farm of that name but a great tract of adjacent, less fertile, land is now under latter-day conifers, not least the world-renowned Pinetum.

During the two very formative centuries 1550 - 1750 the Wealden iron industry was for long the most important in Britain, and the cloth industry, too, was of significant status. Together, they put the local sustainable fuel source under unique stress. Ernest Straker notes an official return of 1573 which stated that in the twenty years 1553 - 73, from the small area of the Parish of Cranbrook and seven others adjoining, 6,542 acres of fuelwood had been felled. Nearly two-thirds of the woodland area was already coppice. The two industries indeed brought drama and change to the woodland but, unlike agriculture, not extinction.

From the prosperous years of wool and cloth we are graced with fine churches and enduring half-timbered cloth halls. From the clamorous ironworks we find nothing now except their peaceful ponds. In the nature of trees, we ought to find some evidence of coppice stools from as little as 250 years ago but it is rarely so. Oak, the majority species, was later frequently re-trained to high forest. With the keeping of only one tall stem per stump the stool disappears, although a slight curve at the base of a mature trunk could be an indication of it. A typical scene, to-day, is at the site of the great Horsmonden gun foundry. Beside the placid lake are intensively managed orchards to one side of the gentle valley and early-20th Century conifers at the dam wall. Further round is pasture and a quite young spinney before a swamp. Here high alder trees fan upwards from ancient stools which might be a rare living link with that small valley before the stream was dammed. There are no buildings left. At the bay outlet the water cascades down, to disappear below hazel catkins, under the hard, clean roadway and onward to the Teise. Gone - and almost forgotten - John Browne, Gunfounder to the King.

THE COMMONWEALTH - THEN SILVICULTURE

Introduction

In Kent, after Queen Elizabeth's reign, a new awareness grew in the minds of men concerning woodland and, particularly, timber trees. It was the result of many causes, in part a slow severance from tradition but also the shock of vandalism. The dramatic moments of change came, perhaps, from the excesses under Cromwell's regime but the greater status of woodland and silviculture was not fully observed until after 1700.

Since Norman times and even before, the management of tall trees had been carried out directly by the agent for the prior, for the archbishop or for the secular lord of the manor. These trees, with a minimum cycle of a man's lifetime or twice that, or even five lives if they were oak pollards, stood as the landmark of the demesne, close to the manor, as well as in the lord's distant woods. Younger members of the family sought, for their gavelkind inheritance, land more suitable for agriculture with an annual cash return. The very long timber cycle was to them a luxury not yet affordable. Tenants whose land included timber trees had been unable to fell them, in usual custom, except with the owner's grudging permission. Now, however, the changing pattern in Kent of land ownership and stronger tenancies was noticeable as some of the monastery and church lands became available to gentry and to yeomen families possessed of increasing wealth from the national recovery in agriculture or, locally, the industries of iron and cloth and the opportunities in merchant trade.

The agrarian innovators now were not the monasteries and the church but the keener secular landholders. Among such men the acquisition of parcels of timber trees and full rights to them removed a sign of inferiority which in the past had been all too visible. In Kent the number of property holders with an interest in this forestry increased more than elsewhere because of the greater number of independent properties, smaller than other counties, and improved wealth in much of the county.

The Statutes referring to woodland enacted by the Henrys and Elizabeth probably gained only limited observance, even in the counties to which they applied. As so often with wood products, the stronger influence came from the side-effects of other affairs of State. Eighteen Acts directly aimed at woods and wood products were imposed between 1540 and 1700 but it was the Navigation Laws, especially that of 1672, which meant most to the home timber market. These Laws of Cromwell and Charles II increasingly debarred foreign ships from carrying English exports or imports. The discrimination was a prime factor in the Dutch Wars and, later, the American War of Independence; but for Kent, as London's maritime service station, the measures guaranteed a huge demand for timber for shipbuilding at Greenwich, Deptford and Chatham (which last town saw a population increase from below 1,000 to 5,000 during the 17th Century). Inland landowners near navigable water on the Medway and elsewhere began to pay more heed to regeneration, or new plantations, of trees for timber.

The acreage of coppiced woodland in the iron area of west Kent was still needed. Elsewhere, the advent of sea-coal, much deferred during the Civil Wars, and the greater use of bricks instead of wattle for house-walling, were two more of the developments in the 17th Century which encouraged the trend of converting woodland back from coppice height to standard trees for heavier timbers. However, this move came in parallel with the gathering demand for coppice poles from hop-growers, fuel for lime-burners and other developing uses.

During the Civil Wars and the following Protectorate, serious damage was inflicted on Kentish woodlands (to be described further in a moment). Seen as part of a drive to punish some estate owners and gain revenue, the depredations compelled heads of families to work doggedly at the recovery and welfare of their lands for a generation thereafter. The Restoration of the Monarchy encouraged public exponents of silviculture, John Evelyn among the foremost, while correspondents turned from politics to writing in detail on this and other forms of husbandry. Tall trees were to be their necessity but also their pride as they restored the family wealth and the land's health, that which for most of them had been hard-earned by their forefathers.

'Looking upon happy times and sad'. This Younger Yew at Ulcombe began life 1,400 years ago - several centuries before the stone church was built.

The Pattern of Landed Families in Stuart and Cromwellian Times

The century which separated the Dissolution of the Monasteries from the Civil Wars, 1540 - 1642, completed the close and complex mesh of Kentish gentry families and the leading yeoman names now threaded tightly into it. The best-known gentle-names, thirty of them, were intermarried across the county, yet spread little beyond it. They featured, doughty but not rigid, throughout the reigns of Tudors and Stuarts, the Commonwealth and Protectorate and then Stuart again. In fact, they formed a social and landholding pattern which was not fundamentally changed in Kent until the coming of the railways, three centuries after Becket's shrine was carted away from Canterbury. Politically, and even militarily, the families opposed each other and changed sides but their names were always there to be recognised by the population at large. Among Kent's 130,000 total in the year 1600 (Zell) fewer than one thousand influenced the county's progress.

This influence of the gentry at the time of the Civil Wars was more real than in many other lowland counties. England's aristocracy, apart from the Earl of Thanet (the Tufton family), was not an active power among Kent landholders. The Earl of Dorset (the Sackvilles of Knole) had little local influence at this time owing to the deep indebtedness of the 3rd Earl. However, families with a London background prospered in the Sevenoaks area, among them the Bosvilles and Amhersts and the Lambardes, whose lawyer son, William, wrote *A Perambulation of Kent* in 1576 - England's first and famous county guide. The trickle of incomers from London had long been breaching the north-west of the county; these were occasionally merchants but more usually the favoured servants of court circles and the law. That they were not greater in number was due to several connecting causes.

The earlier Dissolution did not throw open a large acreage to London buyers. Much land had been transferred directly from prior to dean and chapter of the church, and many other parcels were acquired by the prior's lay tenants or, via the Crown, by neighbouring landowners. Established Kent families had developed a keen instinct for improving wealth by means of marriage. As to inheritance, (according to Lambarde, later) in the mid-15th Century not more than forty families in Kent with their tenures of socage had estates already released from gavelkind. His figure excluded the larger estates held by other means of tenure and bound by the first-born son's rights of primogeniture. But by Lambarde's own time, many more landowners had managed to disgavel their land by applying to the Court of Requests. Primogeniture, 'making eldest sons the owners of broad acres and throwing cadets upon the world', is credited even with founding the British Empire. Certainly it helped to avoid the minute parcelling of land seen still in the inherited peasant farming of some European countries.

Despite the disgavelments, the Kentish estate remained not large, and typically one of scattered farms in several parishes - a complication for a newcomer to assess or manage. If the geography of property and the tangle of intermingled family relations were obstacles to the incomer, they were also a puzzle to the locals. The county survey, intimate and astonishingly complete, by Edward Hasted in the distant late-18th Century could not have been applied to a more wanting subject.

From London into much of Kent, at least until the making of toll roads in the 18th Century, meant a tedious journey of several days, and sailing the long coastline beyond Gravesend was an alternative not suitable for gentlefolk. Rich Londoners preferred to seek the simpler ownership and easier access to the north of the metropolis. In all these ways it came about, as the notable commentators CW Chalklin and Alan Everitt have described for us in detail, that the gentry of early-modern Kent were 'largely native in origin'. 'The greater gentry,' Everitt further explains, 'were concentrated on the rich loams of East Kent or the wooded chartlands to the south of the Downs, or towards the Sussex border. The heavy wealden clays were primarily the province of Kentish yeomen, and the high, flinty fields of the Downland in the main supported smaller gentry and husbandmen.' (A.M.Everitt, 1966. *The Community of Kent and the Great Rebellion 1640 - 60*).

A baker's dozen of the best known gentle-names among perhaps 170 families were Boys, Culpeper, Dering, Digges, Finch, Hales, Hardres, Honeywood, Knatchbull, Oxinden of Deene, Roper, Sondes, Twysden. Within the county there might be many branches of the family: from ten branches of the Boyses to three of the Twysdens. In addition to their estates being on average quite small, another common feature was that of an ancestral home which had been first built in the 15th Century then added to or modified down the generations.

In our 21st Century world of businesses financed by anonymous shareholders and involving central government down to, literally, field level, we have to remind ourselves that until the 18th Century 'the firm' was 'the family'. Apart from the church, nearly all wealth was in the hands of a family, powered along by connections with other families. In Kent the successful ones were deeply knowledgeable about their surroundings in which their forebears had risen through agrarian husbandry or maritime trade during centuries of famine and fever and plenty. Such families included those who had gained from the good fortune of monastery or church land cheaply come by or from iron ore found upon their estates.

The structure was in no way a dependency of aristocratic control, or even presence, other than the Nevills (Lords of Abergavenny and one-time Clares) and the Earl of Thanet. Gentry such as the Hardres family from the time of the Conquest were less illustrious in their ancestors than such as the Scotts lying in Brabourne church, who could be traced back to the eminence of a 13th Century king of Scotland and to a knight Marshal and Lord Chief Justice who died during the ravage of the Black Death. Among the families well-known in the 17th Century but with an unsung history were two at least, the Twysdens and Knatchbulls (Knechebole), who gained wealth from wool on the Romney and Rother marshlands in late-medieval times before moving their home inland to more congenial living and increased prosperity. If such men's wealth came from close attention to farming and dealing aided by their long establishment, it was spurred along by a brisk curiosity in new situations, new inventions and opportunities.

Back in Tudor times, with the growing importance locally of decisions made by Crown and Parliament, the gentry of Kent had become relied upon by the monarch for new endeavours and local projects. Henry VIII, with his concern about invasion from the Continent, and supplies meanwhile to his Calais garrison, was active in demands for service. His newly-acquired palaces of Knole and Otford in the west of the county, and his wooing of Anne Boleyn at Hever, went alongside visits in East Kent to such as the Hardres family and to his new defence installations. On the Channel coast Reynold Scott of Scott's Hall was entrusted to take over the faltering building progress of Sandgate Castle which employed at its peak 900 men, including 66 carpenters and sawyers. Master Scott, soon to be Sir Reynold, used a quantity of large timber from his own woodland, ten miles inland, and the adjoining Horton Priory, but his local knowledge told him where else to choose beams and planks, from nearby or as far away as Great Chart. (See Appendix 6/1)

Yeomen of the same period were drawn more into office as justices and, later, as the elected knights of the shire. By the first half of the 17th Century their own names and those of their relations were listed in the county's petitions upon king and Parliament to right England's wrongs. Sir Roger Twysden and Sir Norton Knatchbull had been elected the two knights of the shire for the pre-war Short Parliament in 1639. Such men and their counterparts from boroughs and Cinque Ports mounted as formidable a group as any seen at Westminster. Alan Everitt, having a detailed knowledge also of other English counties, gives that opinion of Kent's representatives and explains how the would-be elected went about securing support from his fellows:-

> First the knight or baronet who set out to rule the county secured the support of the countryside around his own manor-house. Then his kinsmen among the greater gentry obtained the allegiance of their own labourers, tenants and neighbours. Finally, each major family secured the adherence of those groups of minor gentry whose social influence depended on their place in these galaxies of greater gentry. In this way, the whole community of the county gradually gathered into a series of rival family connexions.

For all that, Kent's voice of moderation was not heard at Westminster.

Abuse of Woodland Property

As civil war came, the intertwined nature of the great families was to increase the personal bitterness at the hardships brought on by the strife. Attacks on the property of 'delinquents' during the Puritan regime affected woodland more than the estate's other assets. In the days of the Sequestration Committee (1643) and then by means of Composition, where royalist owners paid a fine and regained their estates, outright sales were also made, often in penny-numbers of land owned by the church, while other sequestered woods were sold separately by the Committee of Woods.

Sir Roger Twysden's intellect and dignity were sorely tried by old acquaintances, now his enemies, on the republican County Committee. Incarcerated by a sort of lodging-house arrest, he had to

AN HISTORICALL, NAR-
RAtive of the two
howſes of Parliament and either of
them, their committees and Agents
violent proceedings againſt Sʳ Roger Twyſ-
den their impriſoning his perſon, ſequeſtring
his eſtate, cutting down his woods, and Tymber to his allmoſt undoing, and foreing him
in the end to Compoſition for his own.

Top Left: Sir Roger Twysden aged 51
Top Right: Sir Norton Knatchbull, 1st Baronet 1601 - 1685
(Based on portraits from the period)

Above: Title page of Twysden's narrative

Right: Deer park oaks at Mersham Hatch

rely upon his sick wife to come to Westminster and plead his case. None of her early efforts, or their friends', could undo the damage to his mature woodlands at East Peckham. To Twysden, one even more than usually dedicated to his timber trees, the spiteful activities from 1643 of the County Committee were particularly distressing. For Stockenbury Woods, as an example, his plea that timber trees grown from coppice tillers must not be downgraded to fuelwood met with no response. Even the Committee for the Supply of London etc. with Wood for Fuel was unable to abate the felling. The local malice of the County Committee and such men as Walter Brooke and son, wood merchants, ensured that the felling in Stockenbury Wood continued. By 1647 half the trees there had been felled and 'Prior's Broom, Motewood and Oven's Wood had all been cleared' (F W Jessup.) The county properties most affected in this way were those sequestered because their owners were in disfavour and whose timber or smallwood lay near to the navigable Medway or the Thames estuary. The owners, in addition to Twysden, included Sir George Sondes (near Faversham) and Sir Peter Richant (New Hythe), while the Earl of Thanet also lost loads of faggots already assembled at the Rainham wharf.

For other woodlands the violation came 'from the poor'; stealing by local people or soldiers quartered nearby, with the acquiescence of the Committees. Earlier, the official demand on woodland had been for repairs to castles and ships but, by 1643, it was a matter, too, of the lack of sea-coal reaching people of London and harbour towns who had grown used to having it. As in Twysden's Narrative:-

Upon a pretence of saving timber trees which the poor, necessitated for want of fuel, His Majesty having Newcastle, did in many parts destroy, they allowed certain to enter in to and cut only the fellable (small) *wood of Bishops, etc, and such as were described in an Act of Sequestration. But finding the King's army either not willing or not able to help the oppressed, and* (with) *men ready to execute their commands, on the 16th April 1644, they* (the Committees?) *fell upon the timber of sundry persons.*

The Earl of Thanet's loss of coppice product and timber 'by authority of Parliament' is listed in the Tufton sequestration papers. The special sense of violation felt by the victims of theft from their woods is indicated by its relative importance in the order of wording used in his draft petition in 1664/5....*his whole estate hath been under sequestration for a year and a halfe, and his Lady and 5 children have not had £200 to mayntayne them, his woods to a very great volume have been cutt and all his personal estate taken for the use of Parliament.* And again....*whereas there was but £5,000 per annum settled uppon marriage of the Earl of Thanet whereof £1,000 per annum did consist in coppice woods which the Parliament hath for the most part totally felled...*

At the three royal parks of Eltham the park palings were destroyed, no doubt for fuelwood, by soldiers or common people and the deer taken. A quotation from a book of 1660 claims that Sir Thomas Walsingham, after the king's execution, 'has cut down £5,000 worth of timber, and has scarcely left a tree to make gibbet'.

Of course, the majority of estates in Kent were not physically plundered. Many remained little affected by events. Sir Norton Knatchbull, not being selected as a leader for Westminster, retired in 1647 almost to seclusion upon his estate and apparently was spared the tribulations of so many of his close Kentish circle. The Kentish Rebellion of 1648 occupied mightily many leading landowners, by now hardened into Royalist sympathies, until it was savagely put down. Three hundred rebels were slain at Maidstone by Government troops. More insidiously, many smaller estates had slipped into debt and some were forced to sell up; a trend which was to reduce markedly Kent's unusually fractionated land ownership. The 1640s in Kent were characterised not so much by battle and siege as by loss of trust and a coarsening of attitude to property. There is no better an example to depict it than that from Mercurius Rusticus in 1647. In the nave of Rochester Cathedral, it is recorded, men 'so far profaned this place as to make as of it in the quality of a tippling place, as well as dug several saw pits, and the city joiners made frames for houses in it'.

An estate saw pit; the normal method of cutting the length of timber during the 16th to 18th Centuries

The Restoration - of the Monarch and of the estates

Even by the relatively peaceful 1655, the major-general for Kent and Surrey could inflict special taxes of one-tenth of their property value upon the larger delinquent estates. The Earl of Thanet and ninety gentry were fined by this tax called Decimation. However, after the long-sought Restoration of the Monarchy the affected men, most of whom relied chiefly upon agrarian output for their income, could begin to show recovery. At the parliamentary elections the marshmen of New Romney once again chose Sir Norton Knatchbull to serve in a Parliament whose Kent members were predominantly Cavaliers. That a mood of enjoyment, even frivolity, had returned to England may be read into the housekeeping accounts of his son John: a tip for John Evelyn's gardener, and a shilling paid to Lord Brewerson's man for a pet grey squirrel.

In the troubled mid-17th Century and through all such swings of temper and changing values, the concern of the English landholder for the tall trees in his woodland has to be gauged as deeper than, say, for an arable field. This has not always been due to market value: in phases of the Tudor and Stuart period, and many times since, timber did not keep up with the rise in most other staples. Most English people find from trees in the landscape a sort of spiritual well-being, although a sober forester might not admit it. There is sub-conscious respect for the grandeur of the highest living thing and for its longevity. Probably, too, an instinct remains from our very many past generations when the master - feudal or priestly or family head - held his timber trees in demesne. Here is continuity, a most observable good stewardship, an assurance beyond the span of one man's life.

Six Generations of Estate Improvement

The financial and visual appeal of woodland was strong among landowners throughout Stuart and Hanoverian times. Always a predilection of the wealthy, it was now combined with a broader zest for land 'improvements'. An extraordinary and sustained drive had begun to build up in Kent before the Civil War. Between woodland owners, the printed word and their own personal correspondence pointed the way to a more rational, modern silviculture. Demand for both timber and underwood led men away from some long-held lore such as the need to fell trees at the right phase of the moon. Yet Twysden, that most dedicated of owners, still instructed his son not to fell while the wind was in the east for fear that the timber would be worm-eaten. In the more enlightened generation it is unlikely that his heir obeyed. The new force for improvements was aimed at differing objectives but always was fired by the clarity and enthusiasm of its speakers and writers whatever the goal. ·

Early in the period Gervaise Markham in *The Inrichment of the Weald of Kent* (1625 and 1636) gave his treatise on the value of marling and other improvements to the clay of the Weald ' for it will grow to frith and wood if it be not continually manured and laboured with the plough'. In contrast to the Weald, nearly half the county, that part north of a line from Tonbridge to Hythe, was anciently inclined to arable farming. Now, in both regions, came an expanding acreage of hops, orchards and other market gardening in ventures well-justified by the demand from London. Henry Oxinden of Barham, forced to sell up in 1652, could claim that his 550 acres there were 'most of them of a nature fit to be planted with fruit trees, by reason of which fitness for plantation, improvable to double value of the rent they now go at.' Indeed the most popular of 'improvements' could be said to be an increase from the tenants' rents.

However, simultaneously the hunt for fuelwood and timber intensified. The following year W.Blith dedicated *The English Improver Improved*, 3rd Edition, to the Right Honourable the Lord General Cromwell. Blith's Six Pieces of Improvement had 'No.6. By doubling the growth of wood by a new Plantation.' It spoke of planting sets rather than seed and described plashing as a way of thickening existing coppice. In the wings of this stage was the key figure of John Evelyn. By his address in 1662 to the Royal Society he did much to ensure that landowners nationally would become more aware of timber trees, the need to plant them and to be familiar with woodland subjects.

This great advocate of woodland improvements was born at Wotton on the slope of Leith Hill, a well-wooded estate kept by his father who was aware of timber values. As a young man, John, after taking a sort of excusatory army commission, broadened his perspective by a long sojourn on the Continent during the Civil War. Back in England he soon established a home at Sayes Court, Deptford in Kent which allowed him daily forays into London society or on his work in the shipbuilding towns and further afield.

His most influential work 'Sylva' was read to the Royal Society just two years after that body was formed upon the return of Charles II as monarch. The uplift in spirits among property owners due to the Restoration and the added demand for timber from the royal and merchant navies made his ideas, in book form, topical and popular through several leather-bound editions. His wide circle of acquaintances, from Samuel Pepys at the Admiralty to the Knatchbulls among many county gentry, and his work as travelling diarist, councillor of plantations, member of the Board of Trade and Treasurer of Greenwich Hospital all made him a figure of influence in the new awareness of silviculture, both in Kent and nationally.

Evelyn's Discourse of Forest Trees, to be published as *Sylva,* is still exhilarating for the modern reader.

> How goodly a sight were it if most of the Demesnes of our Country Gentlemen were crown'd and encircl'd with such stately rows of Firs, Elms and other ample shady and venerable Trees as adorn New-Hall in Essex and our neighbouring Pastures at Barnes. Yet were these Plantations but of late years in comparison : It were a noble and immortal providence to imitate these good Husbands in larger and more august Plantations of such useful trees for Timber and Fuel, as well as for shade and ornament to our dwellings.

Narrowing from the grand to the specific, Evelyn has been proved sound in so many aspects; from Of Copses to Of Pruning and even charcoaling his findings have stood the test of time. On nurserywork, that critical start-point, he added

That great care be had of the Seeds which we intend to sow has already been advised; for it has been seen that Woods of the same age planted in the same soil discover a visible difference in this Timber and growth; and where this variety should happen if not from the seed will be hard to interpret; therefore let the place, soil and growth of such Trees from whence you have your seeds be diligently examined.

Ravaged woodlands, new orchards and ornamental bowers required more resources than local seed gathering. Nursery smallholdings had developed outwards from central London after early beginnings in the 16th Century. Some growers concentrated on trees and shrubs more selectively. By the early 18th Century John Parkinson of Lambeth was able to prosper as a specialist in evergreens. After a further century a Swede, Pehr Kalm, could comment, 'In England there is the advantage that in nearly every town and village there is one or more nurserymen, whose principal occupation is to sow and plant the seeds of different kinds of trees.'

To see this southern nursery practice at its climax we may, for a moment, stray 160 years beyond Evelyn's discourse, to read a report from the land agent for the 4th Earl of Aylesford (CKS archives). With the aid of his now famous estate atlas, R K Summerfield described progress in 1825. His reports exemplify the long-sighted but practical approach to woodland of the wealthy landowner through the 18th Century.

He wrote that his plan from the old century had been achieved. During eighteen years 'from 20 to 30,000 Ash and Chestnut plants were supplied from this nursery annually and planted in the Rainham, Bredhurst and other woods in the Estate.' Allowing 500 plants per acre for 'filling up', fifty acres could be covered each year. Then 25,000 seedlings were bought as replacements (from an unnamed source). By now the nursery had done its job, the planting up of the coppice woodland was virtually complete and so he had converted the $2\frac{1}{2}$ acre nursery to a future orchard of 'Cherry, Filberts, etc.' A smaller nursery had been started, under the supervision now of a tenant farmer, to cope with maintenance. As a postscript this contented agent showed fallibility - 'The oaks hitherto put in the nursery have not succeeded but I mean to make another trial.'

Although nowadays kept in separate compartments, the practices of horticulture and silviculture were intermingled for owners and staff in the past. In Kent, the cherry was the far-famed crop which, from its seas of blossom, first earned the county its title, Garden of England. Gascoignes (now Gaskins) were the dessert cherries said to have been brought from Gascony by Joan of Kent, wife of the Black Prince. Another name for them was Guigne. Sweet cherries of this sort are all cultivars of silviculture's wild cherry (Prunus avium), otherwise known still as Gean. Wild cherry wood was used as a coppice product and, more importantly, it was grown to larger girth specifically for its decorative timber. Paradoxically, apple and pear trees provided wood for furniture making but seem not to have been planted for that purpose.

That Summerfield report was made at the end of a long, little-changing but virile span of years (1660 - 1820) which in Kent gave continuity enough for woodland working methods to be established and passed to younger generations by means of many estate books.

Other archive material at the Centre for Kentish Studies which may be seen and handled includes a set of 18th Century 'Timber Books', five in all, the first of which begins in the hand of Sir Edward Filmer of East Sutton. He starts his items of memoranda without preamble.

> NB That Sir Robert Filmer my Father in the year 1698 let all his Underwood in Lamberhurst to Mr William Benge containing by Estimate 100 acres more or less at 6 sh a cord to be cut and corded by Mr Benge - Each cord to contain 3 foot in height, 3 foot in breadth and 14 foot in length for ye term of 21 years. The Woode to be 15 years growth or upwards. Benge to fell so many acres as should be assigned by Sir R Filmer. Benge to have the Brush for clearing the wood. Wood to be cleared by Michaelmas Day. Money to be paid upon Michaelmas Day and the fence to be made by Mr Benge.

This intensely detailed record or instruction is carried on into a hasp-bound book of 'Woods at Chartham' by Edward Boxfield, noting events for eleven woodlands up to 1798, a working continuity of nearly a century. The regular felling regimen for all the Filmer underwood in that period is from 7 to 18 years with the majority between 10 and 14 years. Because the writers are so close to their subject the coppice species is often unmentioned, just as at the manor of Wye four hundred years earlier. We may guess that in the 18th Century the Kentish underwood was likely to be ash/oak or part of the increasing acreage of sweet chestnut. That the underwood usually had its complement of timber-sized oak or ash can be seen in the sales details.

> 1721 Truman's Grove Sold to Browning, a Carpenter in Canterbury at £105-0-0 by the Lump. Measured the last Fellet which was in 1710 at 18 acres. Fences to be made by thePurchaser.
>
> Timber Sold to said Browning 122 oaks then growing in Truman's Grove & 8 other pieces then growing in Miln's Bank Coppice, in all 130 - all at 50 sh. a Tun, Top and Tan containing by measure 53 tons 2 ft 6. = £134.02.06

Nearly seventy years later in Truman's Grove we read of Oak Timber at 'Twenty-five Tun and thirteen feet' and, elsewhere, of 'Six Tun and two feet' - a perplexing combination of measurements. The terms are discussed in Appendix 6/2.

'Tan' or oak bark was not yet, it seems, up to the great value which for a while in the 19th Century made it worth more than the tree's timber. Nevertheless the wood book counselled felling timber trees after coppice cutting 'level with ye Ground with a Saw in April or May when the bark will run (peel) easily and let them be carried out by Michaelmas'.

Felling the oak trees at bud-burst time but allowing until Michaelmas Day, 29th September, to haul away the round trunks or planks sawn on site gave usually enough time to get the timber away on passable tracks. Turnpiking had been spreading through Kent since 1709 but the roads were, at best, patchily maintained by the parish workless or by often-reluctant employers who must put their men to work on a local stretch. Underwood cutting, as now, might well be done by the tree-faller in the winter months if the product was to be poles rather than woven work. Again, he should be off that land by Michaelmas to ensure a settled ground for the next coppice regeneration.

Much of the practice was as old as the woods themselves but now was reinforced by somewhat arbitrary rule in the Chartham and Crundale coppice. After a cutting at less than fourteen years growth, 'stock should not be allowed to graze for four years and if above fourteen years growth no animal to enter for six years. And then with new wean'd Calves and some say Colts of a year old - from November to March.' While the cutters were working in the woods 'Waggon horses to be muzzled at the expense of the seller.'

At Chartham the norm was to sell a whole wood as one lot, the crop being chiefly cut for hop poles in that area and the acreage perhaps smaller. At Crundale, on the other hand, the woods should be 'washed' which meant, and still does, marked into sections known as cants for the buyers to bid upon and work within. 'Wash' may seem obviously to have come from marking the boundary stems with whitewash or quicklime solution but the ancient word might also fit the practice of cutting a distinguishing clearance through the foliage. Both marking methods are used still. Another annual practice, which continues still in Kent, was to excite the auction day with a little ale. 'Brew a Bushel of Malt for Beer against the Sale Day, to adjourn of ye wood to his house where ye price of each Cant is to be declared.' In the 20th Century the usually solitary woodcutters were still invited to a favoured pub to make their bids.

For standlings (one of the many names for those coppice poles to be kept and grown on for timber) the woodreeve must mark them individually and could be expected to add a penalty for any then cut down. For the rooted stools left after cutting it was good to runt

Cutting a wash today

them if they were big in circumference. To runt was to cut them, in winter, level to the ground, and by axe 'not saw because the fretting of the saw would kill them'. This piece of lore was long-held, even into the first chain-saw years, but has been disproved by that machine.

At Highfield Springs Wood, Chartham, twenty-five acres were to be felled in two falls during 1743 and 1744. (In woodsman parlance, fellet might be used for the past tense, fall as the noun and faller as the worker's name to distinguish better between feller and fellow; the latter often used pejoratively.) The owner's man was to mark out 50 sheddles of Oak on an Acre, if there be so many, for future timber. The cutters were to leave 50 stocks (coppice stools) of the best sort of wood, 4 or 5 Wavers (pliable stems) on each stock for the benefit of the next Underwood.

By the 1750s in Kent wood buyers came from an assortment of fuelwood merchants, fencers, carpenters, mill- and wheel-wrights, hop pole buyers or brewers, and now specialist timber merchants. Mr Joseph Mercer, Timber Merchant of Maidstone, bought from the Filmer lands 155 oaks containing by measure 64 tuns 14 ft Top and Tan, as they stood, of 32 sh. per Tun. The selling of woodland produce was becoming more commercialised but at a time when communications were still not quick. Letters direct by post to Mr Edward Horsefield at Chartham (Filmer's tenant) were to be left at the Mermaid near the fish market in Canterbury. Peter Ellis, Carrier, went from Maidstone to Canterbury, twenty-eight miles on roads not yet fully turnpiked, every Friday to return on Saturday. In these circumstances forthcoming auctions were still 'cry'd' at Canterbury, Chartham and Chilham.

A restored Kent wagon (Mr R H Bazell). Oak for shafts and spokes, ash for rims and outrails, elm for hubs and baseboards.

Printed advertising was now appearing in newspapers, using pseudo-legal terms not found in the clear English of the timber books.

> **To be Sold Tithe Free**
>
> **An Under Wood of Sir Edward Filmer's called Clay Forstal Hill containing by estimation 12 ac. 13 rds 19 p lying in the Parish of Chartham (Mr Horsefield-Tenant) to be felled this Winter. For further particulars Enquire at the Three Tuns Canterbury where Sir Edward Filmer's Bayliff may be spoke with Saturday who will treat for the same.**

> **Timber to be Sold**
>
> **Whereas there are 50 middling Oak trees marked out for sale in an Underwood called Highfield Springs in Chartham, Edmund Fairbree - Tenant, These are to give Notice to all Buyers of Timber that they may view and that there will be a Person ready to treat with such Persons as are disposed to buy the same on Saturday ye 23rd March at the Three Tuns in Canterbury.**

What was meant by Tithe Free as far as the underwood buyer was concerned is not clear now. The woodland at Chartham was assessed for Land Tax, 'the Poor' and 'the Church'; for the latter two the Sessing was calculated per 20 acres. In the matter of tax and tithe additives the owner's servant needed to be alert. An advanced case of doubt is sensed from a Sheppey writer.

> Beech trees regularly are titheable, yet in a County where there is a scarcity of Timber, and where Beech is used as Timber for Building and ye like, there possibly they may be discharged of paying of tithes. Beeches in their own nature are not computed Timber-trees, and therefore are titheable, except where by the Custom of the country where there is Scarcity of Wood they are accounted Timber-trees in which case they are not titheable.

The splendid elm, of beauty and of many uses, was now managed more carefully in hedgerows surrounding the long-enclosed fields of Kent. Later, in 1825, R K Summerfield would be able to write to the Earl of Aylesford about his Eccles and Roe Place farms.

> The hedgerows in these two last described Farms abound in Elm Timber which grows very fast in this soil and is of the best quality; formerly the Tenants cut and made their hedges as they pleased, consequently the workmen paid no regard to the young Timber; but I have never suffered a fence on any part of the Estate to be new laid, where there is Timber, without the young plants, however small, being first carefully marked whereby a full and regular succession has been secured. In 1819 upwards of £1800 value in Elm was sold, principally from these Farms, tho' the price at that time was not as high by one-third as now. £400 or £500 in value of large sized trees might now be taken down to advantage, if your Lordship is so inclined, and it would make room for the quicker better growth of the young trees adjoining.

Before this report, while still in the 18th Century, the benefits of the General Highways Acts of 1773 begin to be seen. In this, internationally, most formative period the prospect of better roads was one encouragement in men's thoughts to wider horizons and new opportunities. First, at the county level, a greater traffic rumbled between London and the still-fashionable spa society of Tunbridge Wells and the newly-splendid parks or county seats of the wealthy. On a higher plane events, including the Seven Years War in Europe, the fantastic voyages of discovery by James Cook out of Greenwich, the commercial effects of the American War of Independence and the incoming bounty from the Orient, all had their impact on men's minds and pockets - none more so than the Revolution in France and the Napoleonic wars to follow it.

Even the parochial nature of England's woodland produce began to be affected, by the philosophical influences and, at the level of trade, by such as the competition of foreign steam-driven sawmills. Meanwhile, a unique, and therefore absurdly untypical, example which illustrates two strands of influence, at least, was seen at Chilham Castle. The owner, George, Earl of Tankerville, had all the wealth of a Chairman of the East India Company and the convenience of its marine base at Gravesend. He or his successors caused two elephants to be installed in very high-ceilinged stables by his castle wall so that they might, with their imported mahouts, work the timber of Chilham Park.

PARKLAND AND THE NAVY

The English Parkland Garden with Trees

Landscape expressions of family wealth had traditionally featured timber-trees on the demesne and a deer pound and park for the most affluent. As late as 1598 a foreign visitor, Hentzner, observed at Greenwich: 'Near this place is the Queen's Park, stocked with deer; such parks are common throughout England, belonging to those that are distinguished for their rank or riches'. However, owing to the cost of labour the number of fully-fenced parks in Kent was much reduced even before the Civil War. William Lambarde's *Perambulation* commented on the prosperity of Kent around 1570 but his list of fifty-four Forrestes and Parks noted that twenty-three had been disemparked; their cleft-wood pale or hedge and bank and ditch all now breached by neglect. A far cry from the days around 1332 when the prior gave six deer to Elham to start yet another new park.

From that ancient style of wealthy prudence there developed through the centuries, and latterly by several quick steps in severe fashion, a softer landscaped design which in the mid-1700s would display the new Georgian house to great advantage. And huge sums were spent in the landscaping. The more usual alternative declaration of increased wealth, buying more land, had lost some of its attraction when food-growing profit in Kent came to depend on the type of crop rather than acreage. Land tax, too, was a new dissuader. The landlord's competitive nature had already turned to lavish spending upon the fashionable appearance of his buildings. The many-times altered Wealden hall/house was a thing of the past and the splendid new mansion must be set in suitable surroundings. Tall trees, whether woodland or singly on the lawn, enhanced the house and became even more a mark of prosperity in the hands of landscape designers.

A map of Kent to interest the gentry, by John Seller, was updated for the bookseller H Moll and his rival P Overton at a date that cannot have been earlier than about 1720. The map is accurate enough to show, for example, Knole deer park beside but separate from The Wilderness. Seller's total of thirty-one fenced parks has fourteen in Kent's westernmost lathe of Sutton-at-Hone (roughly west of a line Gravesend - Wrotham - Tonbridge). In the north-west corner it included the now-forgotten Scadbury by Chislehurst but not the royal Eltham. The park of Plumstead, its great house in the centre of the little village, was shown but not Langley at Bromley. It is possible that when the surveyor passed through he did not record properties as having deer parks unless the beasts were evident and fenced in. Eltham parks had been breached terminally and their deer slain during republican times. Mapmakers often treated woodland as they did parks: ancient sites of some size might not be shown if they had recently been coppiced or their timber clear-felled.

There was little likelihood of deer being stocked while major

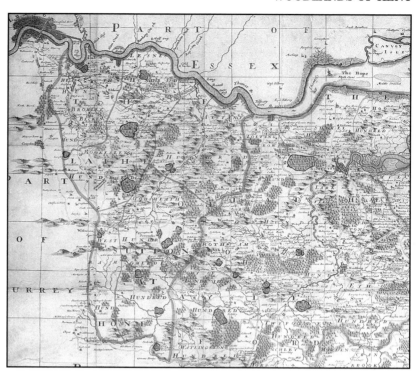

From John Seller's map of Kent, updated to about 1720 or later.

landscape engineering was in progress. From the 1720s onwards very many Kentish estates underwent dramatic changes in their physical appearance. Following the more house-formal disciplines of Dutch, French and Italian gardens, the English style sought to carry the eye out to the farthest horizon and bring back that vision to the house by means of rolling pasture, then lawn, separated only by a sunken ha-ha and with the middle ground beyond the ditch organised by hillocks, perhaps a lake, and well-placed copses or avenues of lime. The method was applied by many landscapers beginning with William Kent, who died in 1748, then 'Capability' Brown in the mid-century, who was succeeded by Humphry Repton, and there were others in parallel although less well remembered.

Brown wrote little about his ideas but Humphry Repton left us the evidence of his dramatic sales literature, the Red Books, a dozen of which are still in existence from the west of the county. He showed, by attractive illustrations, how country seats old and new might receive his landscape treatment. The contrasting effect worked best with neglected or very conservative properties such as Bayham Abbey. So compelling was the fashion, however, that a number of owners had their views adapted by a contractor to this pastoral landscape, even quite soon after much labour had been spent on a formal design as at Squerryes Court.

In the centre and east of the county physical alteration came to estates old and new. Leeds Castle, so magnificent to-day, had been neglected to the point when John Evelyn, in one of his Thames-side roles, could billet Dutch and French captured sailors there. Its owners, more concerned with their kingdom-sized holdings in Virginia colony, returned for Robert Fairfax to have Leeds park landscaped about 1770. Thomas Best, 'next door' at the large Chilston Park, had his formal gardens broadened out at about the same time. Both landlords had the scenic advantage of the five-mile stretch of King's Wood above them although it is thought that they owned no part of it. On the other side of the ridge the Filmer family maintained the deer park at East Sutton they had created a hundred years earlier.

The recruitment of a mass of adjacent woodland, owned or not by their client, gave English-style landscapers a common feature of 'ordered wilderness', as Elizabeth Jenkin puts it in her biography of Jane Austen (1775 - 1817). Well-travelled gentlemen likened the scene to a painting by Poussin or Claude Lorraine. 'It was disposed with the aim of achieving an emotional effect on the spectator.' The biographer follows with an extract from an unattributed essay which suits that mood as well as the fact of forestry adapted by the early exponent William Kent

> When the united plumage of an ancient wood extended wide its undulatory canopy, and stood venerable in darkness, Kent thinned the foremost ranks, and left but so many detached and scattered trees as softened the approach of gloom and blended the chequered light with the thus lengthened shadows of the remaining columns.

The H Moll version of Seller's map (and allowing that the deer may have been only temporarily absent) shows not a single park on the Stour valley banks between Wye and Canterbury, where so soon were to be Godmersham, Olantigh and Chilham. Only Eastwell, with one thousand deer in its park of ancient fame, stands above and towards the wooded hills. Along the Canterbury to Dover road the string of parks - Bifrons, Charlton, Barham and Broome - are not marked. 'Capability' Brown drew up plans for Chilham Park in 1777 (uncompleted, it would seem.) All these near together parks, plus Mersham Hatch and others a little more distant, can be said to have had major work done on their grounds between 1750 and 1800.

Parks across the county, however much landscaped, took their character to a large extent from the surrounding landform and topography. At Cobham, near Rochester, Repton and the Earl of Darnley made expansive use of the scarp's gentle fall to estuary level and were influenced by the great woods of 1,400 acres on the estate beyond the park, which itself enclosed 538 acres. Species, natural or introduced long ago, ash, oak, sweet chestnut and hornbeam, and also sycamore, were nurtured in the park, and the horticulturally inclined earl would have known the seasonal beauty of horse chestnut and other recently introduced trees. In the far west of the county, Chevening and Combe Park for the Duke of Argyll were influenced by the tree horizons of the Westerham Greensand hills and valleys. On the Sussex border at Bedgebury the site of the earlier mansion of the Colepeppers, where Queen Elizabeth stayed, now lies beneath an ornamental lake.

That there were no parks on the coastal marshes or Thanet's treeless island is not surprising but less obvious is the lack of them on the Low Weald. The wooded but clay-bound land was not a chosen home for wealthy families. There, to-day, may be seen a misleading effect of old oak veterans standing singly, and handsomely, in pasture fields. These are not the relics of abandoned parkland; they are trees, many once pollarded for poles and smallwood, remaining after hedgerows were rooted out in recent time to form a larger field. Like the single, placed oak grown up in open parkland, the one-time hedgerow tree has heavier, more-lateral branches and a wider canopy than its woodland brethren.

The altogether more accurate map of the county of Kent by the Surveying Draftsmen of His Majesty's Honourable Board of Ordnance in 1801 (England's first Ordnance map) used symbols which also leave inconclusive the matter of deer-fenced park boundaries. The draughtsmen showed any roadway along the perimeter by means of two continuous lines which might also be read as walling. Those parks near Canterbury missing from Seller's map were all on the OS map with their distinctive symbol of stippled lawn and trees. Some parks, such as Godmersham, may have got their deer after this date. However, in Kent and elsewhere the term *park* no longer applied only to deer enclosures. The smaller parks of gentry, such as those newly created surroundings for mansions near London, avoided the problems of deer keeping, even though by doing so they lessened the elegance and standing of their property.The fallow deer of lowland parks, as farmers know too well, are voracious grazers as well as browsers of higher vegetation. The deer-owning landlord had to protect with paling the new tree seedlings planted in his park but, as a grazier, he needed to shift his herd from one part of the park to the next. Tree lines and clumps, fenced around or ditched, were adapted to this practical purpose as well as for viewing from the house. This pattern was the reverse of medieval deer-parks where woodlands of trees with grazing below them was the norm, and pollards on the occasional open lawn. The method and manner of it all were important to the owner and his family. Sir Wyndham at Mersham kept up his 'Hatch journal of country work' (as distinct from his months each year in London). Writing in 1773, just before Robert Adam built the new mansion, he makes frequent first hand observations

| Tues 10 July. | James Clark & 2 men setting up ye Park pale --- there was then set up in all 50 rods of new pale |
| Wed 11 July | --- there will be about 104 pannels (of posts and close railing) when the whole is finished. |

The panels were of oak felled and converted on the estate.

The acreage of named parks in Kent was indeed large by the end of the century; by extrapolating from sixteen parks of known size, a conservative total estimate is not less than 10,000 acres. That, however, would have been little more than one-tenth of Kent's total woodland acreage, and the parks included a large portion of open ground. Park woodland, on the other hand, contained a bigger ration of timber-sized trees than the county's whole, which was at least two-thirds under coppice with standards.

The degree of attention required from his lordship to the positioning of trees and copses undoubtedly gave him, and his ladies, an interest in the species and their provenance and health. Jane Austen wrote in a letter from Godmersham Park

Yesterday passed quite a la Godmersham: the gentlemen rode about Edward's farm, and returned in time to saunter along Bentigh with us; and after dinner we visited the Temple Plantation, which, to be sure, is a Chevalier Bayard of a plantation. James and Mary are much struck with the beauty of the place.

Whilst not, in this history of woodland management, tackling the sociological impact of the landscaping movement, it should be noted that the rich man's interest in trees made more likely the survival of woodland <u>outside</u> his park as well as that inside. Failing that interest, and an acceptable market for timber, he would have had available skills enough to turn woodland on indifferent soil into farm field or orchard. This leaning towards forestry percolated through the lesser gentry as a study worthy of imitation and it was encouraged further by the patriotic and profitable notion of tree-planting for the very long-term future of the Thames-side royal shipyards. So interwoven were the ideals of deer park land and woodland that the combined thought persisted until at least the end of the following century. As far ahead as 1908 that towering series the Victorian County History devoted, in its Kent volumes, more than four of the seven pages on Forestry to a description of deer parks. By then there were only fifteen parks with deer. Today the visitor to Knole or the walker across Mersham Hatch may still enjoy the gracious air that deer bring to the parkland scene.

That extraordinary chronicler Edward Hasted reflected contemporary thinking in his survey of Kent. In 1798 he described Cobham Hall with this balance of interests

> Cobham Hall is a noble and stately mansion, which cost upwards of sixty thousand pounds building; it consists of a centre and two wings, the former is the work of Inigo Jones; the latter were made uniform, new cased with brick work, and sashed by the late earl. It stands in the midst of an extensive park, formerly much more so, which is finely interspersed with woods and stately timber trees, many of the latter being of great age and size; some of the oaks are twenty feet and upwards, in circumference; the noted chesnut tree, called the four sisters, from its dividing into four very large arms, stands in the grove, about a mile from the hall, near the path leading to Knights-place farm, and is thirty-two feet in circumference. The herbage of this park is so excellent, that the venison produced from it is highly esteemed, as being of a finer flavour than most others in this county.

He commented that ' the woods and foliage in Cobham-park give it in general a gloomy appearance'. And then, 'The antient Roman-road or Watling-street-way goes on to Cobham-park where the pales seem to stand on it for some little space soon after which it leaves them - - from thence it runs into a thick wood which is not to be followed'. Humphry Repton agreed that the estate looked neglected when he began his sixteen years of work there in 1790.

But Repton, of course, preserved the greater trees. For commercial value, woodland timber was routinely felled at 80 - 100 years, yet in most Georgian, and then Victorian, parkland alterations the veterans were kept. The ubiquitous oak, so often pollarded, was featured on grazing land with sweet chestnut and the smaller hornbeam. Regular cutting of the pollard branches continued if the park owner knew it to be for their health. It seems that a life of alternating limb amputation and recovery adds to the longevity of broadleaved trees.

In the hedgerows and woodland edge were tall or pollarded elm among the field maple and ash, sometimes as boundary markers cut at lower stub height. With these and the great full-height specimens, notably of beech on sandy soils, the owner thus prolonged the lives of his ancients of several centuries.

His own planting alongside ensured for us more giants of the future. A reminder that such familiar trees are not for ever was delivered brutally to park trees by the Great Storm of 1987. The appearance of parkland a few years later, the open grass now dotted with frail new park trees guarded up to horse-height, would have been at once recognised by our forebears of 200 years ago. In 1790 a passer-by wrote of Mersham Hatch as an unseemly mansion with 'fir trees and suchlike minutiae around it; and a common in front, and backed by a staring park'. Nearly two centuries later Sir Hughe Knatchbull-Hugessen had very good reason to respond, 'Today no one looking across the Park, with the great trees of Barracks Wood, the hornbeams of Bockhanger and giant oaks dotted about on the sweep down to the two small lakes could possibly call it *staring*.'

The 18th Century planters worked largely still by trial and instinct and had, for example, little scientific awareness of the ecological value of an old broadleafed tree. Indeed, considering their ability in all aspects of silviculture, it is strange how little was determinable by scientific analysis concerning tree species and their origins. The argument over when sweet chestnut became known in England brought Hasted into the arena of the Royal Society's journal *Philosophical Transactions*. In 1777 his considerable knowledge of the long-established sweet chestnut area around Sittingbourne was highlighted among reports from across Britain and the finding of its charred wood near old iron-workings. *Castanea vulgaris* was not really proved to have existed here since before Britain's watery separation but the anecdotal evidence was rich and wide, and it was of major interest to the readers of the day. For most planters the interest lay in a more commercial direction. Mr W Randall, the Maidstone nurseryman and author, was a great promoter of chestnut coppice for the galloping increase in hop production. He wrote fulsomely to encourage the end-product:-

> In a political view, we must perceive in the Hop, as in the oak, and in the iron, a source of defence arising from its powers of revenue; not only by its direct supply of a duty averaged at about £115,000 per annum, but by its being also the great preservative of beer; that congenial beverage of Britons, and to which immense duties are attached in all its stages.

On a more factually martial note, the gunpowder millers at Faversham were beginning to seek ways out of a shortage of suitable wood species in nearby coppices. The army had to be served in America now as well as Europe and the East. The town mills had been taken over by the Ordnance Board before Edward Jacobs wrote, in 1774, 'The only considerable manufacture here is that dreadful composition gun-powder.' The mills, by then much improved in quality and safety, had an output of up to 8,000 lbs per week, while at Oare more mills made the explosive mixture for the East India Company. Hazel, willow and alder (and its unrelated shrub namesake Alder Buckthorn) were all used for charcoal in large quantities. There is a record of colliers being sent from Faversham to set up kilns at Hythe, Wye and Charing - their output, no doubt, going as river and sea cargo to the home town's Powder Quay.

GENERAL VIEW OF BAYHAM.

GENERAL VIEW OF BAYHAM.

Bayham Abbey. Humphry Repton's proposal to build and landscape, circa 1790. Open parkland with positioned trees and retained woodland are to frame the mansion and its new lake.

Heart of Oak Have Our Ships

Jane Austen's brief adult years from, say, 1790 to 1817 were, for her, a world of parkland beauty, elegance and articulate society. But beyond the park gate there was cardinal change. The kingdom (now to include Ireland) began adjusting to the loss of its American colonies, to Britain's growing dominion over India, new settlements in the Antipodes and, nervously, nearer home the economic and military effect from Napoleon's armies and alliances. In these times a hugely expanded British maritime activity arose from the vital import tonnage for a wealthy island with its multiplying population, and from the middleman trade on the high seas, including the slave trade still, and the urgent expansion of the Royal Navy. Until mid-century the Navigation Laws required that all ships going about British business must be made in Britain.

In Kent the warship had been locally significant from as far back as classis Britannica and then the medieval Cinque Ports. By late-Tudor times shipbuilding for the monarch's navy was based on six English shipyards - Deptford, Woolwich, Chatham, Sheerness, Plymouth and Portsmouth - all but two being in Kent. The dominant timber was oak, and the unassailable belief was that the best naval oak in the world grew on the clays of the Weald. Here were sought not only the thousands of loads of woodland oak stems but also the few but prized shapes of 'compass' oak from parkland, pasture or hedgerow trees' those legendary wide-branched trees which admirals on leave were said to replace from a pocketful of acorns for the navy of the next century. Their branches of curved or forked shapes provided key parts of the wooden ship's frame.

Although Wealden, or 'Sussex', oak was the most preferred, the archives contain little about its purchase specifically for shipbuilding. One rare exception is that of Petts Wood, east of Bromley, which takes its name from the Pett family who owned or had a very long lease upon the oak wood there. Phinias Pett built *Sovereign of the Seas* in 1637 for the Ship Money fleet and it was he who, unusually, took his timber moulds (templates) to the forest to convert the tree most suitably. His son Peter, master-shipwright at Chatham, was continually recommending the purchase of timber, at a good price, from a certain Moorcock. When it was found that Moorcock was really a dummy contractor, the selling agent for Pett's own timber, the misdemeanour was used to have Peter suspended from office (source R G Albion.) In general, the Kentish woodland owners sold perforce to agents of the Navy, men often corrupt at the London end and disinclined to go on record. There is scant record either of their timber purchases for the much larger merchant fleet but, in contrast, the royal dockyard supplies from the Royal Forests were subjected at this period to anxious and high-level inquiries. In parallel at the shipyards, the shortage of supply or mishandling of timber was exercising the Lords of the Admiralty quite as much as during the days of Samuel Pepys one hundred years earlier. This way, for example, Lord Sandwich gained some badly-needed improvements such as the first home timber seasoning sheds at Chatham in 1772. Commissioners were appointed, from 1787, to 'Enquire into the State and Conditions of the Woods, Forests and Land Revenues of the Crown'.

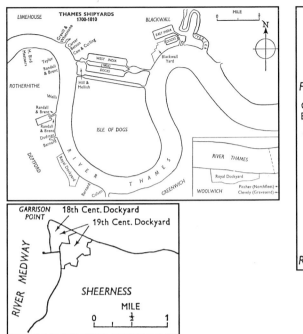

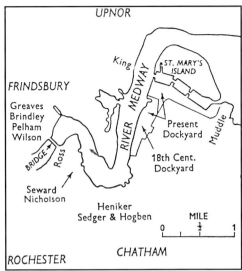

On the Kentish banks of the Thames and Medway Shipyards of the 18th and 19th Centuries

Four of the six main dockyards of the Royal Navy and twenty-two for the merchant fleet.
(From Shipbuilders of the Thames and Medway - Philip Banbury - 1971. David & Charles).

By 1803 even the great Admiral Lord Nelson was apparently drawn into the Royal Forest problem. Two years before he died in action at Trafalgar, the victor of the Nile and Copenhagen stepped aside to attend to the Forest of Dean, spread between the rivers Wye and Severn. The report given his name is introduced with this paragraph.

'The Forest of Dean contains about 23 000 acres of the finest land in the kingdom, which I am informed if in a high state of cultivation of oak, would produce about 9200 loads of timber fit for building ships of the line every year; that is, the Forest would grow in full vigour 920 000 oak trees. The state of the Forest at this moment is deplorable, for if my information is true, there is not 3500 loads of timber in the whole Forest fit for building, and none coming forward. It is useless I admit, to state the causes of such a want of timber where so much could be produced, except that by knowing the faults we may be better able to amend ourselves. First, the generality of trees for these last 50 years have been allowed to stand to long; they are passed by instead of removed, and thus occupy a space which ought to have been re-planted with young trees. Secondly, that where good timber is felled, nothing is planted, and nothing can grow self-sown: for the deer (of which now only a few remain) bark all the young trees. Vast droves of hogs are allowed to go into the woods in the autumn, and if any fortunate acorn escapes their search, and takes root, then flocks of sheep are allowed to go into the Forest, and they bite off the tender shoot. These are sufficient reasons why timber does not grow in the Forest of Dean.'

It was forgotten that the Royal Forests were not created expressly for timber production. From reports like this, and the steadfast effort by some foresters against lethargy and selfish interests, the timber output of the Dean and other royal lands would eventually be improved but not in time to build many Wooden Walls. According to Professor Albion (1926), the heavily-documented forests provided barely one-tenth of the Navy's needs in the Napoleonic era, and after 1833 the Navy received no timber at all from them for fifteen years. Ever since Tudor times official record-keeping by the Crown servants in forest and dockyard had been matched by political debate and Parliamentary minutes concerning the seemingly endless crisis of the Navy's oak shortage. They left a rich source for 20th Century writers on warship forestry; notably R G Albion (USA), and, more recently, C E Hart (Senior Verderer at Dean) and N D G James (Land Agent for the Oxford University Chest). A thread running through all their work is the problem of holding men's minds and responsibility to a crop which will only become right for harvesting 100 years hence.

During her 'Twenty Years' at war against France, the British Navy much extended the dockyards at Chatham and its fortification was improved. Defence works were built or updated right around the Kentish shore, from the Thames Estuary to Romney Marsh with its military canal and Martello towers. Navy press gangs roamed that littoral looking for able-bodied men for warship crews while its local defence was strengthened by water-going volunteers such as the Sea and River Fencibles. For a time, large army camps were set up on commandeered land along the lines of the North Downs from Coxheath to Shorncliffe and Dover. This traditional role for Kent when invasion threatened affected the landholder in many ways; perhaps in helping to raise militia or resisting the press hunting his men, and certainly in gaining improved prices for all his produce. Despite the excuse of wartime emergency, however, there was no return to the sequestration of woods so crudely applied during the Civil War and Commonwealth. Apart from a short-lived attempt to form contracts directly between timber owner and royal dockyard, the long-established ways of procurement continued.

Well *after* the great sea-battles at the turn of the century the new parameters of Britain's interests, now truly global for the first time, meant no reduction, in fact an astonishing increase, in wooden shipbuilding and repairs. It is considered by Oliver Rackham (1989) that 'despite minor uncertainties the conclusion seems inescapable that roughly half of all the timber shipping ever built in Britain was launched between 1800 and 1860'. The symbol of the age was the 74-gun warship, the Navy's most versatile vessel. The hull (about 165 ft x 47 ft max) and decking consumed 3,000 - 3,200 loads (about 4,000 tons) of oak, that is the wood from some 2,500 maturing trees. A merchant ship of the period registered as 2,000 tons required 3,000 loads of oak according to the East India Company. In Kent or Sussex, to find an offer of oak timber from a felling of as many as 1,000 trees - even by landowners in combination - was quite exceptional.

Until late in that period, foreign oak was only reluctantly used because of its perceived inferiority or for more calculable reasons such as the extra cost of import duties. The reverse was the position for masts and spars. Since medieval days these long, straight, strong but light poles had been shipped from the vast forests around the Baltic Sea. Virtually unobtainable in Britain, a mainmast for a '74' man-o'-war was 108ft high and 36 inches in diameter at base. Yet just how unremarked a part of maritime trade this was can be illustrated by the Whitby colliers' routine. These strong little ships, the very design adapted for world exploration by Captain James Cook, carried coal to the Thames, then sailed square-rigged to a

James Cook's world explorations were fitted out at Greenwich. Here the Australian-built replica of Endeavour returned in 1997.

Timber hauling wagons of the time

Norwegian port. There they took a cargo of deal or pit props below but up on deck, with an overhang at each end, one of the long mast timbers so much needed by the north-eastern shipyards. Sawn oak board had long come from the Baltic because of the adaptation there of watermill and windmill power to plank sawing but this had traditionally found use only ashore. Now heavier naval planks were allowed in. The established trade route between the Baltic and Britain was what Napoleon hoped to sever by his political alliance with Denmark but he was thwarted by Nelson's defeat of the Danish fleet off Copenhagen in 1801.

That the hub of shipbuilding activity was on the rivers Thames and Medway was due partly to the nearness of the source of best oak but it also had the advantage of closeness for Government and commercial men in London. Chatham, Woolwich and Deptford yards were handy for inspections and experiments in design or materials. For example, with the Government's ability to control timber work in the Royal Forests, a most intricate test was ordered to determine the optimum time and method of oak felling for timber and tanbark. The Navy Board letter in the Maritime Museum archives which details the test, and two other indicative contemporaries, are in Appendices 7/1 - 3.

The subject of that trial was vital because of the interminable problem of constructing with saturated timber, made worse if some sapwood was left untrimmed, which then rotted in the airless confines of the ship. A ship laid up, or even untimely sunk, for reason of rot meant a loss of shipping tonnage as clearly as if it had never been built. The shipyard deterioration affected fighting ships more than the merchantmen because the Admiralty insisted, whenever it could achieve it, upon an average three-years' requirement as the level of timber in store to meet the exigencies of war. From 1801 Timber Masters were employed at the yards to inspect for quality and reduce cutting waste; an unpopular task indeed.

Almost with the same timing as the upsurge in shipbuilding came an escalation in leather-making. Tanbark thus became a principal factor in the business of oakwood. The tannin obtained from oak bark (and also, but less effectively, from alder, birch and willow) had always been used in preparing leather and in ink-making. From 1780 onwards, until late in the 19th Century when a substitute from chrome salts was found, the demand for tannin for leather was at its highest ever. Much of the bark came from underwood or stunted trees on higher land. In lowland England the traditional term 'Ton, Top and Tan' may have denoted the previously lesser importance of tanbark in the timber tree's price. In this boom period, even alongside the stronger market for oak timber, tanbark was so much in demand that it was said sometimes to have earned more than the wood. To peel the bark in the required strips, especially from mature boles, meant felling in springtime or, a rarely used alternative, stripping the bark from the bole in that season and leaving the tree standing until the internal sap had dried away.

Of all the modern reviews of the English naval oak supply problem in the early 1800s, perhaps the most succinct summary is recorded in N D G James's *History of English Forestry*. In an extract from the Report of the Commissioners for Woods in 1812 the key figure was the British Navy's estimated requirement of oak: an annual total of 60,000 loads (3 million cubic feet). The Commissioners' on-going Enquiry had used what they saw as a conservative figure of 40 oak trees to an acre at an average 100 years old. Then, they extrapolated

.....100,000 acres would be requisite and adequate if so planted and managed that the timber in each 1,000 acres could be felled in successive years and that 1,000 immediately replanted for maintaining a Navy like the present for ever.

(As an indication of comparative surface area only, Kent's total woodland acreage at the time was perhaps 120 - 150,000 acres for all purposes.) The Commissioners' Report did not care to guess at the merchant shipping requirement for great yards such as Blackwall and Rotherhithe. Albion gave figures for the Royal Navy of 300 ships having a total tonnage of 391,400. On the British registry of merchantmen there were no fewer than 15,000 vessels totalling 1,460,800 tons.

Modern comment on contemporary records reveals a possible confusion between round timber weight and sawn timber but, from a detailed listing in 1756 of the *Royal George* construction, Philip Banbury (1971) gives percentages (whatever the true weight). More than 90 per cent of the timber in a ship-of-the-line was in her keel, ribs, beams, knees, pillars, etc. and less than 10 per cent in decks and planking. In the *Royal George* half of that small planking came from Danzig. Albion adds that elm or beech were used below the waterline and a little fir where strength was not paramount but these amounted to fewer than 400 loads out of 3200 and even that 12.5 per cent would have been dispensed with in Napoleonic times if native oak had been available. After the early years of the 19th Century the use of foreign timber for hulls as well as decking and spars began to increase. It came from North America as well as the Baltic but for oak the traffic, after the war crisis, was small in proportion until the late-1830s; with imports finally exceeding home-grown oak by 1840. However, compass oak, specified as 'any large timber that curves five inches and upwards in 12 feet', was rarely imported. Uncut, the branched trunk was too unwieldy, and the shipwright was not abroad to supervise the cutting.

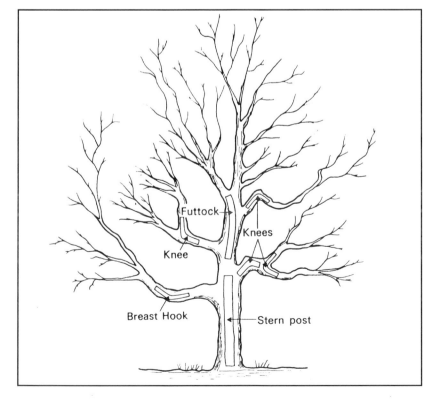

Compass timber. These curved members, before they were made from iron, came from oak trees; not overmature and found in hedgerow, country park or as standard trees in coppice.

Sawing had become the worst bottleneck in shipbuilding, especially of small pieces. In 1803 at Portsmouth, first, then at Chatham, Marc Brunel and Jeremy Bentham developed a machine saw for making rigging blocks; one of the earliest examples of machine tools being used in mass production. By 1808 the machines are reported to have turned out 130,000 blocks in a year, 'enabling ten men to do the work of one hundred and ten'. For the vital rigging blocks elm was as firm a choice as oak for the ships' sides.

Wealden Trees to Chatham

For the Royal Navy, in all its shipyards, the choice of civilian timber agent between 1817 and 1847 was narrowed to one man. John (or James) Morris 'for thirty years continued to supply the entire naval demands for English oak except for the small amount received from the Royal Forests' (Albion). Morris did so through sub-agent buyers of trees grown very largely in the south-east. For Kent merchants the assured market of the Thames and Medway shipyards justified heavy cargoes by sea; sailing out of Rye from the southern High Weald woods and from Dover and Faversham for the mainly church-owned timber woodland of East Kent.

Down the Medway, itself, timber was carried from Yalding. There were eleven private shipyards below Rochester bridge in addition to Chatham and Sheerness. The extensive canal navigation development of the day, as seen elsewhere in Britain, never got past the talking stage in Kent except for a short-lived linking of Thames and Medway at Strood. The more ambitious scheme would have linked the river Medway at Yalding with the Rother near Tenterden. This Wealden Canal, stillborn for lack of funds, was promoted partly to take iron products and timber from the deep Weald to the shipyards. An added advantage over the Channel route from Rye was that the canal would have obviated a sea-passage under the threat of French privateers.

The *Maidstone Journal* in the years stepping into the 19th Century had many advertisements for timber auctions or private sale featured among estates and other property for sale. The usual offer was one or more lots of standing oak trees; in the name of the land occupier, the tenant, or the bailiff, not of the titled gentleman. The journal, reflecting its readers' interests, had an eclectic range of other advertisements which included the current issue of the *Landscape Magazine* and perhaps a sale at the Custom House, Rye of seized goods; '2800 gallons of Geneva' and rum and brandy. At Westerham '1046 trees of Large Oak Timber' were to be sold from five tenant farmers. Another large quantity of fine oak trees came from Black Hoath Wood in Leigh and Courtland Wood, Penshurst. At Lamberhurst one hundred oak would be on offer from Mr Joseph Witherden's Catsweasle Farm, Biddenden. At the King's Head, Rochester in 1807 Mr Boys would sell elm trees, oak trees 'well adapted for the use of the Navy' and five hundred oak posts and rails, all the property of Mr Brown at Upchurch who evidently had a busy sawpit and cleavers. Beech fellies or felloes for wheelwrights at Maidstone wharves, and pairs of shafts and planks, could be bought privately from Mr Hill's wharf at the bottom of Earl Street, Maidstone.

In the first trade directory, 1828 - 1829, Pigot's National Commercial Directory, Kent Section, lists timber merchants in each town; five at Maidstone for example. This was not a large number relative to some other trades. Chatham's four timber businesses, all in the High Street - Wm. Ashenden, Joslin & Manlove, Matt.Nicholson and Thomas Wells - were matched by no fewer than thirteen coal merchants; the demand for sea-coal shipments to urban areas was evidently much expanded before the coming of the railway. Although steam locomotion was on the horizon, this form of power had scarcely yet begun to be used in the south, even for standing work. Marc Isambard Brunel, father of Kingdom, had developed a steam-driven sawmill at Battersea between 1805 and 1810 which was quickly to have an impressive successor in the Brunel-Bentham sawmill at Chatham Dockyard. Otherwise, power-driven mills were held back by the smallness of the local timber merchant's throughput and by the old bogey of the Kent roads which still were difficult enough to encourage piece-meal manual sawing at the felling site, in a pit or over a trestle. As far ahead as 1835, more than a century after Defoe's famous comment, the poor roads for heavy goods would be criticised by Mr Stedley of Ashford, timber merchant, when speaking as a witness for the proposed South Eastern Railway. Forced to ship via Rye, Faversham and Maidstone, he indicted particularly the parish of Smarden where roads even then were impassable for heavy traffic in winter.

The oak of Kent and Sussex became again notoriously scarce as the years of building against the threat of Napoleon's fleet drained the woodlands anew. The shortage threatened the private shipyards despite their paying a higher price. A surge of oak planting in the mid-18th Century for the apparently never-ending future demand had not yet grown trees of a useful size. Back in 1798, the year of the Battle of the Nile, William Marshall (he who later advised the Commissioners of Woods) had published his *Rural Economy of the Southern Counties*. Glooming over Sussex county in a way which many may have thought to be exaggerated, he wrote

AGE OF FELLING TIMBER Either from an extraordinary demand for ship timber, and other timber of size, or from the price which bark has borne for some time past, or a concurrence of other circumstances, there is no oak timber left standing in the Weald of Sussex (except on the demesne of lands of men of fortune) which, either in growth or in size, is applicable to the purpose of building ships of burden and strength. In 1791 there were very few woods of more than half a century standing: and woods even of less than that age were then paying not the debt of nature but the debts of the owners.

THE APPLICATION of the timber of the Weald is chiefly to SHIP BUILDING. For although at present there is very little large timber left, such is the estimation of the timber of Sussex that trees of twenty feet measurement upwards are eagerly purchased by the builders. In 1791 I saw very few trees taken down of more than a ton of timber each.

The date in his text, 1791, may be a pointer that explains his despair at the dearth of oak. By then the Wealden iron industry had been in patchy decline for some fifty years only. Following that decline, however, more attention was given by owners to training up tellers or singles, from oak stools to become acceptable building timber by about 1800 onwards. Marshall, himself, perhaps unwittingly supports this probability -

> Unless in the particular of setting out young stands with sufficient freedom, I perceived no superiority of treatment in Sussex compared with other woodland districts of the kingdom. With respect to the practice of training oak timber trees from seedling plants, and scrupulously rejecting sapling shoots, the propriety or impropriety of it depends entirely on circumstances.

> In a situation where a sufficiency of seedling plants can be had, IN A FEW YEARS, and where a straightness of timber, either for the house carpenter's use or for planks to be used in ship building, and especially where coppice ware is wanted, the practice of training seedlings appears to be perfectly eligible. But in situations where the oak is less NATIVE; where a sufficiency of seedlings could not be expected to fill up the ground in the course of a few years; more especially where mere coppice wood is of little value (as in the coal countries) and where ship timber is the main object - training the first stools of felled trees is, indisputedly, the more eligible practice.

> A Yorkshire wood, trained from the stools, agreeably to the common practice of that county, has an hundredfold the number of crooks and KNEES that a wood of Weald of Sussex has when trained, agreeably to the practice of that district, from seedling plants.

Even with sufficient store of average-sized beams, spars and planking, the building of a ship could be brought to a halt for the want of a few pieces of special dimensions. The timber merchant had to scour the southern countryside for 'great' timber, most notably the stern post; its girth and length must come from a tree which had been allowed to grow beyond normal felling age yet was tall and with a sound heartwood. Except in the Royal Forests, the Navy's own men did not join the hunt. Compass pieces must come from trees also mature but of open growth and therefore more evident location. In his 1798 report on the District of Maidstone, Marshall noted that here, in the hedgerows, there was oak timber still left. But, good agriculturalist, he praised the trees as 'well stemmed, clean, and of middle height'; not, therefore, likely to overshadow the arable field crop. Most compass timber would come in Kent from coppice-with-standards woodland; the high, single trees being seen as a cyclical product even if on a very long cycle. But the merchant also coveted parkland trees. Owners of great trees might well be reluctant to sell them if, by their nature and setting, they had become sentimentally regarded over several generations. On the other hand, in times of high prices, and also of a now more common change of land ownership, sellers were tempted to sell oak below the traditional minimum of eighty years growth. Less concerned, perhaps, than long-service estate workers, specialist woodsmen and contract hauliers were ready to do their bidding.

More and more, the shipbuilder had to make use of the scarf joint, diagonal overlapping of the ends of beams, to gain the length needed for the keel. Nevertheless, a strict maximum to the length of a made-up beam was needed for strength and the Navy and East India Company were able to increase by only a little the wooden ship's overall length during the last two hundred years before iron took over. The later years, moreover, saw iron parts used regularly to replace the scarce curved members sought in compass timber. By then, too, the steaming of wood to allow it to be bent to shape was much practised in the yards.

For the Navy the religion of 'English oak only' had at last weakened. In 1827 Admiral Stirling declared that 'the British Oak, however great its name, is not the best timber in the world' - and he was not struck down by a thunderbolt. English woodland owners seem, though, to have ignored any threat to future oak sales. Moreover, during these post-Waterloo years a numbing depression had settled upon agricultural England so that any return to grubbing up of woodland for food crops was likely to be postponed. Oak, therefore, continued to be grown, but for straight lengths now because of the replacement of compass oak by iron. There is a strange lack of comment in local records upon the launching at Bristol of Brunel's *Great Britain*. Then, 1843, it was the largest ship ever built and it was steam powered - and it was of iron. By the late 1850s, reacting quickly to developments by the French and Americans, the Navy experimented with four timber-hulled iron-cased warships.

Supremacy in iron was granted to the Royal Navy by the construction of HMS *Warrior,* the first iron-hulled warship. In 1858 the French had launched *La Gloire*, a formidable ironclad 256 feet (79m) long. In response, *Warrior* was built, towering above the houses of Blackwall at Wells' Thames Ironworks, while the engines and boilers were made by Penn's at Greenwich. The largest, fastest and most powerful warship in the world was more than one-and-a-half times the dimensions of *La Gloire*. Her $4^{1}/_{2}$ inch (11 cm) armoured plates were bolted to a wooden decking of East India teak. *Warrior* was launched in December 1860, to national acclaim. But it was a small, distant defeat at sea just over a year later which brought home to the public the full significance of iron warships.

Wooden warships were traditionally damaged by roundshot and captured but rarely sunk. There was not one sinking of a British ship at the hard-fought Trafalgar. From 1840 explosive shells were to prove much more effective. It was against this background that startling news, only too easy to grasp, reached Britain in March 1862. Off the coast of Virginia a small naval engagement was fought in which the American warship *Merrimac*, its hull sheathed in iron, faced two British Navy wooden ships and, its iron being impervious to their guns, it forthwith sank them both. The long, long saga of Britain's wooden warships - the Roman defence against Saxons, the king's retained ships of the Cinque Ports, the threat of the Spanish Armada and British victories over Napoleon's fleet - one thousand five hundred years of reliance upon English oak had ended as suddenly as an explosion at sea.

The Parliamentary appropriation for naval timber and masts and deals fell from £723,000 in 1860 to a mere topping-up of £15,600 ten years later. With the universal adoption of iron the annual marine market in Britain suffered a permanent sales reduction of 150,000 or more large oak trees during the next couple of decades as iron and steel and steam-power took over the ocean trading routes and naval stations.

From the early 19th Century the demand for marine timber was never going to be wholly met from this country's woodlands, but the suddenly lost potential was a bewildering jolt to the plans of British foresters. In Kent and the Weald, that most favoured home of oak, the cold reality was underlined by the shipbuilders' transfer away to the northern rivermouths of Clyde, Tyne and Mersey and their adjacent coalfields. Before the dramatic and splendid century had reached its end the British Navy had become more powerful than all other navies put together and the British merchant fleet dominated commerce around the globe. By 1870 the nation's furnaces produced more pig-iron than the whole of the rest of the world.

Account of Wood Cutt at Knole in the Year 1819

Where Cutt and by Whom	Hop Poles				Fence Poles	Faggots			Rods		Stakes			Bundles of Birch	Bundles of Pea Boughs
	Feet 16	Feet 14	Feet 12	Feet 10		Best	Kiln	Brush	Bund Gate	Bund Hedge	Bund Gate	Bund Hedge	Bund Fand		
James 25 Jany. White Hart	-	200	312	-	53	454	1437	-	-	-	-	-	-	93	
Dodd 6 Feb. Godden	125	525	750	-	164	225	1000	-	10	14½	9	31	6	189	
Dodd 13 March Godden	-	175	600	-	39	137	800	-	10	11	5	17	9	160	
Dodd 27 do. Godden	-	-	-	-	-	27	313	-	2	4½	1	6	3		
Total	125	700	1350	-	203	389	2113	-	30	30	15	54	18	349	
Richd. Webb 20 Feb. Godden Road	-	-	-	-	10	100	-	200	-	-	-	-	-	-	
Giles 6th March Baker	-	450	1500	1800	213	189	2075	25	37	36½	21	37	-	161	21
Parker 13 do. Baker		150	1350	1550	136	137	1512	25	33	34½	17	38	-	101	16
Wm. Webb 13 do. Baker	-	25	1275	1450	144	52	1450	100	37	32½	19	49	-	145	44
Total	-	625	4125	4800	493	378	5037	150	107	103½	57	124	-	407	81
Parker 3 Apl. Make	-	300	650	-	112	117	948	50	7	13½	4	24		24	
Webb do. Make	-	175	500	-	110	75	412	37	4	8	2	16		40	
Smart Make		50	113	-	11	13	232	75	4		3			43	
		525	1263	-	233	205	1612	162	15	21½	9	40	-	77	
James Coach Wood		225	225		604	2085	225							81	

VICTORIAN WOODLAND - THE REIGN OF GREATEST CHANGE

Introduction

The sixty-three years of Victoria's reign contained the high peak and then the deepest trough of that role for woodland in southern England which Defoe had described as being 'an inexhaustible storehouse' for human needs. At the time of the young queen's coronation in 1837 the steam-train was still a phenomenon, seen in Kent only as the little railway from Canterbury to Whitstable. 'Coal' was the word for charcoal still, except in harbour towns. The rural family depended for its house-fuel, fencing and building repairs on local woodland resources often based on traditional agreement with the landowner. Many such people had relocated their homes for reasons deriving from wood because ship-building was Kent's foremost manufacture. (Chatham's population had become greater than Canterbury's.) Kentish coppice had never been harder worked nor the timber in greater demand. The contrast with the close of Victoria's reign at the end of the century is dramatic. By 1901 nearly all Kent people lived within a few miles of a railway station, for goods and for their own travel, and domestic coal was ubiquitous. Now, ocean-going ships were made in the north country; the steamships were built of iron and steel and teak decking. Whole woodlands had been cleared long since for more dwellings and, on better soils, for orchards and hop-gardens. Despite all of that, Kent's woodland acreage survived better than in most of England. The vagaries of economic and social change had removed traditional demand from tree and coppice yet had once again allowed much of the wooded terrain to stay.

More Than Half the Nation's Hops.

At the beginning of the 19th Century woodland was still, like the farmer's soil and the fisherman's sea, an indispensable resource. The demand for underwood produce changed only in detail. In Kent the turn had come for poles for hop-growing to take the lead; that crop which, reflecting Kent's enormous acreage of it, became the characteristic of the county's husbandry with the oasthouse cone as its symbol. Since the early 1700s, thanks partly to an imposed duty from 1710 which penalised imports from Flanders, the trade had expanded strongly. Hop-growing had become an exciting business for those with skills based on orchard work, and with strong nerves. It was notorious for wide annual swings of fortune from high profit to loss, but more often to profitable.

Farming landholders with woodland in Kent might be very aware of the search for oak timber to supply the many shipyards on their doorstep but they instinctively preferred the shorter money cycle of the underwood trade, perhaps sweetened further by the occasional felling of open-grown 'compass' timber trees among the coppice. Foremost in the horticultural mind, though, was hops. More important now than even cherries, the acreage increased along the North Downs dip-slope and in East Kent, where quality was reputed the highest, and in the dominant triangle of Maidstone-Tenterden-Tonbridge.

Richard Hayes, yeoman and diarist of Cobham at the beginning of its heyday, had written with fierce interest about his varying fortunes in hop-growing

19 September 1761: I am again honoured with ye best sample of hops in the Borough.

(Borough Market at Southwark)

17 September 1764: As to our hops, they were never known to be so bad in general.

In short, I never saw my grounds so bad before by being scorched up like the blight.

Considering the prospects of profit which they dangled, hop-gardens did not require many acres to make worthwhile money but the initial and replacement costs of hop-poles was high. Like many landowners, Hayes had coppice of his own to cut but, cyclically, needed to buy from others. One source was at Cobham Park, that august neighbour with the venison acclaimed by Hasted.

27 September 1773: Brother & Self dined with Lord and Lady Darnley on Haunch of Venison, Soup, etc. with a Dessert of Fruit, Pineapple etc. This was on purpose to buy his woods, as he did in '64.

Then, and for another hundred years, hop-poles were usually erected three or sometimes four in each little growing-mound or 'hill'. Indeed, the practice had hardly changed since the oft-quoted publication *A Perfite Platform of a Hoppe Garden* by Reynolde Scott of Scott's Hall in Queen Elizabeth's day. The number of hills per

The hop-poles at Ham Street, ca.1890, were little changed since the 16th Century but most hop gardens had by then adopted the bine system using now widely available steel wire

Left: Poles and wire at Wye 100 years later

Below:- Five oasts at Goudhurst

acre varied, so that the range of requirement of hop-poles for an acre was as wide as from 2,000 to 3,600. By 1835 the brewers' sales of beer, with its flavour and keeping quality improved by adding the hop, had roared ahead on the crest of an enormously increasing population. Kent hop-gardens amounted to 25,740 acres that year, almost half the total for Britain, and both the county acreage and its national percentage would go on increasing for another forty years. To the coppice worker and hop-pole maker here was real income from a huge, dependable market; it was additional to his commonplace products and nearer for delivery than the other big customers in London.

That poles were of such importance to the hop grower is shown in a table from the work books of Tatlingbury farm, four miles east of Tonbridge (ex Dennis Baker in Cantium 1971).

ONE ACRE OF TATLINGBURY HOPS: ESTIMATED ANNUAL AVERAGE
EXPENDITURE AND INCOME
(based on an average yield of 7 cwt. per acre)

EXPENDITURE (1745-57 average)	£	s	d	as a percentage of total expenditure.
1) Labour (all 'hop ground work' including digging, dressing, poleing, tying, hoeing and picking)	7	13	4	40.9
2) Manure		16	8	4.4
3) Poles	2	2	6	11.3
*4) Bagging material	1	8	0	7.5
*5) Drying		18	0	4.8
*6) Freightage: Tatlingbury to London		14	0	3.7
7) Selling commission		7	0	1.9
8) Hop duty	3	5	4	17.4
9) Tithe		10	0	2.7
10) Rent	1	0	0	5.3
	18	14	10	99.9
omitting items marked *	15	14	10	
INCOME (1744-57 average)	22	5	0	
NET PROFIT	3	10	2	
omitting items marked*	6	10	2	

At 11 per cent of average total expenditure during thirteen years, the cost of poles was second only to labour if Hop Duty is excluded.

John Boys of Betshanger, Farmer, in his 1805 review for the Board of Agriculture, did not report on heavy timber business because it was outside his remit but he saw the need to include a detailed comment on hop-poles by R Tilden which he introduced thus -

> The woodlands of the eastern part of Kent are dispersed principally between the great road from Rochester to Dover and the chalk-hill that runs from Folkestone by Charing to Detling. These woods furnish the country with fire-wood, tillers for husbandry uses, and the dockyards with timber for ship-building; but the most material part of their produce is the immense quantity of hop-poles cut out of the neighbouring plantations.

In Appendix 8/1 a full version is given of Mr Tilden's paper to the Kent Agricultural Society and, in 8/2, a table on west Kent woodlands provided for J. Boys by Mr Randall, the Maidstone nurseryman.

An example of the sweeping progress of chestnut coppice across the county is seen at King's Wood. In his table, Mr Randall describes the woodland surface there as stone shatter and gravelly loam on a subsoil of strong loam with some ragstone. Not unsuitable for chestnut. He notes impatiently that the wood has had 'no improvements recently', having still a traditional cover of oak with hazel and birch and offering 'many oaken tillers, small timber poles and co'. This sketch at the end of the 18th Century is of a possibly heedless management. The mention of many tillers (standards left to grow on the stool) implies that for many years the coppice has not been cut very demandingly. Mrs Bouverie, Sir John Filmer and others - the several owners - need the chestnut planting services of Mr Randall. King's Wood has a large acreage of chestnut coppice today.

Long ago, Scott had recommended alder for hop-poles, a species still, though rather unusually, favoured at Tatlingbury; it was probably locally and cheaply available alongside the Medway river and Hammer Dyke. Before 1800 the importance of the pole trade had led to grading by size and species. In Kent and east Sussex (but not in other parts) a rapid advance to the fore was then made by Spanish, or Sweet, chestnut ahead of ash, oak and birch. Chestnut had the ability to grow quickly and straight on chalky, flinty or other soils not too cold, and where not vital for orchards. The species also had clear advantages in use: it has little sapwood so is relatively resistant to rot when in contact with the ground; it has a fibrous strength which allows the use of slimmer poles for a given height, around which the hop-bine will climb more readily.

In his *Rural Economy* series, Mr Marshall considered that 'In the MANAGEMENT of coppice woods, as of hedges, the yeomen of Kent excel'. And he went on to describe the creation of a new chestnut plantation from agricultural land, thus to enlighten landholders of lesser skill. By modern times the method for creating new chestnut coppice has changed little. Alan Ault, woodreeve at Leeds Castle, describes the work in the 1950s before the decline of interest in growing more acres of coppice, even of chestnut as the most profitable underwood.

> 'On an acre of cleaned, ploughed land plant the chestnuts, like potatoes, along a furrow a yard apart, then fill over the row with

a prong hoe. Thin out the seedlings for up to three years at most, then leave to grow for twelve years before cutting as maiden chestnut. Meanwhile start another acre alongside. This way a quite large plantation may still be called Nursery Wood but, whether or not, you can still tell its man-made origin by the straight line of the stumps, later the stools, and lack of undergrowth.'

In Kent, the straight boundary line of a wood with a field may well have been formed by extending new coppice planting into the field, the opposite of the more usual explanation that an assart of farmland has been cut out of woodland.

Such was the dominance of the underwood harvest that Marshall, when visiting the county, took the locally common word shaw to mean coppice - as he put it 'in the management of grown coppices, provincially shaws'. Coppice, as a noun and verb, is close enough to its derivative copse, to-day's usual word for a small and separate wooded area but in Kent shaw (sometimes shave if narrow in shape) means a small wooded area, not confined to underwood. In Marshall's day, so saleable was underwood produce, the shaw would habitually have been cut over for coppice articles except where it formed shelter for house or farm building. Before the great hops century, 1780 - 1880, and since then, the tiniest shaw would have included its complement of timber trees; until the 1970s the mighty and useful elm was its familiar feature.

In the 1800s the demand for hop poles was met by converting ancient woodland, by spreading back into agricultural land and by husbanding every copse, spinney or thicket. The Kentish hop-gardens increased from the 25,740 acres of 1835 to 46,600 acres in 1878 (such accuracy comes from the duty inspectors). During the forty-three years probably *sixty million poles had to be found for the new grounds alone* while the poles in those new gardens and the even larger existing area had to be replaced about every sixth year. From the supply side, an acre of coppice would have yielded some 3,000 hop-poles every twelve to fourteen years; say 9,000 or more in the forty-three years. The sums amounted to a dedication of more than 60,000 acres to coppiced woodland products (although much of that area also bore scattered timber trees). Of underwood products, the first call in this county was for the hop-growers but after him came a long list of other end-users. That the county's overall woodland acreage should become more than two-thirds devoted to underwood production was based on sound market reasoning, and who should call it short-term thinking when the crop needed twelve, fourteen or even twenty years to harvest?

Underwood Output at its Peak

Among the estate wood-books of the time, none has a better tabulation than the Account of Wood Cutt at Knole in the year 1819 (see page 132). The cant of coppice out at Godden Green was cut by Dodd to yield 2,175 hop-poles from that compartment alone but Mr Dodd and his helpers in February and March also made a great quantity of fence pales, faggots, rods, stakes and bundles of birch and pea boughs. In line with the authors Marshall and Tilden, the Knole poles were graded in lengths of 10, 12, 14, 16 feet, but also noteworthy is the careful grading into three qualities of faggots and stakes and two of rods. Each would have a price keenly monitored by the agent and the cutter. However, as usual in such estate records, the table does not show the species of plant used for the different artefacts. Rods, for example, would normally have been made from the flexibly workable, then durable, hazel to build hedges, hurdles and barrel hoops, although there is little hazel at Godden Green. It should be surprising, too, that the valuable hop-poles were not named by species but by 1819 sweet chestnut was the preference and the norm in most of Kent for this product.

Godden Green hamlet had, and still has, chestnut coppice to its east and west between the Wilderness (no 'e' in 1819) and the Knole park deer fence. Not much has changed over the years. Competing with chestnut on the sandy soil is self-seeding birch, the first to take over bared ground, perhaps where a standard oak has been removed. On a March day near the park boundary the leafless coppice shoots shiver on their lumpy ground of ancient ant-hills. Thin bramble and grasses contrast with the close-cropped greensward inside the deer perimeter. Dodd, the cutter, straightens up from his work to glance over Holmedale to Otford Mount above the Darent river, the long, shadowed line of the Downs matching his own level on the greensand hill. 'Thank God for hops,' his mind intones for the thousandth time. 'They seem to want more every year and there's no machine yet that will cut coppice and convert it.'

His boy is working beyond the village green, down in the broad ghyll, cutting and tying birch faggots. He can do about fifty a day now which is good enough at his age. Next, the boy could sort out some of the bigger birch poles for the wood-turners. That's if the agent can think of anything but chestnut. It might be better to be independent of the House but with the need to see so many in the family fed that would mean giving up too many extras. And you want to keep in with the Sackvilles' agent for summer work.

AN

EPITOME OF COUNTY HISTORY,

WHEREIN THE

MOST REMARKABLE OBJECTS, PERSONS, AND EVENTS,

ARE BRIEFLY TREATED OF;

THE SEATS, RESIDENCES, ETC.

OF

THE NOBILITY, CLERGY, AND GENTRY,

THEIR

ARCHITECTURE, INTERIOR DECORATIONS, SURROUNDING SCENERY, ETC. DESCRIBED, FROM
PERSONAL OBSERVATION,

AND

THE NAMES, TITLES, AND OTHER DISTINCTIONS,

CIVIL, MILITARY, OR ECCLESIASTICAL,

INSERTED.

With Notices of the principal Churches,

AND THE MONUMENTS AND MEMORIALS OF DISTIN

EACH COUNTY ILLUSTRATED BY A

EXHIBITING IN ONE VIEW THE PARKS, PADDOCKS, SEATS, AND OTH
THEREIN.

VOL. I.—COUNTY OF KEN

BY C. GREENWOOD.

LONDON:

PUBLISHED FOR THE PROPRIETOR, AT THE OFFIC
No. 5, HART STREET, BLOOMSBURY SQUA

1838.

EAST SUTTON PLACE,
The Seat of Sir Edmund Filmer, Bart.
For the Epitome of the History of Kent,
1838.

It is difficult to calculate how many workers were in the Victorian underwood trade but it can be said with certainty that the number grew after 1815 and Waterloo, in the agriculturally depressed years, at least until the 'high farming' period later in the century when men left the land altogether. E J T Collins (Agrarian History of England & Wales, VI - 1989) approaches the subject by allying the 19th Century censuses with his deep knowledge of coppice work. He estimates that in the period of the 1841 and 1861 censuses an annual cutting of 7,000-8,000 acres of coppice was carried out in Kent (implying, thereby, more but not wildly more than the above estimate of 60,000-plus acres of standing coppice). For this he reckons that 'upwards of one thousand men would be needed over the winter whereas the 1841 census records but 225 and the 1861 census 410.'

The published trend, a near-doubling in twenty years, must reflect the increase in the number of men cutting coppice - and then men and women using its conversion into goods to find an income and almost a whole-year occupation. A greater degree of specialism was brought about by the larger demand and the better opportunity to supply one product, broom poles for example, to a wider market through better road transport locally and now the railways. The categories in the table below covered many less-remarked uses of coppice. Under 'woodmen' perhaps were those who supplied sea-defence materials to the Kent marshes in an effort to keep salt water from contaminating fresh water. Downstream from Gravesend, about the year 1800, the Cliffe level was, alone, using annually 4 - 6,000 piles, preferably of oak, and matching quantities of double-length faggots.

Numbers employed in selected woodworking trades in England and Wales in 1841 and 1861

	1841	1861
Basket-makers	5,712	8,899
Birch besom-broom makers	— —	103
Bobbin-makers/turners	1,010	2,177
Brush and broom makers	5,928	11,178
Charcoal burners/dealers	216	443
Clothes-peg makers	— —	131
Crate-makers	550	787
Fence and hurdle makers	256	969
Hoop-makers/benders	726	1,255
Wood-dealers	309	3,342
Woodmen	3,322	8,916

Source: GB Census 1841, 1861.

Professor Collins' table of some work categories dependent on coppice output shows an unexpectedly small number employed throughout England and Wales. The significance for Kent and Sussex is that in the two counties the 'acreage of coppice far exceeded that of Wales, Scotland and northern and eastern England combined'.

[As regards sweet chestnut, separately, the modern legacy for Kent was a 1980 figure of 12,544 hectares out of a total of 19,091 hectares for the United Kingdom.]

Covert Wood, Barham 1998.

Mr Randall of Maidstone, about 1800, opined that 'The employ afforded by the culture of HOPS to the poor is very considerable; twenty thousand families are hereby enabled to inure their children to useful labour from five years old in the plantations'. The country-dwelling children were to find little enough labour in agriculture as they grew up. Hops, however, were long to continue to have great importance for Kent: in the peak year of 1878 the county produced an astonishing 65 per cent of the whole for England and Wales. That year the hop-garden acreage had still to be supplied by a similar acreage of coppice cut for hop-poles but by then the new wire-work system for the bines by Henry Butcher of Sheldwich was gaining rapidly in popularity. The method called for higher, stronger poles but in very much reduced numbers. This squeezing of the coppice-cutter's market was not in itself critical but it was one of several factors which, towards the end of the century, were to enfeeble the county's vibrant woodland industry.

England's Wealth Excludes the Landworker

Starting in the 1820s, the downturn in farming profits and the wretched condition of the labourer and his family led once again in southern England's history to unrest, then violence. The riots and machine-breaking, often under the name of a mythical Captain Swing, have been traced back to their start in the wrecking of a threshing machine at Lower Hardres on 28th August 1830 and another the next day at Newington, near Hythe. Shades of Wat Tyler five centuries earlier, perhaps, but very different from the yeomen's rising under Jack Cade. Eight years after the Lower Hardres outbreak an insane demagogue, calling himself Sir William Courtenay, could still gain peasant support around Canterbury and cause renewed Government alarm. The agitation culminated in the battle of Bossenden Wood and the death of eight of his supporters, killed by the Army.

Improvements to the Poor Law and other measures relieved rural poverty a little but tended also to remove an obligation of concern for the labourers' welfare from the local landholders. They were more intent now upon a level of investment in machinery and buildings; not least in the Weald where improved drainage and better fertility could be gained on the heavy clay. Unfortunately for the rural community, the landowner and labourer at least, investment in 'high farming' was not repaid by sufficiently increased land rents. The Kentish hierarchical landowner, descendant of maybe a dozen generations within the county, found that his independence of command was diminishing, yet not the call on him to administer local matters. His money would work better for him not by traditional investment for future crops and rents but in the effortless London financial markets. New landowners, with wealth from London or the Thames and Medway industries, settled down without a tradition of long social or employment connections in their neighbourhood.

There had arisen since the Civil Wars a ruthless defence against loss of property. If this principle could be seen at all levels of society, not least in the debtors' prison with which Hasted was acquainted, its harshest effect was on the poor of the countryside who were much more easily arraigned than those in the teeming towns. Moreover, whereas wealth often now did not come from agriculture, to demonstrate wealth it was still necessary to own a high acreage of land, and that must be protected. Since misty antiquity the degree of ownership, outside the Royal Forest lands, had been in doubt on commons, heath or waste. Penalties for theft, nominally very severe physically, could be transmuted to a cash fine. Worry about theft, nevertheless, rumbled on through earlier years in Kent as much as elsewhere, and woodland was very often the scene of it.

> 29 February 1484 This indenture made the last day of February the first yere of King Richard the thirde, betwene the reverend fader in God William Pryor of Crystyscherche of Canterbury of that oon party and Richard Knechebole of Mersham of that other partye,wytnessith: that where William Lambarde and Stephen Harry, divers times before the date of this present, hath ben sculkynge in wodys be day and lyinge a wate to rob the Kynges lyege people and your tenantes at Mersham, on Saturday last with force or armes mettyn in your wode called Bockhanger with oon of youre tenantes called John Edwards, and then and there toke from the seyd John a purce of xl d in money —- (etc) (Lit Cant)

And one hundred years later in the Sevenoaks area a letter from Edward Crenewell stated that if the tenements of certain men in

Whitley were to be searched.

> - - you shall not fayle to finde corde wood (i.e. not theirs to use) upon their fyers and in their houses. Goodman Wall hath rayled his tenement in with birchen poles. It is reported that Benkyn hath used continually to carry corde wood or other wood out of Whitley upon horse back with hooks to hang upon each side of the horse for the purpose.

Among country gentlemen, priorities of protection of things dear to them came and went but their abiding passion was sport; above all in the 18th and 19th Centuries that meant gamebird shooting.

To be able to promise flying targets for the improving sporting gun, gamebirds in plenty must be reared. Pheasant in woodland, and partridge outside it, are nursed and guarded until they make admirable sport but then they, even more than wild fowl and fauna on his land, are the master's property. Based on these simple principles, there arose the occupation on larger estates of a differently skilled game-rearer/keeper and destroyer of predators. He, for good reason not often a local man, must oppose fiercely all poaching. The poacher was likely to be a local man, or men, from a hungry family.

In 1722 the Black Act had been passed, an outraged and pitiless reaction to theft of game drawn up by the property-owning gentry of that time and developed over the next one hundred years. The 1722 Act was a formative point in the rising hysteria of game protection measures. The stages were typified by a scarcely noticed Act in 1816 which declared that any person found at night, unarmed but with a net for poaching, in any forest, chase or park was to be punished by transportation for seven years. These enforcers were not interested in cash fines. In 1829 in Warwickshire, when eighteen men were arrested after the wounding by gunshot of a keeper, seven of them were exiled for life, nine exiled for fourteen years, and two were hanged. From 1827 to 1830, nationally, there were 8,502 convictions under the Game Code, one in seven of all criminal convictions. It was a time of inhuman punishment for theft in general: at Maidstone assizes a man would be transported for seven years - found guilty of stealing a jacket. At that time deadly spring guns were placed by keepers in woodland undergrowth but although legal they were abandoned because the machines were too undiscriminating in whom they killed and wounded. In addition to the Game Laws there were Acts such as that of 1820 from which a single Justice of the Peace, under the term Malicious Trespass, could punish a person who damaged a hedge, fence, tree, wood or underwood with three months' hard labour.

These aberrations of property protection were to leave frightening legends long beyond the end of the century. Eventually, however, the savage oppression during the reigns of George II and George III was harnessed. Keeper and poacher fought their midnight battles, now often with gangs, but Victorian rectitude disciplined the level of punishment. Aroused public opinion had its say in admonitory works such as *The Village Labourer* by the Hammonds in 1911. By then, ironically, the sporting value of a large woodland for sale was advertised in larger type than any reference to its devalued timber or underwood.

The difficult times for the labourer on the land of the mid-19th Century accelerated his leaving for beckoning new worlds: to the new cement industry by the Thames and Medway, to the maw of London as always, and even far beyond to North America and Australia, not always involuntarily. The paradox was that these years also saw the busiest ever output from the underwood, of which Kent had such a large acreage. Every scrap of work would be taken up by men and women and children, especially in the five lean winter months. The drive came from the workers in the coppice rather than its owner.

On the other hand, the long-term growing of trees for timber was afforded less attention. Reduced shipbuilding needs and foreign timber threatened its forecast value in maturity. Land agents and the surge of agricultural machinery traders combined to promote with zeal the improved equipment for drainage work and ploughing, able to convert land previously thought suitable only for wet woodland. The farmer's assarting of medieval times could begin again in earnest. The change was often energetically tackled but by now such loss of woodland acreage did not match that due to the dramatic expansion of urban housing and factories outside London or along the estuary, wherever there was a railway to serve it.

Yet most woodland remained protected, not so much for coppice products as for the new sporting obsession of almost every landholder. The shoot. At this time (Nuttall's Dictionary 1901), the farmer's _assart_ regressed in its definition to the ancient meaning which Manwood had used but confined to the royal forests: _the offence of grubbing up trees and destroying coverts._

3 May 1830. The Canterbury - Whitstable railway had the first locomotive ever to haul a passenger train. Within thirty years Canterbury and much of Kent would be served by more powerful engines overland from London. (The tall stylized trees are elm).

Greater, probably never greater, collective wealth among landowners allowed them to indulge in gamekeeping and to overlook the declining demand for English hardwood timber and coppice products. Perhaps, too, the sport was more enjoyable now that the poaching, still rife, no longer incurred such terrible penalties. Modern forestry was, however, becoming vitiated by the combined impact of many causes, some fundamental, all rapid. In order to register the swiftness and extent of change to woodland management prospects, the factors should be listed together.

All the changes below started or became most effective in Kent within a period of just twenty years, 1860 - 1880.

- The oak of wooden-built ships was replaced by iron and steel and teak.

- Railways brought fossil coal from Britain's north or west and timber from five continents to all parts of the county.

- Leather treating with oak tannin was replaced by a process using chrome salts.

- Hop-growing reached its peak output but new methods drastically reduced the hop-pole market.

- Machinery for making continuous (and barbed) wire was invented to replace hurdles, rails and hedgerows, causing a major loss of skilled work.

- Shotguns for game were made faster in loading and then dramatically more accurate.

- A surge in the rabbit population, due to the elimination of their natural predators, made costly fencing essential for tree planting.

- New chemical applications and heavy machinery encouraged the grubbing up of woodland for farming use.

- The soaring population numbers and their new locations required land for new dwellings built of brick and imported softwood.

In England and Wales, astonishing as it will seem to-day, the population doubled in just fifty years up to 1851. The misery of the poorer rural families was by then being partly obscured, partly alleviated, by the exodus to towns and mushrooming industries. The pattern of land ownership nationally had not yet changed. In 1874 Lord Derby's *Return on the Owners of Land* (the so-called New Domesday Survey) reported that 526 members of the nobility owned one-fifth of all land in the United Kingdom, while some 7,000 persons owned as much as four-fifths of it. The nobility may be presumed to have included the Church. The Ecclesiastical Commissioners held nearly 150,000 acres across the nation and the other church bodies a further 90,000 acres.

In Kent the Commissioners held 10,591 acres but only three private individuals were possessed of more than 10,000 acres, namely Viscount Holmesdale, Lord Sondes and Sir H Tufton. Landowners in the county owning more than 10 acres numbered about 4,000. (WE Baxter 1877). Such men, however, suffered a loss of economic power if they relied on rental incomes. This, combined with the introduction of death duties in 1894 and other legislation,

Woodland was 'worked harder than ever before or since' in the 19th Century, but here, near Bromley, circa 1910, the industry was already in decline.

Top & Middle: Peeling oak-bark for tannin and carting it.

Right: Collecting underwood for rods and faggots.

led to a more frequent sale of estates which was to become a flood after the First World War.

In Kent the continuing feature was of incoming owners from rewarding positions in London or Thames-side industries and, to a much lesser extent, from fortunes made in heavy industry further to the north. Not all new arrivals bought whole estates, some preferring to put together a group of available farms and woodland. In general, even then, Kent maintained its unusual ratio of a higher number of owners of smaller properties than the norm in lowland England.

The Capital Sporting Woodlands

Thomas Hardy's *The Woodlanders* was published in 1887. For the 1912 edition, he felt he must explain in a preface to his readers that his strange, hidden world in Wessex was there no longer. *In respect of the occupation of the characters, the adoption of iron utensils and implements in agriculture, and the discontinuance of thatched roofs for cottages, have almost extinguished handicrafts classed formerly as 'copsework' and the type of men who engaged in them.* That the coppice trades had declined so evidently would have been more bewailed across southern England if the estate owners had not been able to adapt this land most readily as game-shooting terrain and to absorb many of its workers into 'keepering.

In Kent, the uniquely large acreage of sweet chestnut was not the best of game habitats. It was not as rich in food for birds as the native species. Here, too, another friction with gamekeeping was that the old gapping-up method of pegging down a long shoot was ruined, by either the teeth of the multiplying rabbit or the boot of the beater as he strode through the cant. Chestnut coppice, however, was highly profitable and had spread right across the county from its early centre around Sittingbourne. Its output for hop-poles was still substantial and now wired lengths of fence-palings were winning a widespread market. The first East Kent collieries, at Tilmanstone and Snowdown, gave promise of a local trade in pit-props although some miners claimed that chestnut would shatter under pressure, without warning. The longer coppice tradition of ash, hornbeam and hazel still found a thin market of many products. But in far too many places the winter woodland lay unpeopled, silently awaiting its annual day of the shoot.

In the one-quarter or so of Kent's total woodland which was devoted to timber-sized trees rather than coppice-with-standards, English oak and Common ash were still predominant species, with beech where the Greensand encouraged it. Plantations, often small, of oak, ash, cherry and sycamore - and alder carrs and latterly poplar - denoted the estates of the more forestry-minded landlords. Their interest, more often now, included using 'nurse' rows of conifers when planting broadleaved species. Larch, the favourite conifer for timber applications, gained further favour when it was known that the wood as a pit-prop gave a warning 'groan' before collapsing.

The method of nursing young broadleaves with parallel rows of straight, fast-growing conifers had become known well enough to the forester but to his master, in Edwardian days, its main recommendation was likely to be that young conifers provided good shelter above ground for the gamekeeper's pheasants. There was no support in the south for pure coniferous plantations, despite the muted appeals for home-grown effort to improve Britain's timber stock. Gamebirds need a habitat of ground flora and protection at the wood edge from cold winds, neither being offered by a maturing conifer stand.

As English woodlands became sporting places first, and natural manufactories a poor second, the divergence of interest between regions became more marked. Some counties had large tracts of countryside linked with fox-hunting by horse and hound. Woodlands reflected the owner's encouragement of sanctuary for the fox and, to the peril of any game-birds present, new coverts were planted for that purpose. Fox-hunting was the sport above all for the countrymen of Leicestershire and Rutland, where 18th and 19th century land enclosures provided splendid riding country which was open yet enlivened by the jumps of recently planted quickthorn hedges and cleft rail fences. With a relatively insignificant enclosure movement since Jutish times, the Kent landscape did not suit fox-hunting to the same degree. In neighbouring Surrey, differently again, late enclosure of heaths led to woodland self-regeneration and tree-planting on a grand scale; it was a major reason for Surrey's high percentage of tree cover thereafter.

In later-Victorian years, one among the rush of inventions had brought a sudden advance in game-shooting accuracy. Earlier, fowling pieces had been made with ever longer barrels in the quest for accuracy, 6 feet (1.8 m) being quite usual, but this made the weapon unwieldy for all but ground targets. The short-barrelled shotgun came into use by 1800, followed by advances in breech-loading and percussion-cap firing during the '50s and '60s. It was, though, the American invention of the choke bore in 1869 - the bored hole in the barrel being slightly smaller at the muzzle end - which provided a new order of accuracy. To maintain the challenge to the hunter, the gamekeeper must ensure not only that hundreds, even thousands, of pheasants would be available on the day but that the cover at the woodland edge made the birds fly up fast ahead of the beaters. The master, to guarantee enough days of shooting in each season for his guests, must have control of large areas of woodland.

The financial contribution of the shoot for the owners at and after the turn of the century became paramount, especially in periods of low profit elsewhere. This and the shoot's social importance were the over-riding factors which meant, with some reason, that the gamekeeper, not the forester, would often decide upon the growing and felling of trees and which year to cut the coppice. The classic of confrontation was when coppice became less valuable to the forester charged with making profit from wood products but still suitable terrain for the shoot. The forester saw ahead fast-growing softwood on that land, one of the new conifers, planted easily, which could be thinned quickly and with little skill. The gamekeeper saw that future as a desert for his birds.

Among forestry plans which the latter might support was the option of returning, now unmarketable, coppice to its own timber.

This contribution to hardwood posts and beams required singling out one stem from those on each coppice stool ('a single' or, with much variation, a teller, standrill, waver, etc.). The other new growth was repressed, at first by cutting but in later years by shade and food competition from the canopy of the single stem. The forester would allow that this practice might not always produce sound timber, but he was not to know that a few years ahead the need for wood and timber would become so pressing that poor quality could be found a buyer readily. In all these matters, however, the owner was ultimately the one responsible, and he had in those days neither official guidance nor hindrance, nor any state subsidy.

Landmarks of the Kent Countryside

The great list of inventions from the 19th Century had brought a transformation for English woodland and the surrounding scene, yet for a while the signs of it were few. Around the turn of the century the confident Englishman showed a lively interest in procuring additions to his home surroundings from far away places which was led by a fascination with the world-wide British Empire. The Darwinian period of stimulation from the natural sciences was shown in fashionable rearing at home of exotic trees, shrubs and ferns. For the big house, staff and estate workers, and tenants' men as well when required, were there in numbers to indulge the fancies of the wealthy. Others copied such enthusiasm as best they could.

On the estate, a plant for ground cover which at first pleased master and gamekeeper was rhododendron in all its related species and hybrids. In the non-chalky woodlands of the county this foreign, lush growth and its vivid flowers were admired and the accounts of courage shown by botanist-explorers, such as the rhododendron specialist Joseph Hooker, were read avidly. Above the leathery foliage now began to rise towards their promised height specimen coniferous trees from explorers among the American Indians. Single trees were usually planted in good view from the house to commemorate an occasion of national or family pride. Trees from Douglas fir seeds, brought home in 1827 by the intrepid but ill-fated David Douglas, were also seen in plantation numbers, although not to the gamekeeper's liking because they offered a particularly poor ground cover.

The intense interest in such colossi from distant lands is best shown by the Giant Sequoia. Quantities of seed were brought to Veitch's nursery by William Lobb when he reached home from journeying in California in 1853, the year that the Duke of Wellington died. The wish to mark the passing of the victorious soldier and statesman was combined with the excitement of this new tree of the Sierra Nevada where seed-hunters beheld its full height of above 80 metres and enormous volume of more than 1,000 cubic metres at an age of some 3,000 years. Such a fitting memento for the national hero was adopted throughout the realm. Neither Veitch's customer nor his great-great-grandchildren would witness the full majesty of Wellingtonia (Sequoiadendron giganteum) but their descendants would live in the unchanging presence of its green tower, a landmark which stood rock-steady in 1987 after the first Great Storm of many to come in its lifetime.

Of the native trees, now that the competition for great size was being lost to imported evergreens, the incentive to grow them to full maturity, even for landscape reasons, had been reduced. Beech had always been commercially more rewarding when felled before full maturity. Fortunately, some boundary trees and many in parkland were left to increase in girth. Future generations would draw up lists of the mighty or venerable such as Maiden Oak at Fredville park (more than 11 metres in girth early in the 20th Century). From the unpollarded trees, long oak beams were still sought for the faithful, and expensive, repair of mansions and churches.

Large and long posts were also needed for another new landmark, the windmill, which at this time saw a surge of building. Before the days of steam and electricity the outstanding manifestation of ·physical power in any community was the watermill or windmill. For Kent, until the 19th Century, this had usually been a water-mill, which had heavy timbers in its working parts but, by its positioning beside the river, was not seen as a striking feature on the horizon. The heyday of the wind-powered mill began in the early years of Victoria's reign, when the Ordnance Survey map of Kent gave a count of 226 landmark mills. A long chain of these lofty wooden engines, the sunlight catching their sail movement, could be seen by local and foreign travellers along the Watling Street corn-growing area. In the age of brick building, the mill's use of timber seemed apparently substantial but it consisted of lightweight board except for the massive oak turning-post and gearing. Eventually, the farming drama of cheap Russian and Canadian wheat, preceded by mills based on fossil fuel, not wind-dependent and sited at harbour or railway junction, brought an end to most country mills.

The county symbol of tall oast houses, their building almost concurrent with the surge in windmills, was another example of apparent timber demand, and one strengthened by the Brick Tax from 1784 - 1850. The considerable use of timber was met, though, by reclaimed oak beams and softwood battens and boarding. At the level of fine wood, the furniture fashions for gentlefolk had broadly changed from walnut and 'fruitwood', either solid or more usually as veneers on inferior wood, to mahogany imported in squared baulks from the Caribbean islands and South American coast. (Indeed, at that time alder and even oak were stained red to offer a mahogany effect.). Rosewood was in vogue, too, from India and South America but, as yet, not many woods from Africa.

A Kentish microcosm of 19th Century change was to be seen at Whitstable. The opening of the Canterbury-Whitstable railway in 1830 and Whitstable's harbour two years later anticipated the future surge of coal traffic. By the end of the century more than fifty collier ships were fuelling the town's new coke and gas works and supplying by rail to merchants over a wide area of East Kent. The local shipping fleet included many brigantines built on Prince Edward Island, Canada, where timber was plentiful and cheap, then sent across the Atlantic for sale at Liverpool or Plymouth. There the traditional wooden trenails were replaced with iron bolts for greater strength. Eventually, some of these brigantines became the coastal collier ships of Whitstable.

In lowland England the land which had been replanted or self-regenerated for timber trees during the peak of anxiety in the Napoleon years now showed good volume and quality (the New Forest being a splendid royal example) which should realise optimum profit from about 1920. In many woodlands, however, oak plantation crops were being sold at around 80 years' growth, overtaken by the prospect of cash when they had reached a girth enough at least for furniture, for which oak was still in good bourgeois demand. This premature felling increased in response to the Finance Act of 1894 with its worsening of death duties. Paradoxically, some felling was postponed beyond the optimum date because the owner felt an obligation to replant that land but the work was just too costly to consider it.

Overall, the Government was showing concern once again about the nation's timber resource, though not any more because of fighting-ship needs of oak. Now the vital need was to grow conifers, softwoods, as fast as and wherever possible. Britain's imported softwood tonnage had trebled between 1840 and 1880. As to home-grown timber, of all sorts, the Board of Agriculture in 1895 estimated that England's woodlands had reduced to 5 per cent of the land area; a level that will probably prove to have been the lowest even after many more centuries.

Within England's total of five per cent, only Kent, Hampshire, Surrey and Sussex retained ten per cent or more as woodland: Kent's land area then was 973,846 acres (394,115 ha) of which 98,302 acres (39,783 ha) was classified as woodland, including coppice. On some of the larger estates, modern commercial forestry was pursued despite the dominance of shooting. James Brown's *The Forester* had set the pace from Scotland as far back as 1850 and, later, German instruction manuals were translated, most notably by Sir William Schlich. But he found the encouragement of landowners to be hard going. Other authoritative writers, such as A C Forbes, doubted the wisdom of translating continental forestry methods to an island of different climate, rapidly changing soils and, above all, smaller woodland parcels than those great forests of France, Germany and beyond.

Indeed, the south-of-England environment was not conducive to new planting. Young broadleaved plants, despite costly wire-netting fences, were likely to be ravaged by the scourge of the multiplying rabbits. The choice of new conifers to plant was theoretically wide but objections were found, not all silvicultural: Sitka spruce, perhaps the best general purpose conifer, was wickedly spiky for beaters to force through on shooting days. Again for shooting reasons, the spacing of young trees was allowed to be too open for straight-stemmed growth.

For mature, or near-mature, timber trees the outlook was more promising where the owner took an interest in running his own sawmill with a now reliable steam engine. In small towns, particularly those with a railway goods yard, men began new enterprises, based on steam-driven or electric mills, as combined timber merchant and sawyer. They often bolstered the patchy home trade with the milling of imported deals and with coal distribution. The countryside timber industry, nevertheless, was a small affair compared with the massively increased timber importing industry at the nation's ports. With limitless supplies from abroad of good dimensions and quality, the Edwardian timber trade directors showed little interest in the future of their inefficient home-grown appendage.

Others, however, saw the strategic dangers of an almost total reliance on imports of a staple material. In the thirty years from 1885 there were ten major committees of parliamentary inquiry into this risk. Yet nothing had been resolved by 1914 when a war, popularly expected to last only a few months, was begun against Germany.

FOUR YEARS OF GLOBAL WAR - THEN SIX YEARS MORE

The War to End Wars

As in most wars, demand for materials increased rapidly above expectations. In the case of home woodland output, oak and ash were vital for gun carriages and all wheeled transport, elm and beech for rifle stocks, poplar and ash for the infant air force, coppice wood for every sort of pole and rod-work and containers but, overall, the huge volume of home and imported timber was sucked into the great maw of the coal mines - pit props, chocks, boards - and for railway-sleepers and wagon timber.

With the land war centred in north-west Europe, Kent resumed its traditional role as supply line to the battlefield. A wartime cargo harbour was built within a mile of Richborough, once the Roman portway into Britain. Wars on the near mainland had traditionally required heavy supplies of wood from Kent and the South but now the French as allies agreed to supply the endless needs for beams, posts, boards and duckboards for the fighting trenches and rear depots.

Woodsmen and gamekeepers were terribly suited to the rigours and accomplishment of war. With the proud blessing of their employers and the anxiety of their families, they volunteered in disproportionate numbers to march with the young officer sons of the manor. For the excitement, for the food and clothing, for newly-discovered patriotism, to be with their friends since boyhood, they crossed by the ferry on the short journey to a cauldron of blood and spilt guts. First as volunteers then as conscripts, from Great Britain and Ireland in all walks of life, during those four years more than 744,000 men were killed; a number beyond comprehension, unheard by the insensate ear. In the countryside a generation of men wise in the ways of woodland and the future heirs of the owners' estates was shredded by death and maiming.

Those who returned to take up again the axe and the estate workbooks found that the output normally of decades had been snatched from the woods in three years. From 1915 the sinking of cargo ships by German submarines and surface craft forced drastic demands upon the home timber trade with hastily erected sawmills and drying kilns and unskilled staff hurriedly trained. Early profiteering had to be contained with untried measures. By 1917, of all the timber used, more than half was from home woods compared with one-tenth in 1913. Such a volume of timber must include a large proportion of inferior stuff from the derelict woods which had been left standing only because clearing would not pay for replanting. Although compulsory powers of purchase were rarely used, it is estimated that between 1914 and 1919 the felling of woodlands in Britain, with virtually all manual labour and horse-

drawn extraction, totalled an astonishing 450,000 acres (182,000 ha).

Even while struggling to administer that herculean effort, a forestry reconstruction committee worked to ensure that never again would there be so critical a dependence upon imports. The members proposed afforestation programmes for future Britain in which conifer plantings would cover almost two million acres (800,000 ha) within eighty years. In the first ten years 150,000 acres (60,000 ha) would be planted by the State and 100,000 acres (40,000 ha) by public bodies or private individuals assisted by government grants. Among the assurances that the target was achievable was cited the now excellent example of modern forestry teaching and practice by government initiative at the Crown Wood of Dean; a report very different from that of Nelson's day. The stewards of the new State forestry, to be called the Forestry Commission, received royal assent during Lloyd George's government of 1919.

In the Kent countryside of the 1920s the drama of wartime receded, the uncommon bustle in the woods had subsided and folk early about no longer strained to hear the pre-dawn rumble of guns from Picardy. But at the centre of each village was now in place a startling monument, the daily reminder of young friends dead.

Two Uneasy Coppice Cycles of Peace

In other ways there seemed for a while to be little change. Kentish estates had to wait until 1925 for the first Forestry Commission purchases, such as West Wood and Park Wood, Lyminge from the Erle-Drax family, and another nine years more to complete the biggest purchase at Challock from Dame Cunliffe-Lister. During the swift passage of twenty years between the War to End All Wars and the Second World War there were no mechanical inventions to bring economies into English forestry practice. Changes of attitude, however, brought lasting value in some quarters. The Bedgebury Pinetum, now of high international repute, was created in 1924 under the joint initiative of the Royal Botanic Gardens at Kew (where there were early worries about air pollution) and the new Forestry Commission.

There was perhaps a change in perception of the rural scene for the mainly urban population of southern England. Books and then magazine photography and the wireless fed the growing, if largely nostalgic, interest in country matters. Suburban trains and Green Line buses brought Outer London people on Sunday forays. Young office-workers looked for and found, and photographed again and again, the coppice-worker on the edge of the wood, he and they aware that his craft was surely drifting away to the power-driven wood turnery and metal workshops.

Bedgebury Pinetum, near Goudhurst, was established by the Forestry Commission from 1924. It is now an international authority on conifers and a splendid public park.

W E Hiley, dedicated forester, was more optimistic in his *Improvement of Woodlands* in 1931-

> Broad-leaved trees are planted less than conifers because they are, on the whole, less profitable. This is to be regretted not only on aesthetic grounds but because most of our traditional woodworking industries employ hardwoods and there is a danger that these industries will become obsolete. So far. however, their decay is due not to lack of raw material on which to work but to their failure to keep pace with the times. Their products are often good and cheap and if they were effectively marketed would be readily saleable. A few enthusiastic landowners have taken up such industries as hurdle making and the wheelwright trade and by introducing modern organisation and conditions of labour have succeeded in preserving them; in this way they have been able to utilise home-grown timber to much better advantage than their neighbours.

His own labours and the efforts of others did not see a return of any magnitude to wooden artefacts before, eventually, he and his peers were to be caught up again in the gross demands of war.

In established woodlands, too often management neglect was allowing unplanned dominance by the introduced but all-conquering sycamore seedlings, by a heavy invasion of native birch trees or by banks of rhododendrons. Broadleaved woodland was selling for the shoot and for eye appeal. Announcing the sale of the Bilsington Estate in 1920, the auctioneers, John D Wood, had written -

THE CAPITAL SPORTING WOODLANDS

known as Priory Wood, Tile Lodge Wood and Finch Wood adjoin on all sides. On the outskirts of Priory Wood is the Pheasantry. These woods undulate prettily and the numerous dips form the fine stands from which high birds are obtained. They contain a vast quantity of thriving oak, ash (-etc-) and valuable underwood of (-etc-).

The Sporting for so small an area is exceptionally good and additional sporting over about 200 acres is reserved to the purchaser of this lot. Attention is called to Lot 20, Good Sporting Woodlands of about 178 acres.

The government's post-World War 1 attitude to forestry was, on the other hand, making silvicultural management more possible for those owners who would take advantage of new measures. Alert weekenders began to see young plantations of Douglas fir or Sitka spruce in monoculture. Others were sadly aware of estates being broken up and the opportunity taken to ravage the woods with excessive felling. But W E Hiley again (1931)

The payment of death duties is often made an excuse for dismissing a part of woodland staff. If a large amount of timber is cut at this time more land will need replanting and more men should be employed. A reduction of the number of men engaged on the estate in commercial forestry can then only be regarded as a sign of reprehensible ignorance of the economics of estate management.

The general conclusion that must be drawn from this examination of taxation is that, although death duties have made it very difficult for large estates to be kept intact, there has never been a time when forestry has been so favoured. The willing forester receives every kind of encouragement and conditions so propitious that forestry pays better than ever before. And yet the area which is annually replanted by private owners is little more than half what it was before the war.

- Only in Britain does the woodland owner receive the lenient treatment explained in this chapter, and only in Britain is a money subsidy paid for planting.

Kent's unusually high proportion of coppice in its total woodland acreage reflected the uniquely large hop-growing area. As the demand for Kent hops weakened to cheaper substitutes, the growers were able to re-adapt their skills and switch to top-fruit orchards on land that had been well-manured for hops. Coppice areas, nevertheless, needed to be cut at something like the normal cycle if the growth was to be kept at reasonable quality and broadleaved timber plantations needed to be thinned out in their first two or three decades. To the rescue, for small diameter wood, came a 'groundwood' pulp mill. Kemsley Mill, near Sittingbourne, was built in1923-25 by a company called Lloyd with four of the world's largest paper-making machines powered by an independent station. In 1936 Bowater acquired the mill and increased the output. For some sixty years, until 1989, 'Sittingbourne' would be the forester's name for this essential customer; a viable one because of the short distance from most of the county's woods.

In these years the East Kent coalfield, now increased to four collieries, took the boards, chocks and props of rough timber and roundwood origin from several small sawmills near the pits. Pulpwood and pitwood, thus, could offer a just acceptable return to help the overall management of Kent woodlands. Wagon timber, gate posts, harbour work took a share of larger sizes. Better grades of timber found better reward; from coachwork and small boat-building along the coast to interior wall panelling and beamwork in houses, through furniture, then sports goods, to, occasionally, telegraph poles or the heady price won for a log good enough to peel into decorative veneers.

Yet, in Kent as in England as a whole, the private forestry scene in the 1930s was abysmal. Addressing his Forestry Sub-section of the British Association in 1937, the Chairman, the Hon. Nigel Orde-Powlett (the future Lord Bolton) admitted...

> At present, with few exceptions, private woodlands are run at a dead loss. Owners regard them, financially speaking, as a nest-egg which must only be realized under the stress of dire necessity, and not at all as the source of annual income which they ought to be. We know that too often, because of this outlook, the annual value of woodlands is allowed to run to waste, and the nest-egg itself is found to be addled when the time for its exploitation is considered to have arrived. One can say without exaggeration that on nine estates out of ten the woodlands are an encumbrance rather than an asset.

The penalty of post-Industrial Revolution progress was to be seen even in the new wood product markets. The pace of improvements, and therefore changes, of industrial processes was already too rapid for the long cycle of silviculture. On the longer view, the need for sustainability of raw materials was not recognised. At the detailed level, in many cases the wooden product was comparatively inefficient.

Manufacturers of crates and chip baskets and, more famously, Bryant & May of the safety match, urged the planting of hybrid poplar. Its particular qualities, especially its growth rate which yielded industrial veneer logs from as young as fifteen years, were enticing to the owner of poorly drained clay land. But its end-products would not be able to compete with the basket of the future made of card or plastic, or with the disposable petrol lighter. There was to be no alternative use to absorb profitably the widespread fashion for poplar planting.

War Again and Shortage

The power of market forces looked set for inexorable progress, and later its course would be resumed. First, though, the thinking of even the most far-seeing economist, and the silviculturalist, was to be halted again by the frenzied demands of full-scale war. Orde-Powlett had put great energy into urging estate owners of the 1930s towards good forestry practice combinable, he insisted, with estate shooting. (The Forestry Commission, not yet committed to private woodlands in any great degree, had left the teaching to such individuals.) Now, as President of the Royal Forestry Society of England and Wales in the Spring of 1940, he addressed the members

PRESIDENTIAL MESSAGE and Woodlands in Wartime

I have been asked to write a few notes for the JOURNAL, indicating in what way owners of woodlands can best help their country in wartime. I will be very brief.

In normal times the Society exists to further the interests of woodlands, foresters, and woodland owners in every possible way; and amongst the most important of our endeavours are the conservation of woodlands and the prevention of excessive fellings. For we know that not only is the destruction of woodlands against the national interest, but it is also against the interests of the owners themselves. Our function, in fact, is to promote good forestry and to increase woodlands - not to destroy them.

But war alters all things: and, not least, the outlook that we must adopt towards our woodlands.

..To come down to brass tacks. It is of the utmost importance that our home supplies of timber, of every size, should be available as and when they are required. Owners, therefore, can render the best service to their country by parting readily with their timber when asked to do so by the Timber Control or by timber merchants, even if the resultant fellings are far in excess of those which would be allowable under good forestry practice, and even if the timber in question is immature.

The country's necessity must come before every other consideration.

With a long-term faith in woodland continuity despite all around him, the President added a characteristic postscript

N.B. - It is hardly necessary to point out to members the immense importance of replanting felled areas with the least possible delay.

N.A. O-P.

The global conflict from 1939 to 1945 began as 'War with Germany' and a flush of memories of the Great War, even for those only thirty years of age. But now people realised, from newsfilm of the recent Spanish civil war and Sino-Japanese attacks, that air warfare would be critical. By the summer of 1940, comparisons with the Great War had lost meaning; they came more easily from Napoleon's war and his threat to invade across the Channel. Fighter planes with single wings rapidly drew patterns of combat on clear skies above Kent, while at ground level Royal Air Force plans were acted upon to augment the pre-war airfields of Hawkinge, Lympne and Manston on the Channel's edge and, further inland, Biggin Hill and Malling. Along the coast, children were evacuated far from their homes and the remaining population was restricted of movement. Suddenly, in June of that year, more than 300,000 troops of the defeated Allies poured back from the mainland through Folkestone, Dover and other south coast harbours, and then for four long years the door was firmly shut.

The woodlands adopted a nervous activity. Throughout the county they were used as cover for secretive bunkers of ammunition and standings for other war materiel. In East Kent, the invasion coast, double lines of concrete pyramids one-metre high, to be known as dragons' teeth, were rushed up as obstacles to enemy motors. Long-since removed from fields, they may still be seen at a wood-edge. Within the woodland, notably at King's Wood, Challock, were hideaways below ground in which trained saboteurs, local volunteers, were to lie until the enemy attack had passed above them. By narrow roadsides, logs were suspended ready to be crashed down at the invasion alarm.

But invasion did not come and Hitler's barges on the French coast were dispersed. The woods became vital suppliers; their proper role of timber and coppice production ran, once again, at a drastic wartime level. There could be no thought for the longer term now, and, in any case, the desire for responsible growing of timber

The nearest land to
Hitler's Europe.
The Kentish scene was
transformed during the
Second World War.

stock had hardly resumed after the First War felling. The nation's
stock of trees of even minimum timber-felling age was pitifully low
after the War to End All Wars. This time, however, there was no
sense of unreadiness in organisation. Helped by the improved
awareness of the British private woodlands industry's structure
which came with the creation of the Forestry Commission, essential
early measures such as the setting of maximum prices for wood
products were put in place from the outset. Indeed, the Commission
had taken charge at the beginning of the war and carried the
responsibility for procurement until handing over to the Ministry of
Supply early in 1941.

'The original plan to meet wartime demand was for three categories of preference for felling: first, pitwood dimensions of trees of 20-35 years and coppice of pitwood dimensions with some mature stands of both hardwoods and softwoods; secondly, stands at 35-40 years and other mature timber; lastly, very young plantations and those of middle age held as a future reserve. This attempt to meet the immediate need without totally wrecking the longer-term management had to give way to heavy demand. Immature stands which should have been preserved for the long term had to be sacrificed to achieve production targets. There was less longer-term loss in cutting the middle age stands which had been neglected and underthinned and had no promising future.' Thus Russell Meiggs who, in 1949, retold the whole story graphically from his first-hand experience as Chief Labour Officer of the Home Timber Production Department at the Ministry of Supply.

A figure for comparison at least as comprehendible as tonnage is that the labour force working in Britain's home timber production increased from fewer than 15,000 in September 1939 to over 73,000 at the peak in 1943. Augmenting the skilled Forestry Commission and timber trade personnel, deferred if necessary from military service, men and women were also drawn from wartime Conscientious Objectors, alien civilians and German and Italian prisoners-of-war with, later, civilian woodsmen from British Honduras. Most effectively, military units of foresters came from Canada, Australia and New Zealand, many of whom went on to the battlefields of the European mainland. Following the precedent of the First War, the Women's Timber Corps now rose to nearly 5,000 members who, in this war, undertook all the physical 'timber-jill' tasks, including felling, as well as the clerical work.

A year after the war began, the night-time bombing of major ports with highly-flammable timber wharves - London, Liverpool, Belfast, Hull - badly disrupted supplies. By now the shortfall could not be made up by imports because of the appalling losses of merchant shipping at sea. In August 1942, the Director of Home Timber Production, Gerald Lenanton, wrote to the Forestry Society, beginning as follows

Dear Sir,   August 7, 1942

The shipping situation makes it absolutely essential that our home production of timber should be speeded up still further. During the last six months British woodlands have been felled at the rate of approximately 1,800 acres a week, in itself a startling figure, but in future some 2,200 acres a week must be felled if we are to produce that volume of timber which is required for the effective prosecution of the war.

I realize only too well that after nearly three years of heavy fellings this will entail a serious depletion of our woodlands, but at this critical stage of the war there is no alternative, and I have no doubt at all that landowners and land agents will co-operate wholeheartedly in helping us to secure sufficient timber to maintain supplies for the Service Departments and essential industries.

While all kinds of utilizable timber are in demand, the most urgent need is for pitwood, of which available supplies are limited. I know that pitwood production entails the sacrifice of young plantations which have not yet attained financial maturity, but the maintenance of supplies for the pits is of vital importance, and I must appeal to owners to part readily with their pitwood stands when asked to do so.

The Deputy President of the Royal English Forestry Society, Major The Hon R Coke, made the reply below. His, effectively 'open', letter in the members' journal was frank, indeed, and reflected the war-weariness, yet not disloyalty, at this low point in the six years, coming just before the victorious Battle of Alamein and the successful Defence of Stalingrad.

Dear Sir,   August 17, 1942

In acknowledging the receipt of your letter of August 7 respecting home timber production I have no doubt that members of the Royal English Forestry Society who own woods will continue to do their best to meet national needs.

I am asking the editor to publish your letter in the next issue of this Society's Journal.

It would be very welcome, however, if your remarks on the 'burden of sacrifice' could at the same time be supplemented by a fairer apportionment as between the owners of woods and sawmills and the rest of the community. For while the prices of timber, both in the round and converted, have remained much as they were in 1939, costs of production have risen appreciably all round. Hitherto applications for price revision have not met with much response.

The incidence of E.P.T. moreover, in the case of large wooded estates, will be likely to leave their owners without timber as well as the money received for its removal.

The reference to EPT or Excess Profits Tax showed clearly that tax worries had not gone away during The Emergency. Russell Meiggs, from a fairly neutral standpoint in 1949, felt he should say this ..

Woodland owners who, like home timber merchants, after a very lean period suddenly found themselves in a seller's market, saw the greater part of their profit taken away by the State. In assessing (their) wartime contribution the profit motive should not be unduly stressed. Taxation fell proportionately more heavily on them than on trades which had fared relatively well before the war. And once again it may be emphasised that unlike most trades they were consuming their capital and jeopardising their own future prospect. Patriotism weighed more heavily in the scale than profit.

Brilliant Improvisation and Exhausted People

Despite the grey facts of life, the contribution from the woodlands was greater than had been expected. Before the war not more than 5 per cent of the entire timber (wood) consumption in the United Kingdom was drawn from home sources but at the end of 1942 the figure had grown to 60 per cent of the, albeit lower, wartime total. By 1944, moreover, out of that year's home timber production of three million tons, around one-third came from the private broadleaved woodlands of lowland counties. These hardwoods were more likely than conifer plantations to require tactful but firm procurement from reluctant owners by an Acquisition Officer, the source of many human stories. In one respect the lowland drive was unfulfilling: large quantities of oak, the commonest species, were difficult to employ because of the low-grade timber coming out of neglected woodlands.

The wartime contribution of timber threw up newsworthy items which became legends. Just as the Women's Timber Corps tended to obscure the other 93 per cent of the workforce, so did the appeal of the Mosquito fighter-bomber (the fastest aircraft in service was built of <u>wood</u>) outshine the huge but humdrum overall timber usage of the war machine. Now the war's appetite affected even North America, making timber imports for Britain still difficult despite the Allies having won the Battle for the Atlantic against the U-boat. In an eye-opening article (1950) on wood requirements for shipbuilding, John G Kuenzel of the US Navy Department pointed out that in the year of 1944 his department used nearly nine million tons of steel but, alongside that, nearly three million tons of wood. That was little less than the entire timber production in Britain for the same year, and a reminder that naval timber needs had not ended with the 'ironclads' even if Wealden oak was no longer a prime timber for naval purposes.

At the smaller end of marine requirements were vessels such as drifters, minesweepers, motor-torpedo boats and speedboats. Many hundreds of these were built in Britain in a myriad of small boatyards and almost entirely of home-grown wood. Usage of timber on land was, of course, over the same wide scale. If Kent had to have its equivalent of the Mosquito story it was the roll of six-foot chestnut paling a-top a photogenic tank. These fascines for filling ditches to make a tank crossing were the most observable example of how the peacetime coppice trade adapted its wired-paling fences to war. With minimum change and vital success it provided temporary passage or trackway for army vehicles. For the campaign in Europe many millions of palings were sent across the Channel.

Timber yard gantry at
Morgans of Strood

The allocation of felled timber to the most appropriate end-use had to be ensured despite an overall pressure for sheer volume. Telegraph poles (though few enough from Kent) were a particularly high softwood specification of length, strength and straightness. Best ash, suitable for aircraft construction, was in short supply because it had been used heavily for the same purpose late in the First War. Beech, which had been used as a replacement for American walnut in rifle stocks, became much used for aircraft-grade plywood. Oak was now massively used for the remarkably durable - in design as well as structure - Utility brand of furniture and also, for its unique structural properties, in beer barrel staves. Larch, more commonly used for fencing before the war, took over from imported mahogany for the outer skins and other parts of boats. The lack of poplar imports for safety matches showed up the then small availability in home supplies. Among substitutes for other imported timbers, sycamore and birch found many more uses in wartime. The biggest users, collieries, railways and boxboard containers, were all customers for enormous quantities and now accepted an unprecedented range of species to meet the demand. Bowaters' pulpwood mill at Sittingbourne was a major local buyer.

With thoughts of victory already in people's minds, Kent received a rude shock from the pilotless aircraft-bomb, the doodlebug. It was launched from occupied northern territory close to the Channel, and all its ramps were aimed at London. Fighter pilots and anti-aircraft batteries strove to shoot down the flying missiles before they could reach London. Many hundreds exploded in Kentish fields and woods, but a few caused great and indiscriminate loss of civilian lives.

Finally, the Second World War ended in August 1945 with the awesome new dimension, physically and mentally, of the Atomic Bomb. Later, men returned to study their profligacy with natural resources during six years of war demand. For British timber the broad estimate was that, out of the stock standing at the outset of war, some 46 per cent had been felled. In 1949 the Forestry Commission Report said that in Britain since 1939 'all the worthwhile timber had been cut'. In England alone that had amounted to felling 254,000 acres (103,000 ha). Talking as a Kentish woodland owner recently, Lord Kingsdown said of Torry Hill and its neighbours, 'We had nothing much left.'

Strangely, the sheer volume removed was not to be casually observed. The clear-felled woodlands, including Bilsington's 'capital' Priory Wood, rather quickly pushed up scrub or a managed new tree crop. With gentle deception the very large number of individual trees in Kent's shaws and hedgerows, from the crest of the Downs and across the Weald, gave the land a still remarkably wooded appearance. The British people, with an end-of-war yearning for calm times, looked upon woodland and thought of it in an uncritical way. Radio readings and cinema propaganda had been instilling a sense of its unchanging, natural world, more readily than in the farming drive for food or the seaside's barbed wire. If woodland had long held a sense of mystery, often unwelcoming, that very emotion had come to seem bitter-sweet, familiar, and more dependable than the unknown perils of war. Woodland, for those emerging from war at last, was the *Greensleeves* of Vaughan Williams and the billowy shaw in a Rowland Hilder landscape.

But the post-war, shocking, fact was that the acreage of healthy trees in middle growth or of productive coppice had, in England, fallen to an almost despairing low. In the nature of men's priorities, however, it can be allowed that the distress of seeing early-felled trees would be deeper for one who was a woodsman first, not a gameshooting sportsman. It was the latter who had been in the majority among landowners who had held woodland since mid-Victorian times, and for many of them the damage to long-term forestry or the quality of coppice was not a matter of profound importance. All owners were, on the other hand, forced to be very aware of the pros and cons of tax impositions, and planting subsidies. Now they were to hear with much interest of woodland management incentives from Government. 'Will there be enough reason again for growing timber trees, and a chance of our woods being allowed to mature until the grandchildren are old? Then all that coppice - - ?'

ALWAYS REGENERATION

Lowland Conifers

The Government's roles of both umpire and coach had reached into every aspect of its citizens' lives since 1939. Unlike Germany, France and Italy, the British post-war political system had changed from the 1930s only in its members of parliament. The same government structure continued. Indeed, problems such as the coal shortage of 1947 were found, wartime-style, to be solvable only at Whitehall level, while food rationing was not lifted until 1954, after nine years of peace. Consciously or not, the people of the British Isles continued to look to the civil service for orders and to accept its guidance in practical matters.

State control of the essentials - coal, rail transport, hospitals - seemed to be a logical progression from the decade of Emergency Powers which had lasted so long as to become the norm. State control, or nationalisation, of the country's woodlands did not happen despite a serious recommendation in earlier years. Instead, with vivid experiences of wartime timber shortages still fresh in the mind, Forestry Commission personnel went forth with energy to acquire land for afforestation and to encourage private woodland owners in timber management.

Land, even poor land, which had been pressed into use for wartime food production was still required for that purpose, and more yet would be taken, but the ravaged woodland left from emergency cutting-over was a problem for the owner who found it difficult to summon up the effort or skills to re-stock it. Death duties, too, which had affected more families in wartime, led to the clear-felling of some remaining timber crops by the timber merchant. For these reasons, even in a South-East England hungry for farming acreage, the Forestry Commission took smoothly into ownership a considerable land area, although its component units were as little as twenty acres in some cases.

In central and eastern Kent, the 'Challock and Lyminge' Forestry Commission area expanded to an accumulation of 5,000 acres (2,000 ha) in the 1950s. At the later peak of 1982, the Commission's landholding throughout Kent would be 11,670 acres (4,723 ha) or 11 per cent of the county's woodland. The remit was 'to grow useable timber, fast'. To that end were employed Douglas fir, spruces (Norway then Sitka), larches (European and Japanese), pines (Corsican and Scots), Western Hemlock, Western Red Cedar and hybrid poplars. For countless years until 1920 the most-planted trees on Kent land had been oak and then beech or ash. Now, with its own land and workers or by influencing others, the Forestry Commission ensured that Corsican pine would be front runner (See Appendix 10/1)

The officers' dedication to their work was high. The Working Plan for the Challock Forest/Lyminge area in 1960, compiled by Dallas Mithen, District Officer, was a masterpiece of erudition and exhaustive research into detail. It recorded that soils and field-layer plants had been studied and the chosen forestry planting mixtures of species and spacing were always under examination. In these years seed origin was a problem, unreliable supplies having to be included, and sources were tactfully filed by code numbers.

By the late 1950s, the Challock/Lyminge area had 3,000 acres (1,214 ha) under management as High Forest of which more than half was pure conifer plantation. The overall picture was that broadleaved timber trees now represented only one-fifth of the Forestry Commission's acquired land in Kent. Being Kent, more than half of the balance of 2,000 acres (809 ha) of Commission woodland remained as productive sweet chestnut coppice. Chestnut does not offer a suitable cover to act as a canopy for newly-planted trees of another species, a method of converting coppice to a High Forest regime which was used after 1952. The chestnut output was, in any case, a valuable earner.

In this period of 'bare ground' post-war woodland the emphasis was on replanting choices. For a mixture of broadleaved species and conifers the Commission favoured alternating three rows each; for example, three rows of beech nursed by three of Lawson's cypress or of 'thuja'. For conifer mixtures, alternating single rows were preferred, such as Douglas fir with 'tsuga' (nomenclature in the plantations became half-English/half-scientific).

Below: Oakover tree nursery today.

Below Right: Plantation oak, 47 years after Forestry Commission planting, 1951

Again, a pure row of one conifer might be alternated with a row containing two conifer species such as Norway spruce and thuja. Each permutation had its advantages in thinning practice and nursing support for the other species. Frequent experimental variations according to soil type and micro-climate were a feature of the Commission's work. The best of such pre-war and post-war practical experience of lowland conifer forestry could now be handed to private woodland owners.

In the post-war decade, long-term forestry in Britain, and more
so in the Colonial Forestry Service, was seen by a wide range of
young men as a great corrective, a restorer of sane balance through
work to be followed in the open-air and with government support.
From this there stemmed enthusiastic forest officers and
researchers with specialist degrees gained at Edinburgh or Oxford
or Bangor, North Wales. They, when advising woodland owners,
found themselves among owners and agents also with a new-found
energy to put right their properties. Gold Medallists of the Royal
Forestry Society, such as Arthur Hills on his land at Redleaf in
Kent, were woodsmen of exceptional vision and practicality.

The dual drive with which these men could make great progress
was the 1948 Dedication Scheme to commit land to forestry and the
tax advantage which respected that long-term commitment. In its
1950s and '60s form, this system ensured a great replanting in the
lowland private sector, augmented by the Forestry Commission's
own planting. Forest management companies were formed to
operate the expansion and the increasing demands of paper-work.
For owners who maintained close interest in their estate forestry
programme, this was an era of working confidently towards
rejuvenation of their woods after more than a generation of war-
directed expedience.

Alongside forestry, and dominating it, was the national drive for
food production. In 1954, G H Garrad remarked in his *Survey of the
Agriculture of Kent*

> - - - when the land comes under the plough, especially in these days of
> tractors and modern machinery, small and irregularly shaped fields,
> surrounded by trees and high hedges are objectionable for many
> reasons.

Of the shaws of Kent, he wrote

> - - -unfortunately these shaws are scattered everywhere among the
> farmland and are ideal cover and breeding grounds for innumerable
> rabbits and noxious weeds.

During the Second World War, Garrad had seen new arable
cultivation wrested out of pasture and other land uses to an area-
equivalent of twice the total woodland acreage of Kent. Writing for
the Royal Agricultural Society of England, he approved of farming
land being won from woodland but added sagely

> - - - it is always worth while, before starting on an expensive
> reclamation scheme (note the term), to try to ascertain the reason why
> the land had remained under woodland for so long, and to satisfy oneself
> that the land will be suitable for arable cultivation or for grassland after
> the trees have been grubbed.

About this time, newly-reliable chainsaws swept away the old
crosscut saw and felling axe. The change within the woods was
remarkable. No longer the low, sweet whisper of a crosscut with two
men working in patient, day-long reciprocity. The clamouring roar
of the one-man chainsaw might not become an enjoyed part of the
scene for years, if ever, but, oh, it was so much quicker! No longer
horses, either. For a choice of tractor, the smaller ones were better
at tricky extracting of logs, so then and thereafter the small, old,
tractor became the lowland cutter's trademark. Other than the
chainsaw, the usually small acreage of individual woodland
operations - and the low profit from them - meant that there would

be little progress in mechanisation. The car, however, had transformed the mobility of rural workers to make them more independent and more specialised in their work.

'Outside the wood', the spheres of science and international politics rushed onwards at an astonishing rate. In 1957, while Britain's drivers were grumbling about petrol rationing as a result of the short Suez Canal war, the first atomic power station came on stream at Calder Hall and the nation's first hydrogen bomb was exploded above the Pacific Ocean. In mainland Europe six countries signed a treaty for a Common Market, and the Russians launched a space satellite with a dog aboard it. In a milestone decision, but one overlooked among all those dramatic events, the British government adopted the Zuckerman Report and accepted that **a strategic reserve of timber would no longer be a national priority.** The announcement came a little over 400 years since the State Act of Henry VIII - his was to be the first of many- entitled An Act for the Preservation of Woods. In our short half-century since 1957 every principle of lowland forestry has been challenged. The individual steps taken have been few and often hesitant but future generations looking back will see that the late-20th century was the watershed of thinking about woodlands in southern England.

Came the Chainsaw and Other Great Changes

In 1968, C A Barrington, Conservator for South-East England, gave his and the Forestry Commission's view of forestry in the Weald (FC Booklet No 22.) Undoubtedly he was influenced by the international opinion from the Food and Agriculture Organization - that there would be a world shortage of softwood timber by 1990.

> (In the Weald region) excluding the Chalk Downlands and with the possible exclusion of the Wadhurst Clay, the growing of hardwoods (other than chestnut coppice, possibly elm and perhaps the odd poplar here and there) is justified only by a love of beautiful scenery. So wherever landowners in the Weald plant hardwoods or keep hardwood standing today for the sake of amenity, and there are a lot who are doing this, they deserve the public's thanks because it is costing them money to do it.

> On the Weald clay, oak, with its slow rates of growth and small increment, does not pay to grow, but whether we like it or not, Norway spruce, Corsican pine and Western hemlock, for example, do pay to grow.... On the sands, the most suitable species to grow, ecologically and economically, are the Scots pine, the Corsican pine, Western hemlock again and larch. The decision has to be the same on the Greensands and the Gault Clay. On purely financial grounds, from the point of view of the forest and timber industries and the nation's trade, hardwoods are not a viable proposition, but on aesthetic grounds they can be priceless - especially along our Wealden hedgerows.

Like Garrad before him (except perhaps on hedgerows) Barrington portrayed the considered land-use objectives of his industry. Both were backed by the official drive to overcome shortage of their produce. Although they were advising the same producer in many cases, the owner of field and forest or his tenant, neither author felt he should give book space to one of the consuming interests of most countrymen, the shoot. Neither man gave more than a word to 'the environment' or 'ecology'. There is no doubt that broadleaved woodland was planted and maintained by most owners, despite the official preference, because they valued it; as an aesthetic amenity, perhaps, but certainly as *sporting* woodland. In the century since the mid-Victorian collapse of demand for home-grown timber and for underwood, other than during two world wars, it was the shoot which preserved the traditional broadleaved woodland scenery of Kent.

Gamekeeping also knew change in its secluded environment. Despite poaching for the pot during years of food rationing, the rabbit population was everywhere referred to as a plague when, in 1953, the plague indeed of myxoma tumours reached the warrens here from the Continent. Within a few years the rabbit was so rarely seen in southern England that foresters gave up the practice of always fencing new tree-planting. For the forester, savings in planting costs were up to half the total. The wire-netting had irritated gamekeepers and they were also pleased to have fewer avian predators, following the loss of rabbit from their diet. Not for thirty years would the rabbit, by then often dwelling above ground, become a major problem again.

'.....it was the shoot which preserved the traditional broadleaved woodland scenery of Kent.'

For the 'keeper, a keenly felt change was the reduction in partridges. Needing a habitat of continuous hedgerows rather than woodland, the partridge family was a victim of agriculture's economies of scale in machine size and grant-seeking. Nevertheless, with massive pheasant-rearing programmes, the shoots were maintained. Earl Mountbatten of Burma wrote to congratulate a 'keeper in Cambridgeshire in 1960 for providing a day's bag of 1,425 high-flying pheasants. His son-in-law, Lord Brabourne, got 335 of them. In later years Lord Brabourne's own gamekeeper ensured good shooting at Mersham Hatch but with the emphasis on high-fliers rather than numbers. Since the 1950s pheasant breeding had been more predictable with improvements to incubator temperature control. It was later to be modified by some shoots by encouraging woodland-rearing of the bird and hence the qualities of 'wild' game high-fliers. Then avian predators also prosper.

For many years past, fallow deer had escaped from Kentish parks, notably along the Stour valley. Unlike the rabbit, they had been kept down to a few, not least by soldiers with rifles who were camped nearby. With the post-war young plantations in east Kent reaching pole size, to the enjoyment of the deer, these beautiful animals with their palmate antlers became a less rare sight, and their depredation of young plants by grazing worsened. To the west, roe deer began to increase in population and to cause severe plant damage in some localities. So, too, did the American grey squirrel. By an Order from 1973 covering most counties, including Kent and its neighbours, Warfarin was specified for use as a poison against the grey. Its population increase and the potential for disastrous damage to trees whose thin bark it would strip - notably beech, young oak, sycamore and some conifers, - was little recognised by the general public; they were told that the grey's crime was that of ousting the red squirrel from its native habitat.

Whatever its crime, the grey squirrel was now a well-known 'foreigner', an Introduced Species. The new lore of the 1970s held that all 'native' species must be OK and only foreigners were vile. This facile grouping came partly from the early talk about biodiversity; the sweet chestnut, having arrived only a couple of thousand years ago, made a poor host environment when compared with the oak tree. 19th Century rhododendron threatened to smother all other plants on soils it enjoyed. The pervasive 16th Century sycamore tree, praised for its shelter in extreme conditions and a producer of useful timber (occasionally to its famous 'fiddle-back' quality) was an invasive force of a thousand seedlings. These flourish in the shade of the parent's deep-green, large-leaved canopy which denies life to other plants. Of introduced mammals, the rabbit appeared by this time to have survived myxomatosis and to be multiplying again. Among all the commonly known introduced plants and creatures, the pheasant alone escaped the tar-brush.

During the 25 - 30 years following the end of World War II a misleading picture of forestry had emerged. Britain's overall figures for new afforestation looked relatively healthy; the tree-covered percentage of the land was swinging up from its nadir earlier in the century. But the planting was very largely in the upland North, where a new environmental concern showed in anxiety about the forestry locations on the moors of Scotland. Over-eager investment consultants contributed much to this still-attractive form of super-tax avoidance. At a City lunch, a noble woodsman of Kent was told by an acquaintance that he, too, had become an owner of great tracts of trees, yet when asked where they were the new forester wasn't sure. His broker would know.

In lowland Kent the post-war enthusiasm for woodland management had lost steam by the mid-1970s (and would lose more with further tax changes in 1988). For the woodland worker, the feller, the contract planter, the coppice cutter, prospects were not bright. Most of the small workforce had only moderate expectations of their labours, but now they were aware of a reduction in planting - the future for most of them - and the continuous piecemeal replacement of the remaining wooden-made articles by metal alloy or plastics. A seasonal use for Kent chestnut palings had been the long lines of snowdrift deflectors parallel to the highway. Came the winter when Kent authorities replaced them all with black plastic screens, and the visual message was only too clear.

World developments and local change caused the forester to lose his old sure sense of the correct path for the long term. Agricultural income was changeable but artificially high, on balance, compared with other rural land uses. The lead over other sciences gained by the chemistry of compounds in the 19th Century was now being challenged in disturbing ways. The imported timber trade had an established infrastructure from importing dock to customer but home-grown wood products did not. Even the 1973 world oil crisis only briefly excited woodfuel prospects. Increasingly the owner and woodsman left the debate to the larger forestry services companies and the Government's laboratories. Inconfident about the new, the private sector forester did not embrace the scientific approach to timber-growing expressed in such phrases as Yield Class, Mean Annual Increment, or the metricated measurements. Tellingly, the measurement of timber in broadleaved trees (not conifers) was still expressed in the Hoppus feet of the 17th Century. (See Appendix 6/2)

Who Shall Conserve the Woodland Habitats ?

Since the word ecology was coined in the 19th Century, its meaning has undergone immense growth and diversification. With the dual crisis of rapid growth of the human population and its consumption and the accelerating deterioration of the earth's environment, ecology has assumed the utmost importance.

- Open weekend course, Epping Forest. Field Studies Council (A May and J Paynter - 1998)

The planting of conifers in Kent was in small minority for most decades of the past hundred years but there was a much higher rate in 1961 - 70; when some 5,000 acres (2,000 ha) were planted, in contrast to only 2000 acres (800 ha) of broadleaved trees. The surge was a combination of the Forestry Commission's work on its newly-owned land and private owners being persuaded about the quicker returns of softwood growth rates. The fashion did not alter the overall position in the county; even by 1982 fewer than a quarter of timber trees (High Forest as the Commission calls it) were softwoods. During this time commercial nurseries local to Kent

Treeshelters 1.8 metres-high safeguard young Wild cherry trees from fallow deer, near Wye.

users, notably Oakover, became able to offer the large quantities of forest trees, conifer and broadleaf, previously thought of as the preserve of more-distant growers. The conifers, all evergreen except larch, were nevertheless a talking-point in landscapes where they erupted spikily from a rounded, broadleaved norm. They were a local, factual reminder of the concern encouraged now by colour television about the changing countryside, and unfairly linked with other new bogeys - air pollution, agrochemicals - in the environment. By the mid-1970s, after thirty years of peace in Europe, the long-term condition of the environment had become a major issue.

Conferences now took place with agendas that would have been most unlikely even ten years before. The woodland owner was rarely at them, but speaking for him were senior members of the Forestry Commission, estate and game management, forestry financial services and the Nature Conservancy Council. Biodiversity entered everyone's vocabulary now that these debaters had been awakened to the need to stop the alarming global reduction in the variety of living things. Among the participants' many problems was the difficulty of pursuing a national code of practical countryside management when different parts of the land required an individual regimen. The conifer plantation might be appropriate to some parts of the British uplands and to lowland sands. Elsewhere in the lowlands it would be more injurious to the biodiversity associated with, say, heavy soils and mixed broadleaf trees. In practice, conifers had often been unwisely chosen as to soil and microclimate.

Relative to before the wars, change in land-use in Kent was less fundamental, but there were very many assarts into woodland for a variety of reasons. At the medieval King's Wood between Leeds Castle and the Suttons, the historically divided ownership had led, in mid-20th Century, to the building of Kingswood village houses, the planting of conifers on ancient woodland and the establishment of orchards alongside 19th Century chestnut coppice.

Local authorities, their organisation much changed during the 1970s, reflected the countryside concerns of their electorates. At that time in south-east England these were more usually the loss of property values owing to encroaching housing, factories and motorways. One outcome was the acquisition by County, Borough or District Council of threatened woodland. Complicated ownership and management became common. For example, Tunbridge Wells Borough Council, originally concerned with the water supply aspect, retains Marshleyharbour and Forest Woods at Pembury, a portion abutting other woodland properties owned by the Royal Society for the Protection of Birds (RSPB), South East Water Ltd and the Hadlow Estate. Its management responds to the Kent Biodiversity Plan in the overall Countryside Stewardship Scheme and also to the Kent High Weald project for recreating lowland heath.

Arriving in the woods in the 1950s, the chainsaw was developed quickly as the all-purpose cutter.

At the eastern end of the county, the historic Blean Woods continue to mirror property affairs as they have done since the priory accounts of the 13th Century. From the Ecclesiastical Commissioners' files Alexander Wheaten recounts the advice of the Forestry Commission to the modern land agent, Cluttons, of 1950. For woodland blocks totalling 3,283 acres (1,329 ha) the FC advice was to replant with oak standards over chestnut coppice, which meant a forty-year planting programme for the biggest block alone. The programme, requiring at least thirty workers, was too onerous and so the Church decided to sell. The early sales were to private buyers who used the woodland for tax advantage. Even at that stage the scientific interest of The Blean attracted the Nature Conservancy Council to setting up a National Nature Reserve, one of the first in the country. Later, tax alleviation for the private buyer having been overtaken by new rules, a large part of the land became available for common management with agreed objectives. A consortium now severally owns and manages this part of The Blean and only one member of it, Mr Gibb, is a private individual. The others are English Nature (once NCC), Kent County Council, Canterbury City Council, Swale Borough Council, the RSPB and the Woodland Trust.

The Woodland Trust has developed strongly from its start in 1972, reflecting the rising concern of the public that woodland should be retained and well-managed. Its subscribers are especially fortunate in Kent where, by 1998, the Trust owned thirty woodlands with a combined area of 2,424 acres (981 ha); about double its holding in any other county. This relatively large collection must stem from the high number of ancient woodland sites in Kent, some needing more sensitive management, and to-day's pressures upon the county environment, both as a throughway for the Continent and as countryside for the people of Greater London. Among the Trust's major purchases in 1997, after a successful combination of local voluntary contributions and grants, was Dering Wood, Pluckley. It is an opportunity to transform 300 acres (121 ha) of neglected woodland into a nature haven for the public, yet also a place to grow high-quality timber in the long term. The most challenging project, and ultimately the most satisfying, has been to buy land around Hucking, near Maidstone, where the existing woodland on ancient sites is to be extended by the Woodland Trust onto some of the very farmland which, long ago, was taken by assart from those woods.

A number of publicly-funded bodies are owners of large woodland acreage in Kent although they are not specifically 'nature' trusts. The Ministry of Defence has its tenanted farming and woodland, mainly near Shorncliffe (Folkestone) and Lydd. The Forestry Commission, in addition to its 4,000 hectares (its preferred measurement) of working woodland, open to the public, has Bedgebury Pinetum, the research arboretum and park-woodland joy for Kent and Sussex people. Of trusts proper, the National Trust has woodland at Toys Hill, Scotney Castle, Ightham Mote in the far west and others besides. On a county membership basis, Kent Wildlife Trust is a major player with twenty-five woodland nature reserves which amount to some 1,300 acres (526 ha) for its conservation of flora and fauna. A common feature of nearly all these woodlands in public or members' ownership is the freedom of access to the footpaths and, in a few cases, off them. The best known and most visited countryside must, though, be the Kent County Council and district authorities' Country Parks and Sites. They are established liberally now, sixteen of them, from Saltwood in the south-east to Bean in the north-west. Community Woodlands are yet another recent initiative which is being promoted by the Forestry Authority with the county council.

The county has a favoured position of public sympathy with the woodlands as they are now in appearance. The hope for more open access will be spurred by the national debate. Gameshooting and silviculture can be responsibly combined with public access on foot, as has been well-evidenced. Attitudes on all sides will modify. The protesters encamped in West Wood, Lyminge for more than a year were defending a mainly coniferous plantation. Off-path roaming was already accepted there by the Forestry Commission and, whether or not the F C woodlands sold retain that degree of access, the trend will spread elsewhere. Payment, simply for access alone, is most unlikely to happen.

It was, surprisingly, as recently as 1984 when government, through the Forestry Commission, put a stop to the conversion of broadleaved woodland to farming use. Around that time, too, came a major change in emphasis from coniferous to broadleaved species for lowland planting. So firm was this step that years later the Timber Growers' Association was still trying to persuade the Forestry Authority to support with grants the planting of conifers as nurse crops to foster young broadleaves - and assist in gamekeeping.

The new directive was the signal for an outpouring of pent-up labours toward improved broadleaf planting techniques and conservation. A relatively trivial but now omnipresent marker of the times was the 'Tuley tube', later known as a treeshelter. The Forestry Commission researcher's plastic cylinder for protection-cum-microclimate has since been used by the million, in public places perhaps more than in woodland. The Forestry Commission's Bulletin 62: *Silviculture of Broadleaved Woodland*, by Julian Evans in 1984, quickly became a lowland forester's vade-mecum. English Nature came to the forefront through naturalists of great authority, notably in George Peterken's writing and, later, the work of Keith Kirby. By the mid-1990s the woodland owner and worker had a library shelf of contemporary guides to the management of broadleafed, and particularly semi-natural, woodlands. In the expanding literature on woodlands, other authors, outstanding among them being Oliver Rackham, have bridged the gap between technical and general readerships.

The conservation of veteran, usually pollarded, trees was urged by these scientists, not least because trees more than, say, 250 years of age are rarely found in the traditional forestry regimes elsewhere in Western Europe. In 1987, taking a very different approach to woodland ecology, Rodney Helliwell, aided by the close involvement of Peter Buckley at Wye College (University of London), saw to the pioneering work of moving the surface layer of an ancient woodland. 11,000 cubic metres of topsoil were removed by Eurotunnel to a prepared site from Biggins Wood, itself now buried beneath the road vehicle quays of the Channel Tunnel at Folkestone. Ten years later, most of the Biggins Wood ground flora species were recorded at the receptor site, helped latterly by the young canopy of replanted trees. The initiative in this sort of new work came now from men and women in large organisations in the public or private sectors, rarely from wealthy individual pioneers. In every case the funding, this time from Eurotunnel, is the vital enabler.

Nature's Dramatic Reminders

Natural phenomena which alter the landscape quickly but permanently are most likely to stir people's interest in their environment. Some part in an awakening public concern about the fate of tall trees came undoubtedly from the Dutch Elm Disease outbreak of 1970 - 1980.

The virus, which few knew then had nearly obliterated elm in prehistory, came upon modern Kent with speed and shocking effect. The town of Hythe stands on the Royal Military Canal where, in Napoleonic times, the army planted elm in close order along the defenders' bank. Until 1975 these trees had been a mature,

The suddenly new horizons. Scene at Emmett's House, Ide Hill, after the Great Storm, 16 Oct 1987.

magnificent line for about one hundred years, their canopies green above the roof-tops and loftily shading the pleasure walks below. Then, within a couple of years from the disease first appearing as withered leaves, almost every tree in the town's three-mile stretch was dead. So high was the emergency cost of felling and clearing that the townsfolk set up a successful appeal for money from their fellows to replant the area with other species. The disease gripped all English country hedgerows and wood-edges and transformed the traditional rural landscape as the elm, so noted for its upward-billowing form, was felled in thousands.

A decade later, in a few hours, the Great Storm swept through Kent and the South-East. Humans witnessed the awesome power of natural forces wreaking an effect rare in any land, let alone clement Britain. Woodlanders will remember the date, October 16, 1987, as surely as their birthday. As Bob Ogley put it in his introduction to *In the Wake of the Hurricane*, 'In a few short hours 15 million trees were blown down and giants which had stood for 200, 300 or even 400 years lay prostrate on the ground, their vast rain-sodden roots towering in the air.' The wind had struck after three months of record rainfall, and the deciduous trees still held a full canopy of leaves. It blew at high speed but, worse, the tortured air twisted and twirled until the fibres of a tree could stand it no longer; for every one that fell there was another with its trunk snapped above the ground like a brittle twig or shredded like a grass-stalk.

The work of clearing the damage was doleful and arduous. In a few cases the thousand jumbled spars, like several spilled matchboxes when seen from the air, were just too much for the owner to contemplate tackling. Nearly all others, however, were cut and hauled and fed into a market of wrecked prices. Chainsaw teams and hauliers from as far away as Scotland descended upon the mess and slowly it was cleared for re-planting. Emergency groups such as Task Force Trees gave advice to smaller casualties. When the worst was over, workers and passers-by looked with amazement at new vistas across the swept land. Ten years later, commentators marking the anniversary concluded that recovery or masking of the dead had been achieved by natural means; indeed, it would have been best if the disaster zones had been left to lie uncleared for their value to forest ecosystems. The comment was repeated often enough to provoke robust replies.

To the Daily Telegraph, October 17, 1997

- - It may come as a great surprise but the woodlands of the South-East consist of more than just parkland, arboretums, nature reserves and scenic woodland. The vast majority, like woods throughout the country, exist to grow saleable timber. It is notable that none of the people asked to reflect on the events of October 1987 were involved in this type of woodland management. To assert that 'nature' has played the major part in the 'healing' process is to ignore the efforts of hundreds of forestry workers in harvesting the fallen trees and re-stocking the cleared land. As establishing woodlands involves much more than planting trees, this work is still continuing.

  - D W MACDONALD, Head Forester, Cowdrey Estate, Midhurst, W.Sussex

Natural Regeneration

Storms come and go - there was another severely damaging gale in January 1990, mainly to the west and north of Kent - but objectives are not blown off course for that reason in the woodland industry. Owners, management and the expanded body of advisers and fundholders had been trying to reconcile differing aims, as was illustrated by the major review of broadleaved woodlands policy by the Forestry Commission in 1984. Its published guidelines made a slim booklet but the headings had a revolutionary width of range. Guidelines for the private sector now included

Wood Production

Landscape

Recreation

Nature Conservation

Game Management

Ten years later *The Management of Semi-Natural Woodlands* (see Appendix 10/1) was the title of a series of eight guides; one for each of the woodland types recognised by its main ecological and silvicultural characteristics. Much of Kent, for example, is covered by Guide 3, Lowland Mixed Broadleaved Woods, which type corresponds broadly with National Vegetation Classifications W8 and W10. The publications form a remarkable work, relying on many skilled people. Fittingly, the foremost was George Peterken who had transferred from the then Nature Conservancy Council to become ecological consultant to the new arm of the Commission, the Forestry Authority.

For ancient semi-natural woodland, there is emphasis on having a wide age-range of trees; to be best achieved by fostering seedlings which have regenerated naturally on site from suitable broadleaved parents. Among forestry workers the planting vocabulary of the tree nursery - 'two-year-ones', 'feathers' - has been joined by the new importance of natural regeneration, or 'regen' as it is known conversationally. For manually planted woods on ancient sites (so many in Kent), if the species is native and long-established the guideline now is 'natural regeneration is preferred'. This would maintain the natural distribution of tree species in relation to site conditions, allow a shrub component to grow with the trees, maintain local genotypes and usually give mixed stands of diverse structure. Even for recent plantations on ancient sites nature conservation values should be 'at the front of management thinking'.

In practice, the protection of fragile seedlings haphazardly sprung from the soil is difficult and the resulting young trees much less assured in number. But their quality, given that the parent trees passed muster, would show the benefit of being evidently suited to their soil. However, 'where timber production is an important aim, planting could be justified if existing genetic quality is poor'. It often is, so that the initiatives to improve it are vital. Across the country, five teams are conducting the British Hardwoods Improvement Programme. There is more allied work in Kent with the study at East Malling of strains of Prunus avium, the timber cherry. Hadlow College is embarked on the micropropagation of oak from Penshurst Place and English Nature has had DNA tests carried out on the post-Ice Age origin of ancient, naturally-seeded, oak pollards at Mersham Hatch.

For lowland England, then, 'forestry' has travelled a long way in the short period since the government, in 1957, finally abandoned its uncomplicated aim of a national strategic timber reserve. Denoting the spread of importance now ascribed to woodland, the Forestry Commission, in all its departments, is intertwined with every aspect of land management, and so, too, is the woodsman. Forty years on, in 1997, the Kent Biodiversity Action Plan (BAP) was published. As it said, biodiversity simply means the variety of life around us, from microscopic bacteria to the tallest tree. But, because of its fundamental importance, the Steering Group has representatives of ten organisations, the county council and all the district councils.

<u>Members of the Kent BAP Steering Group</u>

Country Landowners' Association

English Nature

Environment Agency

Forestry Authority

Government Office of the South-East

Kent County Council

Kent District Councils

Kent Wildlife Trust

Ministry of Agriculture, Fisheries and Food

National Farmers' Union

Royal Society for the Protection of Birds

Somehow these units have to show a singularity of purpose which will not only make people aware that biodiversity is the 'key to the maintenance of the world as we know it' but also cause them to respond.

At Hucking, near Maidstone, digital mapping helps to assess the effect of today's ground plans on the landscape of 2040.

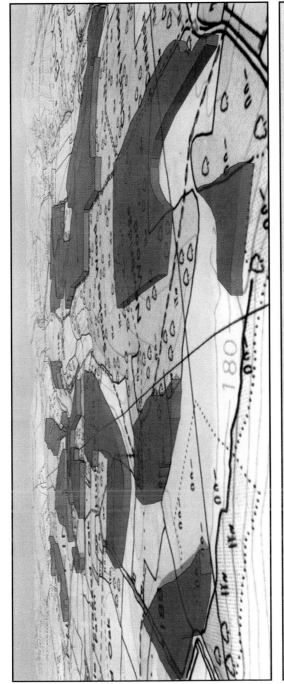

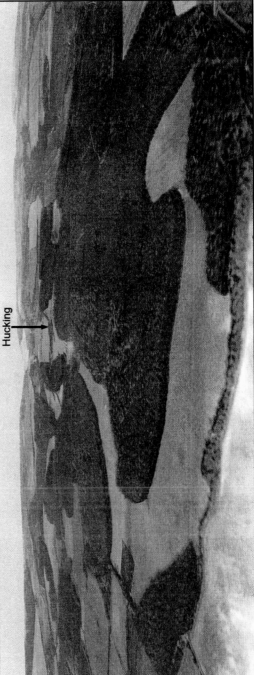

Hucking

Stewardship for Southern Woodlands

The representatives of woodland interests, the Timber Growers' Association, the two Royal Forestry Societies, the Institute of Chartered Foresters, all endeavour to improve their members' prospects but, inevitably, they have to concentrate on national heavyweight factors. They are keenly aware of the better forestry infrastructure in the uplands. In Northumbria, Forest Enterprise runs the great Kielder Forest. It is almost exactly the same size as all the woodlands of Kent put together. With fewer than 300 workers, it fells and re-stocks 1,000 hectares (one-fiftieth of its area) every year, and intends to go on doing so forever.

In Kent woodlands, progress in conservation science is not matched by the commercial side, where problems have not been dustily familiar but, rather, worsening from the financial aspect. Changes in tax law in 1988, which were framed to stop the extremes of tax-avoidance planting in the highlands, removed sensible encouragement to woodsmen in the lowlands. Eight years later the Royal Institute of Chartered Surveyors found from a survey 'that the income tax and forestry grant changes since 1988 had worsened the financial position of most lowland forest estates, some almost to the point of forcing neglect'. In Kent the particular problem lies in its uniquely large coppice acreage. In much of Britain, coppice is an unimportant aspect of woodland but in the South-East (Hampshire, Berkshire, Surrey, W and E Sussex and Kent) it is more of a feature, there being 74,000 acres (30,000 ha) of coppice in 1991. Out of that, Kent had no less than 44,000 acres (18,000 ha.)

In counties where coppice acreage is small it is possible to find a relatively significant market for greenwood coppice articles: hurdles, trugs, rustic furniture. In Kent, where two-thirds of the coppice is sweet chestnut, the sheer volume overwhelms such outlets. Moreover, the handed-down skills are less suited to this trade. Kent cutters' traditional wares of cleft rails, poles, spiles and paling are aimed at what has recently been a further falling in demand. Coppice poles come into the category of small round-wood (SRW) which is dominated in other counties by softwood and hardwood plantation thinnings. The 1991 Forestry Commission figures for coppice acreage are under re-study (see Appendix 10/1) but the author, N. Dannatt, had views that are still valid. He recommended then a search for a new market for low quality SRW in the South-East and a reversal of the downward trend in chestnut product sales.

To take the latter first, the chestnut underwood trade continues to bump along at a low level with an occasional good year to lift expectations again. There is no doubt that the acreage in the county merits more powerful selling. Straight poles, densely grown on the right soil, with their durability, strength and lack of sapwood, should be preferred for rail and paling fencing and similar purposes over preservative-treated softwood. On the other SRW resource, broadleaved timber plantation thinnings, there has also been no marketing progress since the Bowater woodpulp mill at Sittingbourne changed to waste-paper for its raw material in 1989. That shut off a short-haul outlet in the final year for 140,000 tonnes of SRW. Since then, working parties have studied more alternatives

Coppice cutters at Godden Green. Mr Hodder Snr, pictured (standing right) in 1998, keeping up the tradition for more than sixty years.

and lobbied governments. Financial non-viability was the main reason against early proposals for woodfuel power generators and other potential users of big volume. A charcoal-making proposal failed, ostensibly for such reasons, although only £1.3 million was said to have been the investment needed for an intake of 30,000 tonnes of SRW. If a larger sum had been sought, to fund a broader-based plant and ancillaries, there could have developed a business not almost wholly dependant on charcoal for barbecues. (Meanwhile, group marketing of output from traditional kilns in woodlands has made a name for a quality superior to imported charcoal.)

Timber plantation thinnings arise from present silvicultural teaching and, to a lesser extent, the planting density needed to obtain grants. It may yet be that the problem of disposal of thinnings will be overcome by not having them in the first place. In areas like Kent, where there is now insufficient outlet for cut thinnings, more opportunities should be sought to grow, and to maintain carefully, an end-crop of timber trees with hardly any intermediate felling. Versions of this are practised by a few Kent woodsmen with precise attention to seed, soil and humidity. Many more want to adopt and adapt these techniques but have not had wide encouragement yet from grant authorities. In the past half-century, owners and foresters have pursued such options beyond the first experimental stage. Careful reading of established forestry manuals, Cyril Hart's magnificent *Practical Forestry* (1991), for example, and some sections of FC Bulletin 62 bring conviction that this already-known attitude to lowland forestry may be taken up with dedication.

Large dimension roundwood (upward of 40cm mid-diameter) from the surge of planting in the 1950s and '60s will now increase steadily in output. Currently the majority of home-grown planking timber is oak, which is affected by the high-quality oak also available from the Baltic States at prices much reduced in their quest for hard currency. English oak, though, is well appreciated. The striving for quality, that very long-term endeavour, will have to be kept up despite the extremely slow return. To-day, timber buyers at Morgan Timber of Strood are qualified to a British Standards level for visual grading of oak; a confidence-building assurance for the grower.

Of course, by planting softwoods and attending to their growth individually a much higher annual and total volume increment than in hardwood may be achieved with good quality. Non-native conifers such as Douglas fir and the redwoods are, with the right seed, soil and site, very rewarding, as may be seen in the work of

the Hills at Redleaf. The stigma of 'conifer' when referring to ancient woodland sites would need to be removed where there was selective timber production and aesthetic landscaping.

Estate owners with an interest in timber trees are increasingly turning to modern estate sawmills for a more cost-efficient conversion of the roundwood and for transport cost savings. These owners may also be ones to enjoy their woodlands for the shoot and take an effective local chairmanship in the advanced studies of environment and ecology made by countryside and wildlife trusts. However, they have only rarely become involved in the search for a major new small-roundwood market. This quest, in which Henry Holdstock of G.W. Finn has played a prominent part, is seen to depend heavily on understanding financial underpinning by governments.

Kent has this particular problem of too much coppiced woodland, ironically, at a time when the merits of coppice over timber trees in terms of biodiversity are keenly promoted by environmentalists (albeit rather less so for sweet chestnut). The shrunken market for coppice cuttings must mean that, if the total broadleaved woodland acreage is to be maintained, the county needs to see coppice management change widely to the growing of timber trees from selected coppice poles, 'storing' or 'singling'. In this transformation the other underwood around the pole is cut to the stump until it is eventually shaded out by the canopy of the new trees. Good quality demands good pole selection and the right soil and location; it is a technical decision which merits on-site advice and then support grants from the Forestry Authority.

More than half the private woodland acreage of Kent is still not contracted to the Forestry Authority for grant-aid in return for following its management guidelines. Moreover, ownership in Kent is noticeably more fractionated than in East and West Sussex and some other lowland counties. The two factors lead to many styles of active management or benign neglect. At one end of the range is the so-called neglect, where even gameshooting relies on the lie of the land only and not on managed cover. Inactive, but not neglectful, management is to rely on natural succession among woodland species. After the Great Storm of 1987 the National Trust at Toys Hill declared a 30-acre portion of it a non-intervention zone: the Trust accepts natural, dense, re-invasion by birch, the rapid coloniser, and will wait for generations to see the next domination by its successor series, probably oak. At the other end of the spectrum for old woodland sites is the individual protection of naturally regenerating seedlings in order to produce selected timber or landscape trees from scratch. On newer land, every type of broadleaved and conifer plantation practice is followed.

The endless arboreal variety thus resulting will have some worth in furthering nature conservation but it works against effective management as measured in money. The lack of economic size most emphatically reduces the prospects of setting up a county or regional manufactory to absorb woodland produce. Even allowing for major changes, such as reductions in Europe's support of agriculture, it may well mean that for the foreseeable future the optimum outlet for sustained woodland in lowland England is no larger than an estate sawmill or small co-operative mill and turnery. Then trees, broadleaf or conifer, could be sited and grown not just to throw timber onto the open market. Individually maintained stems would become sought after at national or international level and the others would better meet the workaday needs of buyers within a short-haul radius.

Inventive end-products abound, at the laboratory stage or at factory scale; soft clothing fabric from wood fibre became a reality in the 1990s. However, like most processed products from wood, new manufactures will be based on more economic highland forest sources or imported even more cheaply. Given that one-eighth of Kent's land area is woodland, it would be no more than basic stewardship for each generation to maintain it in the best ways of the past - whether for a future of landscape and amenity or for an unknown potential. Experiment must always continue, but for 5,000 years woodland has been managed without final depredation or, yet, a critical loss of biodiversity. Now, in this era of marvellous but uncertain progress, is not the time to abandon those methods for others untried. The theory of global warming is not yet a reason to abandon temperate zone silviculture.

But if there is little cash profit at present in lowland woodlands and only inadequate government financial aid - and a presumption that woodland will not be used for other purposes - who, then, will stiffen the resolve? Recently, since about 1970, the lead in woodland management has been taken by government officers and government-funded organisations. More recently still, the urge of many of the general public to see woodland well maintained has been reflected in the rise of voluntary support. That is clearly instanced by membership numbers of the Woodland Trust as conservers specifically of woodland. Perhaps this voluntary determination today can be linked with past values to give confidence for the future.

THE NEXT CHAPTER?

It is less than 150 years since the huge and commonplace industry of Kentish timber and underwood collapsed when faced with coal and metals and locomotion. In 1859, beside Phineas Pett's wood, with its timber for shipbuilding, railway navvies were transforming the landscape. At Downe, an hour away on horseback, Charles Darwin added to the turmoil of those years when he released his *On the Origin of Species by Means of Natural Selection*. His lifestyle and wealthy circumstance, like those of other fortunate men and women contemporaries, allowed him to apply all his energies to a chosen subject. To-day, wealth is more widely distributed, and knowledge, too. It is quite rational to expect that, in the Europe of the future, not just a few but a host of men and women will have the financial freedom to give priority to conservation of the natural world. Many of them will want to demonstrate their interest, and their good circumstance, by practising a chosen method of silviculture, the better to suit their woodland. Planning ahead for generations to come will show their confidence, just as our forebears have shown us in the landscape of Kent.

APPENDICES

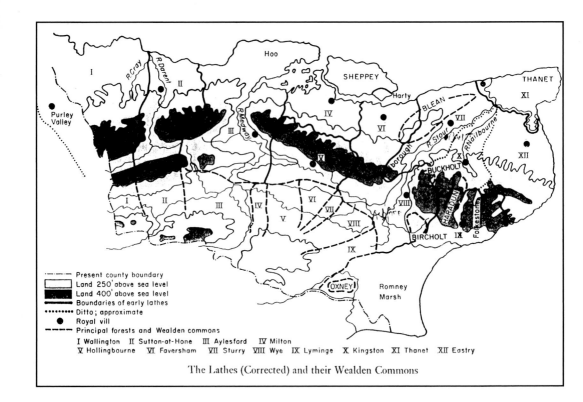

The Lathes (Corrected) and their Wealden Commons

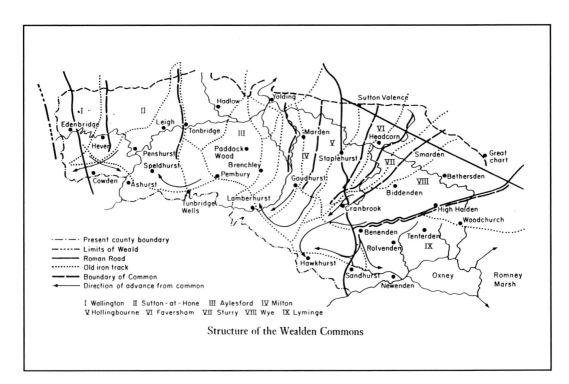

Structure of the Wealden Commons

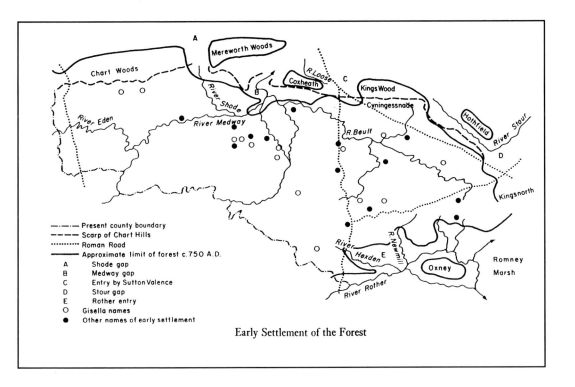

Early Settlement of the Forest

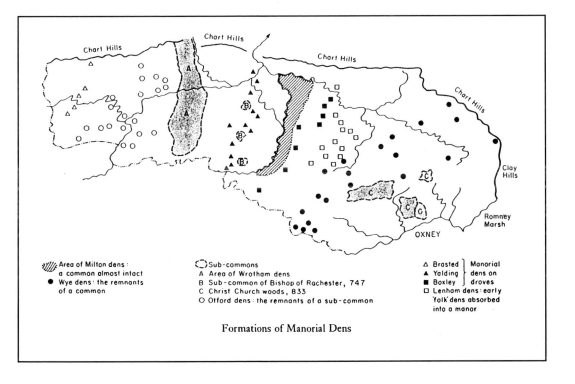

Formations of Manorial Dens

APPENDIX 3/3

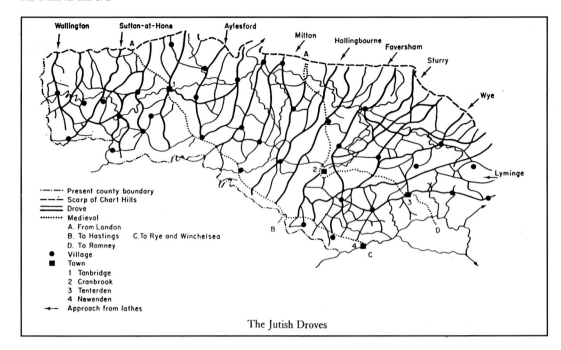

The Jutish Droves

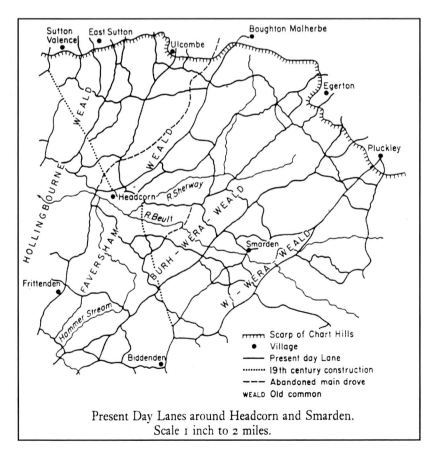

Present Day Lanes around Headcorn and Smarden.
Scale 1 inch to 2 miles.

APPENDIX 4/1

THE TABLE OF MANORS

(after K P Whitney)

In the table of manors below the ownership shown is as it was at the time of Domesday Book.

1. LATHE OF WALLINGTON

Manor	Ownership
Wallington	King
Bexley	Archbishop
Brasted	Archbishop's knights
Orpington	Christ Church
Plumstead	St Augustine's
Limpsfield	Battle Abbey
Bromley	Church of Rochester
Lewisham	St Peter's, Ghent
Cudham	Odo of Bayeux
Eltham	Odo of Bayeux
Beckenham	Odo of Bayeux
Westerham	Eustace of Boulogne
Titsey	Hamo de Valoignes

2. LATHE OF SUTTON-AT-HONE

Manor	Ownership
Dartford with Sutton-at-Hone	King
Otford	Archbishop
Filston in Shoreham	Archbishop
Chevening	Archbishop
Sevenoaks	Archbishop
Sundridge	Archbishop
Darenth	Archbishop
Eynsford	Archbishop's knights
Farningham	Archbishop's knights
Stone	Church of Rochester
Southfleet	Church of Rochester
Fawkham	Church of Rochester
Seal	Odo of Bayeux
Kemsing	Odo of Bayeux
Ash	Odo of Bayeux
Lullingstone	Odo of Bayeux
Horton Kirby	Odo of Bayeux
Swanscombe	Odo of Bayeux
Ridley	Odo of Bayeux

3. LATHE OF AYLESFORD

Manor	Ownership
Aylesford	King
Wrotham	Archbishop
Ightham	Archbishop
Northfleet	Archbishop
Maidstone	Archbishop
Gillingham	Archbishop
Meopham	Christ Church
East Peckham	Christ Church
East Farleigh	Christ Church
Loose	Christ Church
Hunton	Christ Church
Frindsbury	Church of Rochester
Trottescliffe	Church of Rochester
Halling	Church of Rochester
Bromgehaege	Church of Rochester
Borstal	Church of Rochester
Snodland	Church of Rochester
Malling	Church of Rochester
Wouldham	Church of Rochester
Hadlow	Odo of Bayeux
Hoo	Odo of Bayeux
Chatham with Teston and West Farleigh	Odo of Bayeux
Teston and	Odo of Bayeux
West Farleigh	Odo of Bayeux
Nettlestead	Odo of Bayeux
Bensted in Hunton	Odo of Bayeux
Wateringbury	Odo of Bayeux
Burham	Odo of Bayeux
Addington	Odo of Bayeux
West Peckham	Odo of Bayeux
Offham	Odo of Bayeux
Little Wrotham	Odo of Bayeux
Leybourne	Odo of Bayeux
Luddesdown	Odo of Bayeux
Cooling	Odo of Bayeux
Eccles in Aylesford	Odo of Bayeux
Milton by Gravesend	Odo of Bayeux
Yalding	Richard of Tonbridge
Mereworth	Hamo the Sheriff

4. LATHE OF MILTON REGIS

Manor	Ownership
Milton Regis	King
Newington by Sittingbourne	Albert the Chaplain

5. LATHE OF HOLLINGBOURNE

Manor	Ownership
Hollingbourne	Christ Church
Ulcombe	Archbishop's knights
Lenham	St Augustine's
Boxley	Odo of Bayeux
Leeds	Odo of Bayeux
Chart Sutton	Odo of Bayeux
Sutton Valence	Odo of Bayeux
East Sutton	Odo of Bayeux
Detling	Odo of Bayeux
Thornham	Odo of Bayeux
Harrietsham	Odo of Bayeux
Otterden	Odo of Bayeux

6. LATHE OF FAVERSHAM

Manor	Ownership
Faversham	King
Teynham	Archbishop
Ospringe	Odo of Bayeux
Boughton Malherbe	Odo of Bayeux
Chilston in Boughton Malherbe	Odo of Bayeux
Throwley	Odo of Bayeux
Stalisfield	Odo of Bayeux

7. LATHE OF STURRY

Manor	Ownership
Sturry	St Augustine's
Westgate by Canterbury	Archbishop
Godmersham	Christ Church
Chartham	Christ Church
Chilham	Odo of Bayeux
Burh-wara-felda	?Odo of Bayeux

8. LATHE OF WYE

Manor	Ownership
Wye	Battle Abbey
Charing	Archbishop
Pluckley	Archbishop
herland in Pluckley	Archbishop
Hothfield	Archbishop
Mersham	Archbishop
Westwell	Christ Church
Little Chart	Christ Church
Great Chart	Christ Church
Brook	Christ Church
Kennington	St Augustine's
Pevington in Pluckley	Odo of Bayeux
Beaumundestone in Westwell	Odo of Bayeux
Vanne in Crundale	Odo of Bayeux
Brabourne	Hugh de Montfort
Boughton Aluph	Eustace of Boulogne
Wilmington	Eustace of Boulogne

9. LATHE OF LYMINGE

Manor	Ownership
Lyminge	Archbishop
Saltwood (with Newenden)	Archbishop

Aldington	Archbishop
Appledore	Christ Church
Warehorne	Christ Church
Snave	St Augustine's
Bilsington (with Benenden)	Odo of Bayeux
Folkestone	Odo of Bayeux
Acrise	Odo of Bayeux
Orlestone	Hugh de Montfort
Monks Horton	Hugh de Montfort
Tinton in Warehorne	Hugh de Montfort
Postling	Hugh de Montfort
Beechborough in Newington	Hugh de Montfort

10. NORTH-EAST KENT

Manor	Ownership
Reculver	Archbishop
Minster in Thanet	St Augustine's
Bishopsbourne	Archbishop
Petham	Archbishop
Ickham	Christ Church
Wickhambreux	Odo of Bayeux
Eastry	Christ Church
Northbourne	St Augustine's

APPENDIX 6/1

BUILDING SANDGATE CASTLE 1539 - 40

These extracts are from the work of William Loffie Rutton in *Archaeologica Cantiana* (1983 - vol. XX). He had translated, and elucidated, from two ledgers (British Museum - Harleian collection) kept by the clerk at the castle, Thomas Busshe.

The Work resumed and finished 1540. - The building of the Castle had been suspended on the eve of St. Thomas the Apostle (20 December 1539), and it was resumed on the 12th January 1540. A change of administration was then made, or rather this seems to have had effect during the tenth month, which comprised the fourteen days of December before the holidays, and fourteen days of January ending on the 25th. Thomas Cockes disappears as Commissioner, and his late colleague, Richard Keys, is associated in the Commission, as Paymaster, with Reinold Scott, Esq., who has now the chief charge as "Surveyor" or "Comptroller". Reinold or Reginald Scott was of Scott's Hall in Smeeth; on the completion of the Castle, or perhaps a little earlier, he was knighted, and in the next year, 1541, he became Sheriff of Kent.

The Kentish shore did not provide all the material for the fort; much of the stone was of foreign origin, and had come, three centuries before, from that country against a possible attack from which it might now serve. It was in fact second-hand, and came to Sandgate from the lately dismantled priories of St Radigund, Horton, and Christ Church, Canterbury; in the ledger it is called "*cane* stone", easily recognized as Caen stone. The total number of loads thus obtained - the load being reckoned as a ton weight - was 459, of which more than half, *viz.*, 237, came from St Radigunds, 90 from Horton, 32 from Canterbury, 33 from Hythe, 57 from places in the Hundreds of Bircholt Franchise, Hayne, Stowting, and Street, and 10 came by sea from Sandwich. At St Radigunds "the farmer" received for the stone 8d. a load; at Horton nothing was paid; at Canterbury the Prior of Christ Church twice received 4s.8d. a ton, and afterwards "Mr Byngham" had 3s., but it is not said that the stone came from the same site; Michael Carver of Hythe was paid 5s. a ton for stone delivered at the Castle.

Masons found within a circuit of fourteen miles were not sufficient; they had to be brought from the distant "west country" of Somersetshire and Gloucestershire. In the second month, 43 masons, there "pressed", receive a bounty of 4s. a man, being 6d. for every score of miles they had travelled to reach Sandgate; in the following month, June 1539, Thomas Busshe, Clerk of the Ledger, travelling with the same object, enlisted 54 masons; and again in March 1540 a similar journey was made by Richard Tayler, with the result of procuring 71 men in the West and 43 men nearer home.

Coal or Sea Coal ("See Coole") makes its appearance in the second month (April - May 1539), and was brought to Hythe in two ships *"The Nycolas of Sowolde"* and *"The John of Downwithe;"* Southwold and Dunwich are both ports on the Suffolk coast, but the ships hailing thence must have got the coal elsewhere. Again, in the next month, coal is bought of John Marcoll of *Sowold.* The total quantity unshipped at Hythe and thence brought by boats to Sandgate was 96 chaldrons. The chaldron, a varying and therefore ambiguous "dry-measure", is now at London taken to equal 25p cwt., and the result of my own investigations is to put it (for 1539) at nearly 23 cwt. Thus the whole quantity purchased I calculate to have been about 110 tons. From Hythe the coal was transported by boats to Sandgate, and thence 54 tons were carted to the limekiln at Swetton, while 56 tons were retained at Sandgate for the use of the forge, etc. The price paid at Hythe was 6s.8d. a chaldron = 5s.10d. a ton.

Timber. - This material has a special interest on account of the many places named in connection with its supply; it is surprising to find that it was necessary to go so far for it, in some instances even fourteen miles; "the Weald" certainly was not nearer than eight miles from Sandgate, but there were woods at less distance. In the accounts there is mention of oak, ash, and elm; of beech we do not hear. The timber used in the building was as nearly as I can gather 979 loads or tons, the ton or load being taken to measure 50 cubic feet, as is yet the practice, and the bulk of it, doubtless, was oak. The ash, of which I find 46 loads, appears to have been used entirely for barrows and helves of tools; it came chiefly from Hurst and "Roclands" in the parish of Street. Of elm in planks but little was used.

Some items of the timber supply, noting occasionally the cost, follow; the carriage was 2d. per mile per load.

Oak. - Carriage of 36 tons (or loads) of the King's timber for his works at Sandgate, from Horton wood, unto the sawstage, 12s.4d. - Hewed in Oxleys wood at Horton wood, beside the late Priory of Horton, 10 oaks containing 26 tons, price the hewing of every ton 10d. Sm. 21s.8d - Timber hewed in the parish of Horton, 25 great trees felled and hewed in Oxleis wood, containing 38 tons; and out of the same wood 30 small trees containing 14 tons, price the ton 12d. Sm. 52s. - Felled in Master Scott's wood called "Comebe Woode" 7 trees containing 19 tons, Sm. 19s. - For the hewing of 10 oaks in Mostock Wood to William Knight of Sellinge, 28 tons, sm. 28s. - 71 Oaks from "Bonnings Hothes," £4 2s. 4d., and 36 oaks from "Hygh Fryght" or "Frytht" £3 13s. 9d., both woods in the parish of Great Chart, price of the oaks from 1s. to 2s., and the tops of same from 2d. to 4d. - Carriage of 47 loads of plank and board from same places, 13 miles, at 2d. the mile or 2s. 2d. the load. Sm. £5 1s. 10d. - Timber from Mr. Darrell's and Mr Hesnes' woods by the Hundred of Chart, 4 loads. - Timber from Sarles' land called Nacolt by the Hundred of Longbridge, 10 miles, 24 loads. - Paid to Alexand. Jorwood for 40 trees taken upon the ground of Thomas Sarles the younger, which deceased late of Wye, at 2s. the tree. Sm. 80s. - Timber from John Wally's land at Bethersden, 14 miles, 13 loads. - To Andrew Mongeham in Harst (Hurst) wood for hewing of 30 oaks containing 38 tons, price the ton 12d. Sm. 38s. - To Mr Raynolde Scott and Mr. Shelley for 37 oaks from Hurst wood, 2s. the oak. Sm. £3 14s. - Hewing of 5 tons 39 foot of timber in Master Selleng's wood from "Tylhast" (or "Tyle Host" in Hundred of Newchurch), 50 foot the ton, price the ton hewing 10d. - Hewing 21p tons of timber at "Rowstokks" (or "Rowse Stocks," now Rough Stocks, in Ruckinge), William Drew's land and John Drew's wood, and "Mayden's Way" in Hundred of Newchurch (10 miles cartage) - To William Webb of Warehorne for timber, 43 tons 18 feet ready squared at 2s. the ton. Sm. £4 6s. (12 miles cartage). - Timber and plank out of Cornewall's land, Hundred of Blackbourn, 14 miles, 220 feet, 2s. 4d. the load of 50 feet. - Timber from Boddenden wood in the parish of Woodchurch, carriage to Sandgate 14 miles, 21 loads. - To Mr. Thomas Harlakenden of Woodchurch, for 30 oaks at 2s. the oak. Sm. £3. - Also oaks taken upon the lands of Sir William Kempe, Edward Phylyps of Thenterden (Tenterden), John Boll of Warehorne, John Drew of Rockenge (Ruckinge), John Cop of Blessyngton (Bilsington), and upon land sometime the prior's of Crychyrche (Christ Church) in Canterbury. To John Marble, carpenter, for felling and hewing of 56 trees at 5d. the tree. Sm. 23s. 4d.

Ash. - To "Bertylmewe Goddyn of Powltyn" (Poulton), for 3 loads of "Aschyn tymbir" spent in making of hand-barrows, helves for tools and mortar-beaters and other necessaries, at 2s. the load with carriage. Sm. 6s. - Carriage of "Ashe Tymber" from St. Radegunds to Sandgate (6 miles), 4 loads at 12d.; paid for the ash 4s. - "Ashe" from Horton 6 loads at 10d. and 10d. carriage. - Carriage of "Asche Timber" from "Hasrte" (Hurst) Wood to Sandgate, 6 miles, 5 loads at 12d. the load, Sm. 5s., and to Mr. Scott for the said 5 loads 2s. 6d. - Carriage of "assche tymbre" from Cheriton to Sandgate, for making helves for sledges and hammers, 2 loads at 4d. Paid for said wood at 16d. the load. - Paid for felling 12 loads of "asshe timbir" in Rocland in the parish of Street, price the load 2d.

Elm. - To Stephen Ladde of Lyminge for 400 "elm planche borde" of him bought and employed in the King's use at 2s. the 100. Sm. 8s. - Paid Master Nethersole of Dover for two loads of "elme" for scaffolding, 5s. - Carriage of "elmen tymbre" from Selyng Hort of Hartes land, 6 miles, 2 loads at 12d.

Poles for scaffolding, amounting to 146 loads, came chiefly from the vicinity of Horton Priory, the carriage 5 miles. 20 loads - 6d. a load, 2d. felling and 6d. carriage - were brought from "Sandlygs" probably Sandling, and "Brock Hill" 3 miles distant; 16 loads came from the Bishop of Canterbury's wood in the parish of Brabourne, 7 miles, and 28 loads from Brabourne Pound; 10s. for 6 loads from the Hundred of Bewsborough were paid to John Lushyngton and one Horne and Robert Nethersole of Dover.

Wattles were made use of, but in what manner does not appear; possibly in "wattle and dab" party-walls. Some of the entries follow: Provisions made for "watls" at "Lyckwood Oke in Ovyngstone Wood," 6 dozen there and 6 dozen in Bayls Wood. - Paid to Andrew Joncok and Wllyam. Turroll of Elham for 10 dozen of "wattls," price the dozen 10d. - Paid to 3 men for felling of an acre of wood in Assholt Wood (Hundred of Folkestone) for "wattls," 4s. 4d. - Two acres of wood felled to make "wattyls" within the parish of Newnton (Newington), price the acre 15s., and for cutting down of the said two acres 4s. 4d. the acre. Sm. 38s. 8d. - "Watls" made at Rayneden (Raindean), Cristoffer Wyddon for making of 16 dozen "watls" at 16d. the dozen. Sm. 21s. 4d. - To same for felling of 2 acres of wood at Rayneden at 3s. 4d. the acre. Sm. 6s. 8d. - About 120 dozen seem to have been used, of which a third came from Raindean, carriage 4 miles.

Wainscot. - There is repeated mention of wainscot, written "wenskotts" and "Wayneskotts," etc. Thirty pieces are bought of James a Court of Hothfield, and 200 pieces, costing £11 6s. 8d., come from London by ship to Dover Wyck, and thence to Sandgate. I find in all 258 pieces, costing with carriage £15 7s. 6d.; the price generally 14d. the piece, of which, however, I do not find the measurement.

Carpenters. - The work of the carpenters is described as hewing and squaring of timber, rearing building, framing of timber, making of wheelbarrows, handbarrows, bosses (short troughs for mortar), hods, and mortar tubs, helving mattocks, pickaxes, and hammers; and in the last month John Pallmer, the master-carpenter, who has witnessed to the correctness of the accounts by signing every page of them, takes work "by the great," i.e. at the fixed sum of £4 for the making of doors, windows, and other necessaries, and has 12s. besides for making a "portall." The carpenters were not in force until the third month, when their number was 22, which increased to 33 in the fifth; the strongest muster was 40, with 10 apprentices, in the fifteenth month; their wage was 8d. and 7d. per diem; Pallmer the master or warden had 10d. and Richard Smyth the under-warden, 9d. each day.

Sawyers vary in number from 8 to 20, their daily wage being 7d. They are mentioned in the third month's account as sawing and cutting timber boards for the frames, and planks for the stairs going up to the Castle walls, and for wheelbarrows, hods, etc. Besides the sawstages at Sandgate there were others in Harlakenden's, Phillypp's, and Hygh Fryght woods, where planks were sawn before being carted to Sandgate.

Carts. - Unlike other words written variously throughout the ledger, carts are uniformly "courts," an indication perhaps of local pronunciation at the time. It is not clearly gathered of what the ordinary cart and its team consisted; for finding those working between the Castle and the quarry indifferently termed "courts" and "great courts," and reading in the first month's accounts of "great courts with six beestis" bringing lime from St. Radigunds (the only instance in which the team is defined), we ask if six oxen formed the usual team of carts, or of exceptionally large carts only? As the recognized load, one ton, was not generally exceeded, I am inclined to think, even mindful of rough roads or no roads, that a pair of oxen would have sufficed for the ton load. Horses evidently were used only for riding.

Every month during the progress of the work, a large number of carts were hired to bring the stone from the quarry, and to convey other materials. The greatest number was 110 in the fourteenth month (April - May 1540), but these did not work all the four weeks, a certain number worked and were then relieved, 40 being the daily average. The carts were procured from all the country round; for instance in the thirteenth month they came from places in the Hundreds of Folkestone, Street, Bircholt Franchise, Chart, Calehill, Wye, and the Liberty of Ashford; and in the other direction from the Hundreds of Hayne, Worth, St. Martin's Longport, Aloes Bridge, and the towns of Old Romney, New Romney, and Lydd. To whatever place the carts belonged, the hire for those working at Sandgate was 16d. a day; a number were also engaged in the transport of timber and lime, paid, as has been said, at the rate of 2d. a mile for the ton load.

Terms of Measurement for Freshly-Felled Timber

Wood	Description	Tunn
Hasling Wood	Lies for about 60 Acres in each Acre one with the other Six Oaks containing 15 foot each some more some less in all 360 trees and about 130 Tunn.	130
Torne Den Wood	Contains about 600 Acres, and upon about 450 Acres 10 oaks upon each Acre (the other 150 Acres very poor and barron and little or no wood or timber) containing from 4 foot to 10 foot in a butt and as near as can well be computed 4500 oaks and about 750 Tunn.	750
Denge Wood	Contains about 400 Acres and hath about 5 trees upon each Acre containing 10 foot one with another 2000 oaks and about 500 Tunn.	500
Hanger Wood	Lies for about 200 Acres in each Acre one with the other 4 trees containing from 7 and 8 foot in a butt about 800 trees and about 120 Tunn.	120
Godmersham Wood	Lies for about 300 Acres in each Acre one with the other 4 or 5 oaks from 7 to 10 foot in a butt in all about 1250 oaks and about 150 Tunn.	150
Hounsted Wood	Lies for about 70 Acres in each Acre one with the other 5 oaks containing about 10 foot in a butt in all 350 trees and about 95 Tunn	95
1630 acres of wood		1745

Estate records of the 18th Century offer much clearer writing than in earlier times but still leave doubts, which the modern reader should not rush to decide upon: 'cwt' or 'cu ft', for instance. 'Ton' or 'Tun', even when clearly written, were mischievous spellings. The ton, by then, was acknowledged to be a unit of 20 hundredweight (cwt), each of which was 112 pounds - Bradley's Dictionary of 1725 - and thus 2,240 pounds to the ton. That measure might also be spelled tun; a word then more usually employed for a capacity measure of 2,120 pounds of water. Different basic commodities had different volume tons, or tuns; of which timber had a ton/tun of 40 cubic feet. It is quite possible that some clerks used 1 cwt as the equivalent of 2 cu ft; lesser measures being commonly expressed as doubles of a unit.

The timber world did not respond readily to the rationality of Victorian and later times. There long remained a jumble of different measures, both imported (the 'St Petersburg standard' for board was still referred to in the 1950s) and in the home trade with its emphasis on round timber transactions. For home-grown broadleaf trees, attempts were made from the 17th Century to measure large roundwood in a way that allowed for the unavoidable wastage of bark and sapwood and taper in sawing conversion, notably in oak, and so only to reckon the useable timber. In 1736 Edward Hoppus, surveyor, produced timber ready-reckoner tables using the formula of multiplying the square of the quarter-girth in inches by the length of the (straight) piece in feet and dividing the result by 144. This measuring in 'Hoppus feet' or simply 'feet' has remained in use ever since for broadleaf trees of lowland Britain. There are 27.7 Hoppus feet in a cubic metre but 35.3 true cubic feet. The conventional phrase in estate forestry for pricing broadleaf round timber is still '£1 a foot' - one pound sterling for one cubic foot Hoppus. Or many more pounds, hopefully !

In 1971 the Forestry Commission adopted metric measurement for all round timber and the cubic metre is also used in private woodlands for conifers. The cubic metre is loosely equivalent to a metric tonne for oak, beech, sweet chestnut and pines *when freshly-felled* but with vital reductions of as much as 25 percent among other timbers. Smaller roundwood, other than stacked cordwood, is usually measured on a weighbridge and priced by the metric tonne (orally, 'a tun'.) The variation in moisture content of freshly-felled roundwood, owing to the season of felling or the time left lying in the woodland, can then be important to the transaction. Note For timber measurement in general the Timber Growers Association has excellent quick conversion guides in its biennial handbook for members.

Trading in a natural commodity of such variability as wood demands compromise between buyer and seller. This is seen at its best or worst, and often with humour, when dealing in the unit strangely called the cord. The derivative cordwood, usually from the outer branches of felled broadleaf trees nearby, has its own lore. To-day, many variations have gone, leaving one in general use in the south: a cord is a stack of firewood measuring 8ft x 4ft x 4ft (not yet metricated). To get a lower price the firewood buyer will protest that the stack has been laid down too loosely - 'full of daylight'. The cutter in reply will blame the unique crookedness of branches from these particular trees.

A Note on Historic Price Comparisons

Except in a couple of instances for contemporary comparison, units of money have not been employed in this history. The variations of the timber units of measurement (see above) and underwood costing, the undefined grades of quality and all the other surrounding circumstances render fruitless the reprinting and analysing of scattered prices from old documents. The economic health of woodland industries in times past has to be gauged from other evidence.

APPENDIX - 7/1

The efforts behind Britain's supremacy at sea in Georgian and Victorian times are nowhere better illustrated than in correspondence with Chatham officers.

The Increase in Imported Timber. The lifting of controls on the use of imported timber in 1809 and the unprecedented rate of shipbuilding, the river-front hubbub and the ponderous authority are all brought to life in this short letter from an officer at Chatham Yard to the Navy Board on 24th July 1811.

Honourable Sirs

In obedience to your Minute of the 19th Inst. We beg leave to acquaint you, the Timber therein alluded to was imported into this Port on the ship Reprisal & delivered into the charge of the Water Bailiff in the month of January past, which from the great quantity of Foreign Timber landing at that time, we were necessited to secure in rafts near the Mast Pound. When about the 30th of the same Month, a Gale of Wind with considerable quantity of Ice carried away six pieces of Canada White Oak which by taking an average of the quantity delivered from that ship amounts to 4 loads 28 ft. The most diligent search and exertions have been used to recover the above without effect.

APPENDIX - 7/2

English Oak Deliveries to the Royal Navy Shipyards From the dockyard letter-copying book the anxiety to improve the quality of supplies in the Royal Forests may be sensed from the instructions issued by Sir Robert Barlow, Chatham Commissioner from 1808 to 1823.

Evidently, here, Shipwright's officers were being sent to the forest source but in the majority of such trade it seems the buying decision was made by the timber merchant.

3rd December 1814 - to Dockyard Officers.

I herewith transmit a Copy of a report made by the Commissioner of Woods to the Lords of the Treasury dated the 10th of June last, on the subject of Barking at the earliest season of the year and cutting down the latest, all Trees intended for Naval uses in the Royal Forests.

And in pursuance of the Navy Board's letter to me of the 30th ultimo, you are hereby directed to report to me your opinion on the question therein discussed, returning the same with your report.(signed) 'RB'

In general, it was the timber merchant who made the choice of tree and offered it through the monopolist firm led by Morris, as shown by this routine instruction.

30th May 1815

In pursuance of the Navy Board letter to me of yesterday's date, let a proper person be sent to survey some Timber which Messrs Larking & Morris have convenient for delivery to this yard.'RB'

On an apparently separate matter on 7 Nov 1815, 'RB' says

If any of the Shipwright's officers in the Forests have not been furnished with these instructions, no time is to be lost in supplying the deficiency.

That year of Waterloo, painstaking trials were set up with high-level orders to improve the quality of oak coming into the yards for the future man-of-war. RB's letter of 22nd August:

It being the direction of the Lords Commissioners of the Admiralty that 30 Trees set apart in each of the Forests for experiment, conformably to the Report of the Commissioners for Woods (a copy of which was transmitted to you with my Minute of the 3rd December last) shall be tried at Chatham and the Timber having been felled and about to be delivered as follows: viz. That which grew in Dean Forest to Plymouth, in the New Forest to Portsmouth, in Saley by road to the river Lea at Hertford, Holt, Whittlewood and Whichwood by road to the Thames at Brocot near Oxford and to Woolwich. And the Navy Board having, by their letter of yesterday's date acquainted me that they have directed the Officers of the several Yards to take great care to keep the Trees separate and to transmit them, when received, to this Yard where such experiments are to be made as the Lords Commissioners of the Admiralty shall hereinafter direct.

The Trees are marked with the names of the Forest where they grew and with distinguishing numbers and have been treated as follows: viz. The five Trees marked Nos. I,1 to I,5 inclusive have been felled and stripped in the usual way; those marked

Nos.II,1 to II,5 inclusive have been completely stripped both stems and small branches as far as the bark could be taken off in the Spring, and left standing 'till the end of the last Autumn; those Nos. III,1 to III,5 inclusive have been completely stripped in the same manner as Nos.II and left standing 'till the latter end of the Autumn but the sap wood was cut through all round close to the ground as far in as the heart for the purpose of suffering the sap or moisture to dry out. Nos. IV,1 to IV,5 inclusive were felled in the Spring with the bark on and left so 'till the end of Autumn. Nos,V,1 to V,5 inclusive were set apart unstripped and were left standing 'till the latter end of Autumn. Nos. VI,1 to VI,5 inclusive were lopped of all the Limbs as far as they were not of the diameter of 6 ins. and the stems and such limbs as measured more were stripped and left standing 'till the end of Autumn, and the whole of the trees have been selected as of nearly the same size and growth as possible.

You are therefore, in pursuance of the Navy Board's aforesaid letter, hereby directed to receive the said Timber and cause the same to be kept separate, and when the whole of the said Trees have been received at this Yard, you are to report the same to me for the Board's information in order that they may obtain further directions of the Lords Commissioners of the Admiralty relative to their appropriation.

'RB

APPENDIX 8/1

'WOODS AND PLANTATIONS'

[Chapter 10 of Mr Boys' report]

THE woodlands of the eastern part of Kent are dispersed principally between the great road from Rochester to Dover, and the chalk-hill that runs from Folkestone, by Charing, to Detling. These woods furnish the country with fire-wood, tillers for husbandry uses, and the dockyards with timber for ship-building; but the most material part of their produce is the immense quantity of hop-poles cut out for the neighbouring plantations.

THE MANAGEMENT OF WOODLANDS IN THE DISTRICT EXTENDING FROM CHATHAM-HILL TO CHARING.

Copy of a Paper, presented to the Kent Agricultural Society,

by R. TILDEN, Esq. [circa 1795]

"The soil on which these woods grow, is for the most part flint and clay, with chalk at no great distance from the surface. Where chalk is the chief component part of the upper surface, the wood is of slow growth and little value. They are generally cut down from ten to fourteen and to eighteen years growth; and the price varies from 5l. to 15l. per acre, depending in a great measure on the goodness of the wood, the demand, and the price of poles. Hop-poles are the chief article which make woods valuable in this part of the country; there is not only a constant demand for them at home, but they are carried as far as Maidstone, and to a considerable distance beyond, the plantation (planting) there being so very extensive as to require more than the woodlands in that situation produce, and the planters preferring the poles which grow upon the hills to those of quicker growth and nearer home.

"Part of the woodland in this district is in the hands of the proprietors, and part is let to the tenants who occupy the adjoining farms. When fit to fell, it is commonly sold by valuation. After the purchase is made, and the leaf is off, the wood is parcelled out among the different workmen employed by the purchaser. The first step is to clear the stocks of the small spray, bushes, &c. These are made up into bavins, bound with two wifts, and are called winter kiln bavins. They should be six feet long, and two in circumference over the bands: the price of making them is 3s. per hundred; and they sell in the woods for 6s. per hundred. If the bushes are wanted, the best are bound up in bundles with one wift, at 1s.6d. per load, consisting of fifty bundles; and they sell in the woods from 7s. to 10s. per load

"After the stocks are cleared, they are cut down and thrown into ranges, wide enough to admit a team to pass to fetch away the different articles. These are cut out as the stocks are felled, and consist of first and second best poles, first and second ordinary poles, use-poles, stakes, and binders, thatching-rods, austry-rods, hurdle-rods, wheel-timber, piles, and props. The remainder, not fit or wanted for these purposes, is thrown into the range, where it remains to employ the woodmen in the spring.

"The best first poles are chestnut, ash, willow, and maple: their length should be eighteen feet; their price varies from 30s. to 35s. per hundred; chestnut poles are dearest, varying in price from *15l.* to *20l.* per 1000 in the wood.

"The best second poles consist of the same wood as the first, and are only a smaller pole; varying in length from fifteen to sixteen feet. They sell in the wood from 20s. to 21s. per hundred.

"The first ordinary poles consist of oak, gascoign, red birch, beech, and hornbeam; the two last very inferior: their length should be from seventeen to eighteen feet; they sell in the wood from 12s. to 20s. per hundred.

"The second ordinary poles, varying in length from fifteen to sixteen feet, sell in the wood from 10s. to 12s. per hundred.

"Use poles consist of ash, chestnut, willow, oak, asp, and gascoign, which are too large for hop-poles. They are cut at one halfpenny each, and sell in the wood from 4pd. to 6d. according to the size, length, and goodness of the wood. The largest sort are sold by admeasurement, from 8d. to 9d. and 10d. per foot.

"Stakes and binders are cut out of hazel, ash, oak, willow, and maple; they are bound up in bundles, twenty-five in each; the price of cutting is 1pd. each; and they sell in the wood from 4pd. to 6d. per bundle. The length of a stake should be five feet; of a binder, from fifteen to eighteen feet.

"Thatching-rods are cut out of the same kinds of wood as the stakes and binders, or large enough for stakes. They are bound up in bundles, fifty in each; the price of cutting is 2d. per bundle; and they sell in the wood for 6d. The length of a bundle should be six feet.

"Austry-rods are smaller than thatching-rods; cut out of hazel. They are used to bind billet-wood for the London market. They are bound up in bundles, one hundred rods in each; the price of cutting is 2d. and they sell at 6d. per bundle in the wood: their length is five feet.

"Hurdle-rods are cut to make hurdle-gates for folding sheep; they are cut out of the same kind of wood as binders; indeed, they are only a small binder, from ten to fourteen feet long. They are bound up in bundles, fifty in each: the price of cutting is 2d. and they sell in the wood at 6d. per bundle.

"Wheel-timber is cut out of large beech of two or three falls growth: it is used for fellies of wheels; it should not be less than seven inches diameter at the small end. It is cut down for one penny for every length of three feet, and sold in the wood from 7d. to 8d. per length; if sold by admeasurement, the same price per foot; if smaller, it is cut out for axle-trees, plough-cheps, and wrests. Axle-trees should be seven feet long, and six and a half inches in diameter at the small end; they are cut for 1d. each, and sell in the wood for 10d. Plough-cheps should be five feet long, and five inches diameter at the small end: they are cut for one halfpenny each, and sell in the wood for sixpence.

"Plough-wrests should be four feet long and five inches diameter at the small end: they are cut for one halfpenny each, and sell in the wood for 2d.

"Piles are cut out of beech and hornbeam; they are used to prevent the tide from washing away the chalk at the footing of the sea-walls, and are cut of different lengths. (3 feet to 12 feet).

"Props which are used in the coal-mines at Newcastle, are cut out of oak and birch; they should be cut six feet four or five inches long, and be two and-a-half inches diameter at the small end: the price of cutting is a halfpenny; and they sell in the wood at 2d. each.

"These are the chief, if not all the articles which are cut during the winter. In the spring, what remains in the ranges is made up, part into summer kiln-bavins, which are made of the smallest wood, and bound with two withes, and should be six feet long. The price of making is 3s. per hundred. Part is made into household bavins, being the best faggots which are made; they should be six feet long, and two feet over the band;

the price is also 3s. per hundred; and they sell in the woods from 12s. to 14s. per hundred. The remainder is cut out in cordwood; each stick should be three and a half feet long, the length of the cord fourteen feet, and it should be stacked three feet high; the price of cutting and stacking is 2s. per cord; and the cord sells in the wood from 12s. to 16s.

"It has been found by those that have been very attentive to the management of their woodlands, that wood, like everything else, decays and produces fewer poles every fall, unless they are replenished. This is best done in the autumn after the wood is felled. The plants, whether chestnut, ash, or willow, should be taken up from the nursery with as much earth to their roots as can be conveniently done(i), and their small roots should be cut as little as possible. Strong plants taken up in this manner, and planted with care, seldom fail. They should be looked over the next spring, to fasten those which the frost may have loosened.

"The tithe of woodlands was, a few years ago, at 2s. in the pound; but it now varies from 2s.3d. to 2s.6d. and to 3s.(ii). Many clergymen are of opinion that the woods ought not to be cut down only, but to be made up in the different articles for sale; but this is not true: if the clergyman and purchaser should disagree, all that the latter has to do, is to sever every tenth perch and leave it: the expense of doing this is found to be about 3d. in the pound. If wood therefore is sold at a fair valuation, it appears unreasonable for any clergyman to demand more than 2s.3d. in the pound (iii).

(i) Removing earth with the roots of plants of the kind here mentioned, is impracticable and unnecessary; no deciduous plants; but American flowering shrubs, require earth with them, nor will they retain it - *Note by Mr. Randall, of Maidstone.*

(ii) I never heard of 3s. being paid for the tithe of wood; 2s.6d. is a common price, and ought not to be called unreasonable; for if the purchaser gives 20s. for the wood and 2s. for the tithe, amounting in whole to 1*l*.2s., the tithe of which will be found to be nearly 2s.2pd.: add the expense of felling, and in most cases 2s.6d is a reasonable charge. - *Remark by the Rev. Mr. Pryce.*

This mode of estimating tithe is erroneous, because it supposes eleven-tenths of the whole; and by that means makes the tithe too small. The fact is, that the seller can engage only for nine-tenths; and consquently, the parson's share is a ninth part of the sum the wood sells for, with an addition of a tenth of the price of severing; which in most cases will be found to amount to about 2s.3d. in the pound, as Mr. TILDEN very justly observes. - *Editor.*

(iii) The practice of laying down the different sorts from the stock to strike into the ground, is a valuable discovery; and I believe rather a local one. They produce hop-poles more quickly by this, than in any other way. - *Note by a Middle Kent Farmer.*

The method is, to select long healthy young branches from the stocks adjoining to vacancies in the wood, and then to dig holes, each about two feet square, and fifteen inches deep, returning the surface mould into the bottom of the hole, and then bending each branch and fastening it down with a peg, about ten or twelve inches below the surface, treading over it the remainder of the mould - *Editor.*

Mr Boy's General Observations.

The oaks are all cut in the flaying season, for the bark of all sizes. The fencing-poles are either used whole, or cut into gates for sheep-fences. The hop-poles are sorted into three, four, or five sorts, and sold by the hundred. The faggots, or bavins, are made into lengths of five feet; the best for bakers and house-keepers; and on the hills they make inferior sorts, called kiln-brush, which are used for burning lime. Stakes and ethers are cut out before the faggots are made. In the neighbourhood of Chatham they cut some small bundles of brush and cord-wood, for the use of shipping and the metropolis. The woodlands of the Weald are tithe-free.

[By mending the vacant spots of woods with such sorts of plants as are best adapted to the respective soils, a great additional produce of wood has been obtained. This improvement, together with an increased demand for hop-poles, has made some woodlands the most valuable estates in the county. The beautiful woods of Lord ROMNEY, and those of Sir CHARLES MIDDLETON, near Maidstone, are good specimens of what has been done in this way. His Lordship has, not long since, made above 50*l*. per acre of some wood of eleven years growth, on a poor pinnock soil, that was many years ago mended by the late Lord ROMNEY; and Sir CHARLES MIDDLETON, from a better soil on the rock, has made 104*l*. per acre, of a late fall of only nine years growth; but this was from a plantation of chestnut; a sort of wood the most valuable of any, except larich, for hop-poles.

From some hints on the culture of larich, and the value of that wood for hop-poles, published some years ago by the ingenious Dr. ANDERSON, of Edinburgh, I was induced to raise a small plantation, by which I was enable to cut down in July last a fifth part of an acre; the produce of which lies now in the field, and is as follows:

		£. s. d.
440 Faggots, worth	10s. per hundred	2 4 0
475 Best poles -	40s. " "	9 10 0
125 Second ditto,	20s. " "	1 5 0
162 Third ditto,	10s. " "	0 16 2
88 Large pieces,	1s. each,	4 8 0
75 Hedge stakes,	3s. per hundred	0 2 3
		£. 18 5 5
	Multiply by	5
	Worth per acre,	£. 91 7 1

The land on which this valuable produce was reared, is very poor light loam, not worth more than 6 or 7s. per acre rent, when it was planted.

The plants cost 1s. per hundred, and were put in with a dibber after deep ploughing, at a distance of two feet each way. The value of the produce in eleven years is near ten times the original value of the land at thirty years purchase !!!]

APPENDIX 8/2

A TABLE OF THE PRINCIPAL WOODLANDS OF THE WESTERN PART OF THE COUNTY,

AS FURNISHED BY MR. RANDALL, FOR THE FORMER EDITION OF THIS WORK.

Names of Woods.	To whom they belong.	Parishes they are in.	Acres supposed to contain.	Surface Soil, general.	Subsoil.	Produce seemingly natural.	Extra from Improvements.	Articles for Sale.
Stalisfield	Hon. Mr. Watson.	Stalisfield	400	Heavy and gravelly loam	Heavy loam and some chalk	Birch, hornbeam, oak, ash, hazel, beech, &c.	Some ash, chesnuts, and willow, planted, succeed	Some timber, hop-poles, cord-wood, hurdles, and bavins for bakers, and lime
Newenden Bottom	Sir Edward Knatchbull, Bart.	Newenden	350	Sandy loam	Heavy loam	As above	But little done in planting	Produce as above
Bickner Wood	— Chambers, Esq.	Bickner and Hucking	140	Flinty strong loam	Heavy loam	As above	Some good young plantation of ash, willow, and chesnut	Some timber and fencing-poles, in addition to the above
Chesnut Wood	Earl of Aylesford	Newington and Milton	300	Gravelly and sandy loam	Gravelly loam	Some ash, beech, oak, hazel, &c.	Exceeding good chesnut plantation	Quantities of hop-poles, fencing-poles, and all the above
Long Tunn	— Best, Esq.	Thurnham and Stockbury	350	Gravelly and sandy flinty loam	Heavy and gravelly flinty loam	Some good ash, beech, hornbeam, &c. with tolerable loam	No improvements made	Some fencing and hop-poles, cord-wood for charcoal, bavins, &c.
Squirrels Wood	Messrs. Head and Roper	Stockbury	200	Flinty and dry poor gravelly loam	Chalk at 2 feet, some gravelly loam	Some beech, ordinary oak, &c.	No improvements	Cord-wood, bavins, and a few poles
Bimborough Wood	Earl of Aylesford	Thurnham	150	Flinty and gravelly loam	Chalk 4 feet, some deep gravelly loam	Some good ash-poles, a few oaks, hazels, &c.	No improvements	Cord-wood, hop-poles, bavins, ethers, &c.
Mount Down	— Best, Esq.	Detling and Thurnham	200	Flinty and gravelly loam	Same chalky, not quite so good as above	Nearly as above	No improvements	As above
Cockstreet Wood	— Foote, Esq.	Detling	150	Same as above	Few flints, nearly as above	Some oak, hazel, beech, and a few ash	Old woods and plantations of chesnut and ash. They have repeatedly been filled up, many years ago, with chesnut, ash, and willow; and now again filling up, under Mr. Randall's direction.	Abundance of hop-poles, fencing-poles, stakes, cord-wood, &c. &c.
Chatham Wood	— Best, Esq. of Chilson	Chatham and ——	500	Flinty gravelly loam	Strong loam with flints	Some oak, ash-poles, beech, &c.	No improvements going on	Poles, bavins, cord-wood, &c.
Fright Wood		Aylesford and Boxley	300	Chalky flinty gravelly loam	Chalk and some gravelly loam	Some oak, ash, beech, &c.	No improvements	As last
Upper Bell Wood	Messrs. Read, Seager, and others	Aylesford and Boxley	200	Gravelly loam	Heavy, flinty, and poor loam	Very ordinary oak, some ash, hazel, and beech	A most capital improvement for poles, by Mr. Seager, with ash; one acre of which underwood is now of equal value to eight round of the same age	Produce a few poles, cord-wood, bavins, &c. the plantation great; many poles, and the above
Bridge Wood	Wardens of the Bridge	St. Margarets	1000	Gravelly and chalky loam	Gravelly loam and chalk	Some oak, ash-poles, &c.	Beginning to improve by ash and chesnut plants	Poles, cord-wood, &c.
Chatham Woods	— Foote, Esq.	Chatham	300	Gravelly loam	The same as above	Oak, ash, &c.	Old improvements still continued	The same as above
Shawsted Wood	Dean and Chapter of Rochester	Stawsted and Gillingham	300	Gravelly loam	Ditto	Ash, oak, and beech	No improvements	The same
Rainham Park	Earl of Aylesford	Rainham and Newington	400	Ditto	Gravely loam and heavy loam	As above	No improvement	The same
Penenden Heath Woods } King's Wood	— Best, Esq. of Boxley / Mrs. Bouverie, Sir John Filmer, and others	Boxley / Langley, Leeds, Sutton, &c.	50 / 1500	Sandy gravel / Stone shatter, and gravelly loam	Gravelly and sandy loam / Strong loam with some tag-stone	{ Good lop-poles from the few old stocks / Large quantities of oak, some hazel, birch, &c.	{ Capital improvement of chesnuts on poor sand / No improvements	{ Abundance of poles, stakes, ethers, &c. &c. / Many oaken tillers, small timber, poles, &c.
Mess Woods	Lord Romney	Maidstone	160	Stone shatter, and gravelly loam	Gravelly loam and some stone	Oak, birch, aspen, hazel, and some ash	Improved by planting many ash, chesnut, and willow; said to be the most ancient of all the neighbouring improvements	Some very good fencing-poles, hop-poles, cord-wood, &c. &c.
Coxheath Woods	Mr. John Miller	Yalden and Hunton	80	Gravelly loam	Gravelly loam and some stone	Oak of indifferent growth	Some chesnuts in a flourishing state	Hop-poles, fence-poles, &c. &c.
Earming Woods	Lord Romney & Messrs. Amhurst	Earming and Aylesford	300	Sandy loam	Gravelly loam	A variety of birch, oak, hornbeam, &c.	Much improved by planting chesnut, &c.	Quantities of good fence-poles, hop-poles, &c.
East Malling Woods	C. Milner, Esq. and the Hon. Mr. Pacy	Teston and East Malling	300	Sandy loam and stone shatter	Gravelly loam and rag-stone	Oak, beech, birch, hazel, ash	Improved as above	Produce as above
Peckham Wood	Mr. Bouverie, Sir W. Twisden, and Lord Le Despencer	Peckham and Merewroth	800	Gravelly loam and stone shatter	Deep loam, heavy clay, and gravel	As above	As above, with some new plants of chesnut, by Lord Le Despencer, on very gravelly loam	The same
Oldham Wood	Lord Le Despencer, and W. Geary, Esq.	Peckham and Offham	600	The same	Gravelly loam	As above	No improvement	Ditto
King's Wood, by Sussex	— Cartier, Esq. and others	Goudhurst, Cranbrook, &c.	5000	Gravelly loam and sandy ditto	Some strong clay and ditto	As above, but more inclined to oak	But very little improved	Fewer poles, fire-wood, &c. as above
Barham Downs	Waste	Barham and Aylesford	1000	Gravelly loam, flinty	Grave, clay, some flint	Scrubby oak, hazel, &c.	Waste lands	Free from November to March

It is attended with some difficulty and hazard of success, to cause young new-planted trees to thrive well in old wood and wastes, the land close round the new plants being occupied by the roots of the neighbouring trees; grass and weeds likewise growing near them, added to their being much excluded from the free air by the neighbouring wood growing round and above them, the new plants often fail the first or second summer; and several of those that continue alive till the succeeding fall of the wood, and then cut down with it, are, from their weakly state, frequently overpowered by the more rapid growth of the young springs of the established trees, so that they are seen no more. On the average of all that have been planted in these situations, barely a third is to be found succeeding to advantage, and sometimes not a tenth. Several extensive experiments are now pursuing; and, as far as they are carried, promise more success than hitherto; as nearly all the new plants have been preserved alive through those late dry seasons, in the greatest grassy lands. Digging large holes for the plants, and keeping them clean close round them, with some new-invested lines for the purpose, form a considerable part of the plan; and although those woodlands where planting has been followed, are more than double the value of those adjoining which have been neglected, yet it is confessed by the most skilful and experienced, that this practice is still but little understood.

* New Ed. Wm. Gears, Edit.

MANAGEMENT PRINCIPLES FOR SEMI-NATURAL AND NATIVE WOODLANDS

Semi-natural woods are composed of locally native trees and shrubs which derive from natural regeneration or coppicing rather than planting. Because of their natural features and appearance, semi-natural woods are valuable for nature conservation and in the landscape, and many are important for recreation and for historical and cultural interest.

Management should aim to maintain and enhance these values in harmony with securing other benefits, including wood products.

Ancient semi-natural woodlands are of special value because of their long, continuous history. They are the nearest we have to our original natural woodland and include remnants of the post-glacial forest which have never been cleared. They are irreplaceable assets which support many rare plants and animals and make a vital contribution to conserving biodiversity. They also contain a wealth of evidence of our past. Many have been greatly modified in structure and composition by centuries of management, whilst retaining many natural features. Some are threatened by neglect in the face of pressures such as fragmentation and overgrazing. The Forestry Authority encourages management which seeks to maintain or restore their special characteristics, including their natural diversity of species and habitats, aesthetic and cultural values and genetic integrity, whilst taking appropriate opportunities for wood production for a range of markets.

Management proposals should be geared to sensitive and low-key methods which are suited to the natural dynamics of these woodlands. Natural regeneration will be preferred to planting wherever practicable. More detailed guidance is given in the guide for each woodland type.

Other semi-natural woodlands, which have developed from natural colonisation of open ground sometime within the last few centuries, are also normally of high environmental value, particularly in the uplands, although they are not usually so valuable as ancient semi-natural woodlands because of their shorter history.

Appropriate management will vary according to the relative importance of these woodlands. For some, for example many long-established upland woods, management should be similar to that for ancient woods, whilst in woods of lower value a greater range of silvicultural options will be acceptable.

Planted woods of native species may often acquire some of the characteristics of semi-natural woodland, especially where they are on **ancient woodland sites**, where plants and animals have survived from the former semi-natural wood. The development of a varied structure and composition, including diverse native tree, shrub and field layer vegetation and the use of locally native species and genotypes for planted trees, can also increase the naturalness of native plantations.

Where planted native woods have developed a high conservation value in these ways management should be similar to that for semi-natural woods, but generally a wider range of silvicultural systems, including a greater emphasis on planting instead of natural regeneration, will be permitted under the grant aid and felling regulations.

New native woodlands, which are designed and managed from the start to develop a natural character, can help to offset some of the past losses of native woodland and will in time acquire a high environmental value, although they should not be seen as substitutes for any remaining semi-natural woodland.

The Forestry Authority will encourage by grant-aid the creation of new native woodlands on open land by natural colonisation or planting, where species composition and site are suitably matched, especially on areas close to existing semi-natural woods. Further guidance can be obtained in Bulletin 112, published by the Forestry Authority.

APPENDIX 10/2

KENT WOODLAND STATISTICS

In England's densely populated South East, the difficult soils of the Weald were long to protect woodland from the plough and, in Kent particularly, create the sharp contrast of high-yielding coast and sluggish hinterland. The relatively large proportion of woodland cover for the county is thought to have actually improved somewhat since the early 20th Century; to between 10.5 and 12.5 per cent (allowing for standard error). That we ponder the difference between these two low percentages clearly shows both how concerned we are by their smallness and how pleased that the figures are notably greater than the English (not United Kingdom) norm.

The following are extracts from the 1979 - 1982 Forestry Commission Census of Woodlands and Trees in Kent. (At that time the Commission owned 11 per cent of the county's woodland total and influenced the management of a further 14 per cent through generally grant-aided programmes).

Estimated Woodland Area of Kent: 1982 42,664 hectares (+or- 1024 ha), representing 11.4 per cent of the county land area.

Forest Types (All ownerships)	area	percentage of total
Mainly Coniferous High Forest	6327	15.0
Mainly Broadleaved High Forest	14056*	33.0
Coppice (inc. with standards)	17914	42.0
Scrub or Cleared Land	4367	10.0
	42664	100.0

(Standard errors are + or - 9 to 13 per cent)

*The figure for Mainly Broadleaved included 1700 ha of coppice origin.

Coniferous or Broadleaved Forest - Standing trees (hectares) defined by date of planting. All ownerships.

Decade(s)	Mainly Coniferous	Mainly Broadleaved
Pre-1861	113	1422
1861-1900	267	2712
1901-10	17	760
1911-20	40	1609
1921-30	232	274
1931-40	732	891
1941-50	807	2391
1951-60	1426	2572
1961-70	2043	809
1971-80	650	616

Existing High Forest by Principal Species (hectares). All ownerships.

Scots pine	2494	Oak	4660
Corsican pine	1001	Beech	2014
Lodgepole pine	1	Sycamore	763
Sitka spruce	79	Ash	1454
Norway spruce	922	Birch	654
European larch	255	Poplar	481
Jap/Hybrid larch	553	Sweet Chestnut	1119
Douglas fir	521	Elm	4
Other conifers	796	Other broadleaves	1206
Mixed conifers	275	Mixed broadleaves	1131
Total conifers	6897	Total broadleaves	13486

Kent: The broad picture to-day

In 1999 the provisional number of woodlands totalled 2064 above 2 hectares (5 acres) in size. Nearly three-quarters are woodlands of not more than 10 hectares (25 acres), reflecting the characteristic landscape of inland Kent.

The latest survey from Forest Research (now a Forestry Commission agency) will provide a confirmed census soon after this book has been published. The early results show a reduction in Kent woodland from the 11.4 per cent of land area in the last FC census to 10.1 per cent or 37,820 hectares (93,415 acres) but to this has yet to be added the sector for small woodlands, which will probably restore the difference. Among broadleaved species a marked change will be seen from coppice areas now grown up to nominally High Forest or otherwise altered.

A different recent survey - Land Cover Change in Kent, co-ordinated by Linda Davies for the County Council - recorded a woodland area of 45,000 hectares in 1990. This figure, very similar to the earlier FC census, estimated that the loss of woodland during the previous 29 years had been only 11.11 per cent, despite an increase in the category 'developed land' by nearly a quarter in that period. Another study, by the Council for the Protection of Rural England estimated there to be an actual increase in Kent woodland. Comparisons of different dates are best made from only one data source but even they may be affected by changes in working methods. In Kent, of all places, woodland inquirers will note that orchards should not be included, as they sometimes are, in the overall category 'tree cover'.

WHAT IS 'KENT'?

The county of Kent before 1888 included land so close to London that the western boundary marched with Lambeth and Southwark. In that year the County of London was created and Kent retreated eastward but still included Bexley and Bromley. Those local authorities were themselves made London Boroughs in 1965. In 1997 the unitary district authority of Medway was fashioned from the river-mouth towns. The county's land area is considered to be 373,499 hectares (922,916 acres) including Medway's 19,203 ha. In 1998 the population was 1,566,000 including Medway's 240,100.

Kent place-names appearing in the text are located by the TQ or TR number along the top of the county map followed by the downward square number.
Waterways have a reference approximately at their mid-course.

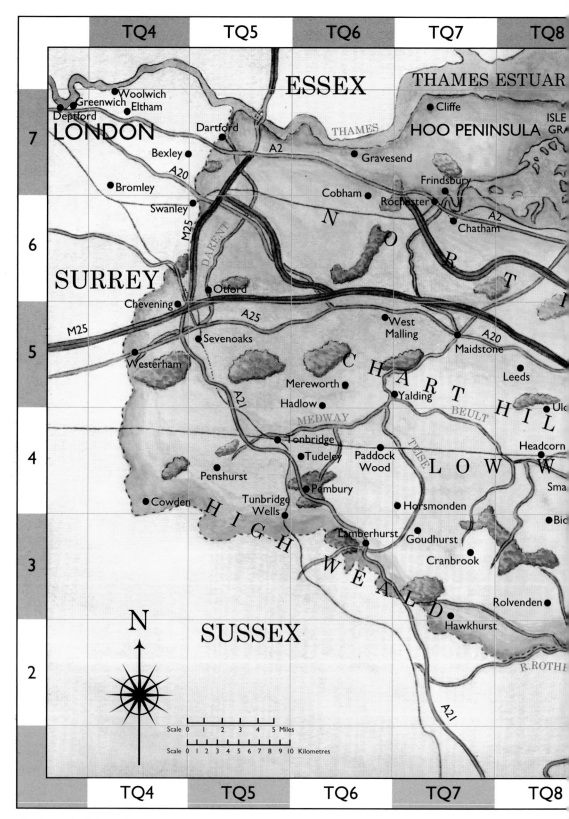